Water Resources Studies
University of Wisconsin
1

Water Resources Law and Policy in the Soviet Union

edited by Irving K. Fox

Published for the
Water Resources Center, University of Wisconsin

THE UNIVERSITY OF WISCONSIN PRESS
Madison, Milwaukee, and London

UNIVERSITY OF VICTORIA
LIBRARY
Victoria, B. C.

Published for
The Water Resources Center, University of Wisconsin, by
The University of Wisconsin Press
Box 1379, Madison, Wisconsin 53701
The University of Wisconsin Press, Ltd.
70 Great Russell Street, London, WC1B 3BY

Copyright © 1971
The Regents of the University of Wisconsin
All rights reserved

First printing

Printed in the United States of America
Cushing-Malloy, Inc., Ann Arbor, Michigan

ISBN 0-299-05990-1; LC 76-157392

Contents

Preface

In the summer of 1966, it was my good fortune to attend a seminar in
the Soviet Union on water resources management, sponsored by the
United Nations and the USSR. O. S. Kolbasov, a Soviet legal scholar,
was a participant in the seminar and gave a copy of his newly published book on Soviet water law to Karl-Erik Hansson, one of the
United Nations representatives. Mr. Hansson loaned me the volume
and upon my return to the United States, my wife, Rosemary Fox,
agreed to translate it into English. Her translation is the basic component of this volume.

In the process of developing a suitable publication, it was decided
that other materials were needed to provide perspective and further
understanding of Soviet water law and policy. Before the task of pre-
paring these materials was completed, the Supreme Soviet of the USSR
in December 1970 enacted a set of Principles of Water Law to provide
a framework for more detailed legislation to be enacted by the government of the USSR and the individual union republics. The need for
such a set of principles is indicated in the study by O. S. Kolbasov.
Since these Principles constitute the basic framework for Soviet water
law and policy, it is appropriate that they should be included in this
book, together with other laws that illustrate the nature of Soviet water legislation.

To provide the perspective and understanding desired, the book
contains four essays which precede the critique of Soviet water law
by O. S. Kolbasov. The legislation, consisting of the recently enacted
Principles of Water Law, two basic decrees, and an excerpt from the
Criminal Code of the Russian Soviet Federated Socialist Republic may
be found in the Appendix.

The first essay, prepared by myself, compares the water resources situation in the Soviet Union with that in the United States, and examines the basic policy issues confronting the two countries. Second is a paper, translated from the Russian, by N. T. Kuznetsov and M. I. L'vovich, two members of the Institute of Geography of the Academy of Sciences of the USSR. This article provides insight into Soviet water development and its problems from the point of view of two Soviet scientists who have specialized in the study of water resources. Third is an essay by Peter Davis which compares the basic features of United States water allocation law with the features of Soviet law as discerned from the Kolbasov study. Fourth is an essay by Zigurds Zile, which outlines the development of Soviet law in general and of Soviet conservation law in particular and provides the context for understanding Kolbasov's work.

One book on water law, together with a set of interpretive essays, does not provide a comprehensive understanding of how the Soviet Union approaches water management and what problems it is encountering. Yet, we believe that this work provides a useful introduction to the situation in the Soviet Union and, therefore, is a contribution to our understanding of water management in that country.

Two technical points merit explanation. In the transliteration of Russian words from the Cyrillic, the system employed is the same as that used by the Library of Congress with the exception of the Cyrillic letters ю and я. Whereas the Library of Congress transliterates these letters as *iu* and *ia*, respectively, they have been transliterated as *yu* and *ya* in this volume. Also, in citing Soviet legislation, where paragraphs in the original are identified by letters, the Cyrillic alphabet has been carried over into the translation.

In the preparation of this volume, I am deeply grateful to my wife for undertaking the translations. They were much more difficult tasks than I had anticipated at the outset. It was my good fortune to find able legal scholars—Zigurds Zile and Peter Davis—who were willing to study the Soviet materials and contribute their essays. Mrs. Lynne Ficken, Mrs. Pat Peters, and Marilyn Schmits were most helpful and cooperative in undertaking the major typing and other secretarial work in connection with the manuscript.

Irving K. Fox

Madison, Wisconsin
May 1971

Water Resources
Law and Policy
in the Soviet Union

Water Resources Management in the Soviet Union and the United States

Some Similarities, Differences,
and Policy Issues

Irving K. Fox

The Kolbasov study of Soviet water law, recently enacted *Principles of Water Law of the USSR and Union Republics*, and the Kuznetsov and L'vovich paper, all of which are translated in this volume, suggest some interesting similarities and differences between the United States and the Soviet Union and also help bring into focus some of the basic water policy issues that confront the two countries.[1] This essay seeks to make a general comparison of the water resources situation in the two countries and examines the policy issues that emerge, particularly from Kolbasov's work. Without considerable study within the Soviet Union itself, there are severe limitations on how well we can understand the policy issues and water problems confronting that country. Nevertheless, these works provide a basis for a preliminary assessment.

---

1. There is relatively little analysis of Soviet water management published in English. The following reports are of interest:

V. V. Zvonkov, *Integrated Water Resources Development in the River Basins of the USSR*, Moscow: Publishing House of the Academy of Sciences, 1957.

U.S. Congress, Senate, Committees on Interior and Insular Affairs and Public Works, *Relative Water and Power Resources Development in the USSR and USA*, 86th Cong., 2d sess., Document No. 71, 1960.

International Seminar—Integrated Utilization of Water Resources (Duplicated for a United Nations Seminar held in Fergana, Uzbekistan, July 1966).

4   Irving K. Fox

A General Comparison

The following table provides certain comparative data on the United
States and the USSR, with emphasis upon water resources development
and use. As this table indicates, both the United States and the Soviet Union have enormous land areas, but the Soviet Union, the nation

Comparative Data: USA and USSR

	USA	USSR
Land area (square miles)[a]	3,549,000	8,647,000
Population (1970)[b]	204,844,000	241,748,000
Gross National Product[c] at factor cost at 1965 U.S. relative prices (1965 figures)	630.5 billion	382.1 billion
Per capita disposable[d] income (1965 figures)	$2,423	$555
Average precipitation[e]	30 inches	15.4 inches
Average runoff[e]	1780 billion gallons per day	3100 billion gallons per day
Miles of inland[f] shipping routes	60,000	88,487
Ton-miles of commerce[g] in inland waterways	281,392,000,000 short ton-miles	106,433,000,000 short ton-miles
Irrigated land (acres)[h]	42 million	26.5 million
Electric power—installed[i] capacity (1968 figures)	Total 290m kw Hydro 52m kw	142.5m kw 27.0m kw
Energy consumption[j] (kwh, thermal—1967)	15.68×10^{12}	7.45×10^{12}

Sources:

a. *The World Almanac*, 1970 edition, ed. by Luman H. Long,
Newspaper Enterprise Assn., New York, 1969, pp. 689, 559.

b. Population estimates: U.S., as of 1 April 1970, U.S. Department of Commerce, Bureau of the Census; USSR, as of 15 January
1970, *Current Digest of the Soviet Press*, 19 May 1970, p. 22.

c. *Economic Growth in Japan and the USSR*, Maddison, Angus;
W. W. Norton and Company, New York, 1969, p. 146.

d. Income figures: U.S., U.S. Department of Commerce, Bureau of
the Census, *Statistical Abstract of the United States* (Washington,
D.C.: U.S. Government Printing Office, 1969), p. xvi; USSR, Joint
Economic Committee, *New Directions in the Soviet Economy* (Wash-

with the largest territory in the world, has two and one-half times the
land area of the United States. In some respects the physical characteristics of the two countries are quite similar. Both have largely
temperate climates. Both have vast desert regions. And both have
cold and inhospitable northern areas. The Soviet Union, however,
lies generally farther north than the United States except for Alaska,
and thus a much larger part of the total land area is in tundra and
other types of slow-growing vegetation than in the United States.
This northern location of a large portion of the USSR, its arid lands in
Central Asia, and its vast extent have been major physical influences
upon the water resources situation.

The average precipitation in the USSR is much less than in the
United States. On the other hand, because of its much larger area,
the total runoff is about twice that in the United States. This may
appear to be an enormous resource, and it is, but 80 percent[2] of this
flow is toward the Arctic and the Pacific where both development and
potential for use are severely limited. Therefore, the major demands
upon the supply of runoff fall upon the 18 percent occurring in European Russia and upon the more limited supply in Central Asia, which
has only 2 percent of the runoff but comprises 30 percent of the total
land area of the USSR.

---

2. *International Seminar*, p. 29.

---

ington, D.C.: U.S. Government Printing Office, 1966), Part II-B, p.
526.

   e. Runoff statistics: U.S., Water Resources Council, *The Nation's
Water Resources* (Washington, D.C.: U.S. Government Printing Office, 1968), p. 1–3; USSR, based on data in Kuznetsov and L'vovich,
Problems of the Complex Use and Conservation of Water Resources,
translated herein.

   f. Inland shipping mileages: U.S., *The Nation's Water Resources*,
p. 4-5-4; USSR, Narodnoe Khozyaistvo SSSR v 1968, *Moscow "Sta-
tistica" 1969*, p. 476 (all figures from this source are for 1968 unless
indicated).

   g. Commerce ton-miles: U.S., *Statistical Abstract*, 1970 (figure
is for 1967), p. 577; USSR, Narodnoe Khozyaistvo SSSR v 1968, p. 459.

   h. Irrigated land acreages: U.S., *The Nation's Water Resources*,
p. 4-4-1; USSR, Kuznetsov and L'vovich, *Problems of the Complex
Use and Conservation of Water Resources*, translated herein (10.6 m
hectares).

   i. Electric power figures: U.S., *Statistical Abstract*, 1970, p.
508; USSR, Narodnoe Khozyaistvo SSSR v 1968, p. 228.

   j. Massachusetts Institute of Technology, *Man's Impact on the
Global Environment* (Cambridge, Mass.: MIT Press, 1970), p. 294.

In spite of its handicaps with regard to climate and location, the
water resources of the Soviet Union have an enormous potential. If
the transport problem can be overcome, the USSR will be capable of
irrigating millions of additional acres. It has many thousands of
miles of waterways that are or can be made navigable. Its hydroelectric power potential is over three times that of the United States.

The comparative water development status reflects the differences
in economic development in the two countries. While the USSR has
many more miles of inland waterways than the United States, the ton-
miles of use are only about 38 percent of the use in the United States.
Furthermore, water transport plays a less significant role in the total
transport system in the USSR than in the United States, as reflected
by the fact that only about 6 percent[3] of the total tonnage of freight
moves by water in the Soviet Union in comparison with about 15 percent in the United States.[4] A similar situation is found with regard to
other kinds of water development. Although the USSR has some hydroelectric power installations that are much larger than any in this
country, the total installed capacity of the USSR is only about half
that of the United States. With regard to irrigation, the United States
has about 42 million acres of irrigated land in comparison with about
26.5 million acres in the Soviet Union.

These comparisons suggest that the water situation in the Soviet
Union differs from that in the United States in several respects. Although the total water resource is larger in the USSR, it is not as
easily adapted to the economic needs of the nation as the water supply of the United States. A substantial part of the major rivers drain
a cold and inhospitable region, far from the centers that are readily
susceptible to economic development. By contrast, with the exception
of the Alaskan rivers, the major rivers of the United States drain rich
valleys where climate, topography, and soils have facilitated economic development. Moreover, in the Soviet Union, most of the streams
flow in a northerly or southerly direction, whereas the major flows of
commerce are east and west. The major difference in the water situation is that the USSR is at an earlier stage of economic development,
and consequently the water resources are less developed than in this
country. With lower per capita incomes, recreation use is not as in-
tense and concern about pollution has only come to the fore within
the last few years.

----

3. Committees on Interior and Insular Affairs and Public Works,
p. 137.

4. Federal Water Resources Council, *The Nations Water Resources*
(Washington, D.C., U.S. Government Printing Office, 1968) p. 4—5—
4.

The System of Development and Management

As the foregoing brief description indicates, there are both striking differences and similarities between the United States and the Soviet Union. However, both nations cover geographic areas of continental proportions with a wide range of topographic and climatic conditions. Both have populations exceeding 200,000,000. Both are highly industrialized. And both have placed a great deal of emphasis on and invested heavily in water development. In turning to the system of development and management, one finds additional similarities as well as some major differences.

With regard to the overall governmental structure, both countries have federal systems. As Professor Zile emphasizes in his essay in this volume, the relationships between the central government and the republics of the USSR differ in fundamental ways from the relationships between the federal government and the states in the United States. Nevertheless, as indicated by the differences among the water laws of the various republics as described by Kolbasov, and by the clear provision for legislation by the Union Republics in the Principles of Water Law enacted in December 1970, the federal nature of the system is a reality.

The *Principles of Water Law of the USSR and Union Republics,* which are translated in this volume, indicate another major difference between the two countries. The USSR now has in one place a set of guiding principles which provides a framework for detailed legislation to be enacted by the Supreme Soviet of the USSR and the Union Republics. This is not a water code but only a set of guiding principles. They are quite general and only specify basic objectives and allocate responsibilities in a general way. Yet no comparable unified set of guidelines exists in the United States.

In another essay in this volume, Peter Davis compares the basic features of the systems of water law in the United States and in the Soviet Union. A striking difference is that under the United States system the use of water is allocated to individuals and organizations in accordance with certain rules of law, whereas in the Soviet Union this allocation is made through the process of planning and implementing specific programs. In other words, in the United States an individual or organization is entitled to use a given water supply in certain ways if certain legal criteria are met and certain procedures are followed. In the Soviet Union, on the other hand, a supply of water is allocated when approval is given to launch a planned program.

The best-known difference between the two countries is, of course, that in the Soviet Union all developmental and management activities are undertaken by governmental organizations. In the United States, only about a quarter of the land under irrigation receives water from federal projects,[5] and most of the remainder has been developed by private individuals and organizations. Similarly, a large proportion of the installed capacity of hydroelectric power in the United States has been privately developed. This means, it would appear, that there is a greater degree of decentralization in developmental decisions about water, and that motivations for development and management are quite different in the United States. Here the market, prices, and profits play a large part in developmental and management decisions. In the Soviet Union the governmental structure, governmentally determined programs and policies, and the kinds of special incentives provided for managers and workers play a much larger part.

Yet the system may not be as different as we sometimes think. In the Soviet Union it has been necessary to establish a large number of enterprises to use and produce the services of water. These are not private organizations, but in some respects they pose the same kinds of problems confronted in water management in the United States. As the Kolbasov study so clearly indicates, Soviet water enterprises have differing objectives, and conflicts among them create problems for government. In its development and use of water, an enterprise may consider only its immediate interests so that some agency must regulate enterprise behavior to serve the larger, overall public interest. Industries may pollute the rivers, the upstream irrigator may deprive the downstream user of his legitimate supply, and the operation of hydropower facilities may conflict with navigation or fishing. As a result, the Soviet Union has had to establish organizations and procedures for dealing with these problems. All of this has a familiar ring to us in the United States.

It is not surprising, therefore, to find that a large number of agencies, as well as productive enterprises, both of the central government and of the republics, are involved in water management in one way or another. The number of agencies involved has necessitated the adoption of elaborate coordination procedures to assure consideration of all interests in both planning and management decisions. The general parallels with practice in the United States are both striking and interesting. Kolbasov does not describe these procedures in detail, but he provides sufficient evidence to indicate that agency coordination is a substantial problem.

Although numerous agencies are involved to some degree in water management, three sets of agencies appear to have the major developmental responsibilities. These are the Ministries of Land Improvement and Water Supply, the Ministries of Energy and Electrification, and

5. U.S. Department of the Interior, Bureau of Reclamation, *Answering Your Questions about Reclamation* (Washington, D.C.: U.S. Government Printing Office, 1970).

the Ministries of Inland Water Transport. The term *ministries* is used because there are counterpart agencies within each republic which work with the national ministry. The Ministries of Land Improvement and Water Supply have coordinating responsibilities at the regional level. It is stated that:

> The local ministries have special boards and river basin inspection departments which are held responsible for the planned utilization of surface and underground water resources, prevention of their exhaustion, pollution by industrial and communal sewage. They supervise measures to combat flooding, waterlogging, soil erosion, and other harmful effects of water....These agencies also see to it that the plants, factories, and communal establishments fulfill the water conservation programme.[6]

In addition to assigning general responsibility for coordination in the foregoing manner, the adopted procedures generally require an agency involved in developing a water resource or engaged in an activity that affects a body of water to secure the agreement of other affected agencies. These include the ministries of land improvement and water supply but also may include other agencies, such as the public health management agencies if health could be affected, or fishery agencies if this resource might be adversely influenced.[7]

It is evident from the controversies described by Kolbasov that harmony among water agencies is as difficult to achieve in the Soviet Union as in the United States. One wonders whether one of these agencies is more powerful than the others, and the evidence suggests that the Ministries of Energy and Electrification may be dominant, especially where power values are at stake. Kolbasov's description of controversies with power enterprises indicates that they do, on occasion, ride roughshod over other interests. Also, it is noteworthy that the Soviet Ministry of Energy and Electrification has responsibility for long-range water resources planning.

It is interesting and significant that both the United States and the Soviet Union are engaged in a nationwide, long-range planning effort. Kuznetsov and L'vovich emphasize the need for such planning in the concluding portion of their paper. In 1961, overall responsibility for this task was assigned to the S. Y. Zhuk Hydroproject Design Institute of the Soviet Ministry of Energy and Electrification. A representative of the Institute has described the objective of the planning effort as follows:

---

6. A. I. L'vovich, "Conservation of Water Resources," in *International Seminar*, p. 228.

7. See, for example, Articles 11 and 22 of the *Principles of Water Law of the USSR and Union Republics*, published in this volume.

To evaluate the surface and groundwater resources and their distribution within river basins and the main economic regions;

To determine the prospectives of water consumption growth, taking into account the recuperation of used water and to determine irretrievable losses;

To formulate basic demands towards water economy on the part of the parties concerned, such as agriculture, water transport, energetics, fishery, population and industry, and so on;

To compile long-term water balances, including the water quality parameter, and on the basis of the said balance to expose regions with the poorest water supply;

To forecast water quality changes in view of all soil and water conservation projects planned for the future;

To determine measures of high priority and to outline the most important structural measures of long-term watershed programs which are earmarked for further development and research efforts.[8]

This national plan for the development and use of water resources is intended to provide a framework to guide the planning of specific projects. The initial stage was designed to cover the period up to 1970 and the second stage was to extend this until 1980. The first stage was reported completed in 1965.

From the available description of the effort, the Hydroproject Design Institute undertook a major share of the work, but assigned portions of the work to other institutes in other ministries. For example, studies of inland navigation potentials were assigned to a water transport institute. A regional organization of the Hydroproject Design Institute coordinated work in the various republics and regions of the country.[9]

The long-range planning effort of the United States Water Resources Council has somewhat similar objectives, although the organization structure for conducting the planning is substantially different. Here, considerable reliance is placed upon the regional federal-state interagency commissions under the leadership of a chairman independent of all participating agencies. Without much more information than is now available, it is not possible to make a comparative appraisal of the two efforts.

The Soviet Union has no agency comparable to TVA in the United States. Nor does it have coordinated river-basin planning arrangements as highly institutionalized as the Water Resources Council and its river-basin commissions in the United States. It would appear that the Hydroproject Design Institute leads the long-range planning

8. *International Seminar*, pp. 30—31.
9. Ibid., pp. 29—41.

effort, various agencies and enterprises develop water resources, and a number of agencies have regulatory responsibility as in the United States, with the Ministry of Land Improvement and Water Supply having a general coordinating responsibility somewhat similar to the combined coordinating responsibilities of the Water Resources Council and the Federal Power Commission.[10]

Problems and Issues

The fundamental questions facing the Soviet Union in the water field are quite similar to those receiving major attention in the United States.

Water pollution has become a serious concern, in part stemming from the increased waste production of a growing population and expanding industry and in part from the growth in demand for recreational use of waterways and a change in value preferences associated with rising income. This, of course, is what has happened in the United States.

The pollution of the unique resources of Lake Baikal by pulp and paper mills became of international concern and drew attention to the seriousness of water pollution in the USSR. A recent paper by Marshall Goldman[11] catalogs some of the more serious cases which have become evident in recent years. Many factories discharge untreated wastes into waterways, and many urban areas do not have sewage treatment facilities. Although a recent report indicated that pollution had been halted in the Soviet Union,[12] experience in other industrialized countries strongly suggests that water pollution will continue to be a major water problem in that country for some time to come.

Closely related to the problem of pollution is that of meeting other needs associated with urbanization, particularly the provision of municipal supplies and opportunities for outdoor recreation. Many urban residences evidently are still not provided with running water,[13] and rising disposable incomes are increasing the demand for water recreation facilities.

---

10. The Water Resources Council seeks to coordinate public agency activities, but the Federal Power Commission is required to see that private water development projects are "best adapted" to comprehensive development of a river basin.

11. Marshall I. Goldman, "The Convergence of Environmental Disruption," *Science*, 2 October 1970, pp. 37–39.

12. "Aide Says Soviet Curbs Pollution," *New York Times*, 29 July 1969.

13. Goldman, "Convergence of Environmental Disruption," p. 38.

A prominent question is whether, and to what extent, the USSR should undertake large-scale diversions of water from the northward flowing rivers of Siberia, in particular to the more arid regions of the Central and Southern Asian republics. This reminds one of the current discussion in the United States of possible large-scale interbasin diversions from the Mississippi to the High Plains of Texas and New Mexico and from the Northwest to the Southwest. In the Soviet Union two factors appear to weigh heavily in the consideration of these possibilities. One is the question of whether such investments constitute an efficient means of increasing agricultural output. The other is the question of whether such programs are desirable in strengthening the economy of Central Asia as a bulwark against China.

As reflected in the matter of large-scale interbasin diversions, the question of how much to invest in irrigation to increase agricultural production is an important policy problem in the Soviet Union as in the United States. It is also evident that considerations other than the relative efficiency of irrigation as a means of increasing agricultural production are weighed in deciding what irrigation to undertake, which is also true in the United States.

It is of interest that hydroelectric facilities provide a little more than one-fifth of the total supply of electric energy in the Soviet Union, which is a little larger proportion than is supplied from hydro sources in the United States. The data indicate that the undeveloped potential in the Soviet Union is much larger than in the United States, although there are substantial undeveloped resources in Alaska. The issue, however, is whether these hydro sources can compete with fossil fuel and nuclear energy, except for peak power demands. With its much larger potential, it seems likely that, in contrast to the United States, hydropower in the USSR will provide a substantial share of electric energy demands for some time to come.

Viewed broadly the problems and issues confronting the two countries are quite similar. Each must face the question of how and to what extent it should transport water long distances to sustain or expand agriculture. Each must weigh investments in hydroelectric power and nagivation facilities against alternative means of providing the same services. Of foremost importance, both must deal with water demands and problems associated with urbanization, industrialization, and higher living standards—recreation, pollution control, metropolitan water supply, and preservation of the physical and biological environment. This is where our major problems lie today. The Soviet Union is just beginning to feel the pressure in these areas, but it no doubt will mount in the years ahead.

This comparison of the water situation in the United States and the Soviet Union indicates that in spite of major differences in the resource base and level of economic development, the water problems which must be dealt with are quite similar. Moreover, in spite of

major differences in economic and governmental institutions, the
decision-making framework has some striking similarities. Yet, there
are fundamental institutional differences, and the central question is
whether one system of decision-making offers greater promise than
the other in dealing with the identifiable water problems and opportunities in the most satisfactory fashion. This is not a question that
can be answered in a conclusive fashion, but it is possible to indicate how the results will tend to differ in the two countries and more
specifically, by using the Soviet system as a backdrop, to highlight
the issues we will face as our own water policies evolve.

Both nations seek to realize what might be called a "social opti-
mum," a best result, through the management and use of its water
resources. For purposes of analysis the manner in which this goal is
pursued in the two countries may be examined by addressing two
basic questions, namely:

1. How and by whom will objectives and priorities be determined?
2. Will the processes through which resources are allocated
   achieve objectives in an efficient and effective manner?

Determining Objectives and Priorities

The determination of objectives and priorities is a complex process
in each society, and this paper does not presume to dissect them.
However, a brief comparison will highlight the differences.

In the United States three features stand out. One is the role of
the market as it functions through a framework of private economic
institutions. Second is the formal political system through which
executives and legislators are elected and their actions are influenced by a large number of organized and unorganized groups. Third
is the governmental establishment—the bureaucracy—which is responsible to political officials, which is also directly influenced by
organized and unorganized groups, and which in some measure is an
independent force governed by its own perceptions and the relationships among agencies. The highly pluralistic nature of the system
and numerous avenues of access to formal decision-makers are noteworthy characteristics.

Committed as we are to the view that each individual should have
the opportunity to participate in the determination of social objectives,
the questions that tend to concern us relate to whether such opportunity is in fact afforded. Do the large corporate bodies which dominate American economic institutions have an undue influence on the
determinations of objectives and priorities?[14] Are politically and

---

14. As suggested by J. K. Galbraith in *The New Industrial State*
(Boston: Houghton-Mifflin Company, 1967), pp. 296—317.

socially disadvantaged groups deprived of access to the political
process with the result that their views are not adequately reflected?
Does the bureaucratic structure operate to limit the generation of information about opportunities and alternatives so that groups cannot
make intelligent decisions about the choices they wish to see pursued? If one accepts the basic tenets of democracy, these are some
of the fundamental questions that face policy makers in the United
States.

Yet, in spite of the validity and significance of these questions,
the fact remains that under the influence of our highly pluralistic
system, objectives and priorities are changing rapidly. In particular,
the provision of amenities and the enhancement and preservation of
the physical and biological environment are beginning to receive high
priority in water resources management in response to changes in
popular value preferences. In addition, the special needs of our
metropolitan communities are receiving increasing attention, and the
question of large-scale interbasin diversions seems destined to involve intensive debate by a wide range of interests.

Within the Soviet Union, it would appear that objectives and priorities are determined through a much more circumscribed process.
An elite—the Communist Party—and the governmental structure have
a very large role in this determination. The large corporations in the
United States find their counterpart in the large public enterprises
responsible for the production of goods and services in the Soviet
Union. As indicated by the Lake Baikal controversy,[15] there are external pressures, but these are much less well organized and less
articulate than in the United States. The perceptions and motivations
of relatively small portions of the total society appear to dominate
the goal-setting process.

In comparing the two systems, it is important to view the Soviet
framework without having one's views colored by the repressive measures that have so frequently characterized Soviet governmental behavior, because such behavior is not necessarily characteristic of an
elitist governmental system. The basic question is whether this system will produce a different set of objectives and priorities than the
system in the United States. There is no clear answer to this question. One might argue that the Communist system, governed by an
elite minority, might arrive at decisions that will serve better the interests of society generally than a more open system—that investments can be weighed more rationally, that pollution can be controlled
more effectively, and that aesthetic considerations will reflect the

15. Philip P. Micklin, "The Baykal Controversy: A Resource Use
Conflict in the USSR," *Natural Resources Journal* 7 (October 1967):
485.

views of the cultured rather than the masses. In this same vein one
might fear that the democratic system may be dominated by special,
narrow interests and mass tastes. This could result in investments
that are "uneconomic" and could produce inequitable distributions of
income and developments which degrade the aesthetic and biological
character of the environment.

Since private individuals and organizations have so little voice in
public affairs, the kinds of objectives and priorities that are adopted
will depend largely upon the structure of relationships and the relative influences of the various governmental organizations which participate in water resources management. How well do they reflect
the range of interests and concerns about water that are important to
the people of the Soviet Union? Do some organizations with a narrow, parochial interest have more power and influence than others so
that final decisions are made without adequate information about alternative opportunities and adequate representation of opposing interests? The structure and balance that exists will largely determine
the character of the major decisions that are made.

In this area of determining objectives and priorities, there can be
no objective measure of whether one system produces a result superior
to the other. The issue is whether there is any reason, practical or
philosophical, for having more and better opportunities for participation in such matters as water management than is afforded by the
Soviet system. My own views are that there are both practical and
ethical reasons for the more open system. The practical justification
is that the more open system will function on the basis of broader
perceptions and better information about the consequences of the
choices it faces. Broader perceptions and better information—if received and used—provide a basis for more intelligent decisions. The
health and success of an organism, including a social organism, is
highly correlated with the effectiveness with which information is per-
ceived and used.[16] Deficiencies in the information system could be
the major weakness of Soviet water resources management. The ethical reason for the more open system is based upon the view that there
is no moral justification for a position that the value preferences of
some individuals and groups are superior to the value preferences of
others. Decisions about objectives and priorities in water management involve value preferences, and the more closed Soviet system
denies a large portion of the population the opportunity to have their
value preferences reflected in water management decisions.

If we accept the concept that all individuals should have effective

---

16. See Karl W. Deutsch, *Nerves of Government, Models of Political Communication and Control* (Chicago: The Free Press, 1966),
pp. 75—97, for an exposition of this view.

access to such decision-making processes, the challenge we face is
to make the concept operable—to see that our large economic institutions do not have an undue influence, that the politically and socially
disadvantaged achieve suitable access to our political processes,
and that the structure produces good information about the opportunities we have and the consequences of alternative courses of action.
From this point of view, the search for deficiencies in our system
would be directed toward those aspects which tend to limit access,
to narrow perceptions, and to inhibit the flow and use of information.

Allocation Processes

   Equally important to the determination of broad objectives and
priorities is the related task of allocating resources to achieve the
objectives sought. In practice these processes are not completely
separate from one another, but a differentiation is useful for analyti-
cal purposes. The process of resource allocation may be thought of
as involving two types of problems. One is the problem of relating
water development opportunities to the demands for a range of services. How can water development planning and program development
take into account in a satisfactory way objectives and priorities for
municipal and industrial needs, agriculture, transportation, power,
waste disposal, and recreation? The other problem is that of allocating the services of water that are produced through such programs
in a manner which will assure the best use of these services.
   The United States has been struggling with the problem of relating
water resources planning and development to the objectives of separate economic activities since the early part of this century. This
struggle has been marked by heated debate and by a gradual evolution
of the means for coordinating water development planning with policy
and program planning for agriculture, power, transportation, and so on.
As a result of this evolution the Federal Water Resources Council now
plays a key role in this coordination process. However, a number of
other agencies also play prominent parts, including the Office of
Management and Budget, the Council of Economic Advisers, and the
Federal Power Commission. Some inconsistencies remain, such as the
evident cross-purposes of land improvement through irrigation, flood
control, and watershed management with national agricultural policy.
These inconsistencies would appear to be less a consequence of inadequate coordination procedures than a reflection of basic differences in the objectives of separate powerful political groups in the
United States.
   The two Soviet studies do not describe precisely the machinery for
the coordination of water resources planning and management with
sectoral programs in the Soviet Union. The description of agency
responsibilities and problems encountered in the Kolbasov study

strongly suggests that there is relatively little in the way of formal
coordination machinery. When this issue was explored with Mr. G. G.
Garngardt of the S. Y. Zhuk Hydroproject Design Institute[17] in 1966,
he indicated that major reliance is placed upon that mysterious institution Gosplan (the State Planning Committee) to see that agency programs are integrated in a rational manner. One might expect such a
powerful central planning organization to prevent inconsistencies between the objectives of water programs and the objectives of sectoral
programs. Unfortunately, the information is not available on which to
base a judgment about this matter.

The other side of this particular problem is that of achieving a
proper balance among potential uses in a regional water development
program, so as to realize the full potential of a hydrologic region. In
the United States we have the TVA, the Delaware River Basin Commission, a state program in California, and the federal-state interagency
commissions and committees, all designed to achieve this result. In
this area most students of water management in the United States
would agree that our most urgent problems are those of (a) incorporating
systematic management of water quality on a regional basis into a
coordinated water management program and (b) coordinating water resources planning in highly urbanized areas with overall plans for
these areas. Much remains to be done before we can say that these
matters are being dealt with in a reasonably satisfactory manner.

The Soviet literature on water resources management, including the
two studies in this volume, emphasize the importance of regionally
coordinated water resources programs which take into account multiple
purposes and multiple means to achieve maximum overall benefits
and which are referred to as "complex" plans. One is led to wonder,
however, from the descriptions of planning and management arrangements, whether efforts to achieve this result have made much progress
toward institutionalization. There does not appear to be any formal
machinery similar to our federal-state interagency commissions to
coordinate water planning and management at the regional level. From
what can be discerned, the Soviet Union is emphasizing the construction of waste treatment facilities to deal with pollution, and no attention, even at the theoretical level, is being given to the possibility
of a systems approach to water quality management. The problem of
coordinating water resources planning with overall urban planning
evidently has not come to the fore in the Soviet Union, whereas in the
United States increasing attention is being given to this matter. In
short, it would appear that the Soviet Union is at a much earlier stage
in the evolution of regional water resources institutions than the
United States.

---

17. Mr. G. G. Garngardt appeared to have a prominent role in developing the national water development scheme.

The allocation of the services of water among potential users and uses once they are produced may be the place where Soviet practice differs most from practice in the United States. It is here, also, that both countries face a basic question about the direction in which their respective policies should evolve.

In the United States, water itself is allocated initially in accord with our complex body of water allocation law. Many of the services of water are priced and a market, often a very crude one, makes the allocation among users and uses. For some services that are highly subsidized, such as flood control and irrigation water supply, the allocation is administratively determined in accord with governmental policies. For waste disposal, use is regulated by government agencies and the allocation is made through these regulatory processes.

Practice in the Soviet Union differs substantially. The initial allocation of water is made through the process of development planning. Kolbasov indicates that the allocation is made when the plan is approved. Municipal and industrial water supplies are priced in the Soviet Union, but certainly the market plays a much lesser role in the allocation process than in the United States. With regard to industrial water use and pollution control, it would appear that major reliance is placed upon administratively determined norms of water use and effluent discharge rather than upon market forces. In fact, there appears to be a strong inclination within the Soviet system to rely upon rules and standards to allocate resources rather than a "process" such as a market process or a regulatory process.[18] This point is well illustrated in the Kolbasov study. He makes a point that industries not requiring potable water should be prevented by law from using available drinking water supplies. We would tend to rely on the market, and if the incremental cost of drinking water is less than alternative sources there would be nothing wrong with using it.

Most western economists tend to view the market as an efficient allocation mechanism, and much of the literature on water resources economics in the United States supports the extension of marketlike forces to encourage efficient use of water and water services. Thus, economists have argued that water law should be modified so as to facilitate operation of the market in the transfer of water rights. This

---

18. As a reflection of the extent of this tendency to rely upon standards, it is of interest that a large volume has been published setting norms for water use and effluent discharge for all types of industry. See *Ukrupnennye Normy Raskhoda Vody i Kolichestva Stochnykh Vod na Edinitsu Produktsii ili Syr'ya* [Consolidated norms for the use of water and quantity of effluent per unit of production or raw material] (Moscow: State Publishing House of Literature on Building [Stroiizdat], 1965).

same argument has been used in advocating the elimination of sub-
sidies. Also, effluent charges have been endorsed as a means of
allocating the assimilative capacity of streams. Those who hold these
views contend that they would simplify allocation procedures, which
thus would reduce administrative costs and increase flexibility in
adjusting to changes in demand.

Here both nations face a somewhat similar issue, but from differing current postures. For the Soviet Union the question is whether it
will move toward reliance upon prices and a marketlike system to allocate water and water services. If it does not, one wonders whether
the administrative procedures will become so complex and cumber-
some that the efficiency of water use will, in fact, be very low.

In the United States the question is whether increasing reliance
will be placed upon standards and administratively determined allocations—as in the Soviet Union—or whether instead an effort will
be made to extend the use of the market, including greater application
of marketlike forces to the public enterprise sector of water resources
management.

Conclusion

Admittedly we have only a modest insight into water resources
management institutions of the Soviet Union. The similarity in the
kinds of problems and policy issues confronting the United States and
the Soviet Union are striking in spite of some significant differences.
Our interest centers upon how the two quite different sets of economic
and political institutions will respond to these problems and issues.
This comparative analysis tends to highlight the two broad policy
questions confronting both countries, and the way in which these
questions are answered will be the most important determinants of
how well the two countries respond to their respective problems.
These may be briefly stated as follows: First, to what extent should
the arrangements for deciding upon broad objectives, policies, and
overall programs permit participation and influence by all groups in
society? Second, to what extent should the use of prices and the
application of marketlike forces be utilized to allocate the water services which are produced and to what extent should such allocations
be administratively determined?

On the first of these questions the United States subscribes to an
open system, but the growing population and the increasing complexity of social institutions and technologies of management have caused
us to drift toward a more closed system. Should we move toward our
ostensible ideal or should we overtly assign such decision-making to
an elite? The Soviet Union has taken the latter course. Can this elite
produce and maintain a healthy and effective political-economic sys-

tem or will its effectiveness be impaired by deficiencies in its intelligence function?

On the second question the United States has tended to subscribe to the use of market forces. Yet, it has drifted toward administratively determined allocations. The Soviet Union, on the other hand, has traditionally favored administrative determinations. In both countries economists are calling for greater reliance upon prices and market forces. One approach permits the individual to express his measure of value by his willingness to pay. The other leaves this matter to political-administrative behavior.

These are the larger questions with which policy-makers in both countries will no doubt be struggling for some time to come. Their answers will help determine not only how water is developed and used, but also in some measure the quality of life in the two countries.

Problems of the Complex Use and Conservation of Water Resources

Theoretical Prerequisites

N. T. Kuznetsov and M. I. L'vovich

Water is notable for its high mobility. Natural waters are in continuous motion. All sources of water—rivers, lakes, underground water and soil moisture—are connected with each other through the water cycle. Use of one cannot but affect the condition of the others. This leads to an important practical conclusion: that the exploitation of water resources, planning for the utilization and study of them, must be carried out on an integrated basis.

Water, however, is only one unit in the intricate complex of nature. Its connection with climate, with topsoil, with vegetation, with minerals is well known. Climate influences its condition and quantitative characteristics chiefly through other components of nature—soil and vegetation. This leads to two important conclusions, namely: (1) that in planning the use of water resources it is necessary to take into account the condition of the other components of nature; and (2) that it is possible to influence the condition and quantitative characteristics of water through these components.

In agronomy and integrated forest and land improvement measures, changes in the local water balance are brought about extensively by increasing the infiltration capacity of the soil. However, water management officials sometimes underestimate the role of soil moisture, although it is one of the most important sources of water, used, in particular, in agriculture. Soil moisture is essential to the growth of vegetation—food products, fodder, industrial crops, timber.

In this connection, the law on the protection of nature of the RSFSR,*

---

*Russian Soviet Federated Socialist Republic.

ratified by the Supreme Soviet of the RSFSR in October 1960, is of particular importance. It states that all sources of water are subject to
conservation, including soil moisture. Similarly, it was officially
recognized that the use of soil moisture for agriculture and forestry
should be planned in advance. This has a beneficial influence on
other water resources: rivers, lakes, and underground water.

An accurate and complete idea of water resources may be obtained
by evaluating the structure and correlation of the elements of the
water cycle, that is, on the basis of the water balance. Without considering the total water balance, it is possible to evaluate only the
reserves of water present at a given time in the atmosphere, soil,
water bodies, and so on. There are 200 to 250 km^3 of water at any
one time in the rivers of the USSR, but this figure does not character-
ize the water resources. River water resources are the water flowing
in rivers, that is, the annual renewable reserves of river water, the
river flow. Similarly groundwater resources should not be considered
to be the reserves of any one moment, but renewable reserves, that is,
the recharge of underground waters. Their use in a quantity above the
annual recharge leads to the depletion of age-old reserves and does
not ensure their sustained yield.

At the present time the "water consuming" national economy can
only in rare cases be supplied by age-old reserves of underground
water. Usually such use of underground water gives temporary results, but when these reserves begin to be depleted the whole water
management system of the area is upset. It follows that the permanent and reliable source of groundwater for use in the national economy
is that supply which is renewed in the process of the water cycle.

The concept of water resources is not limited to renewable reserves
of different sources of natural waters existing at any one time. It applies also to certain water objects: rivers and lakes, which are used
for transport purposes—shipping and timber-floating.

The protection of water resources, and similarly other forms of natural resources, from quantitative depletion must be simultaneous with
their use. The implementation of this principle of conservation begins
with planning water resource use. Accurate calculations are important
in order to apply it.

A plan for the development of water resources must proceed from
workable, renewable reserves and provide a basis for the protection
of the water from quantitative depletion in the process of use. If the
consumption of water exceeds the renewable reserves and draws upon
the long-standing reserves of water, such consumption is generally of
a rapacious nature: it fails to provide for a sustained yield of the reserves and leads to their depletion.

This situation applies principally to underground and lake waters,
although in the practice of water management there are cases where a
nonrenewable volume of underground water and lake water is used.

Lake Sevan may serve as an example. The principle of sustained yield on a large-scale basis applies to water resources in the same way that it does to biological resources. It consists not in a simple increase in the quantity of water, but in an increase in usable water by making available water that is inaccessible and reached with difficulty. This is achieved by changing the water balance and increasing or regulating those elements which can be utilized.

A common method of obtaining a sustained yield of water on a large-scale basis is by regulating river flow with the aid of reservoirs which permit an unstable high-flood flow, which is difficult to use, to be transformed into a stable, regulated flow, suitable for water supply, irrigation, power, water transport, and so on. Other effective methods of obtaining the sustained yield of water on a large scale lie in flow regulation—the conversion of surface water into underground flow or soil moisture by means of integrated measures for forest and land improvement. Improvement of water quality is another way of achieving the sustained yield of water on a large scale. Water pollution, increasing annually as the economy develops, has become so great in certain areas that it is being felt even in localities which get their water entirely from natural sources. An improvement in the quality of polluted water increases the supply suitable for use.

The sustained yield of water resources on a large-scale basis is obtained by different methods of transforming the water regime and the water balance. These methods are divided into two groups: hydrotechnical, by means of which river, lake, and underground water is transformed; and integrated measures for forest, land, and water management which permit the water balance of areas to be influenced before it becomes concentrated in the form of stream flows or lakes or underground water.

The Water Balance and Water Resources of the USSR

Only comparatively recently the water balance of regions and river basins, over long periods of time, was defined by the equation:

$$P = R + E$$

where P equals precipitation, R river flow, and E evaporation.

The elements on the right side of the equation are heterogeneous. River flow (R) consists of an underground, more or less stable part U, which is of the greatest economic value, and of unregulated surface, high-water flow S. Evaporation (E) also consists of two parts: nonproductive evaporation (N), evaporation directly from the soil, and productive transpiration (T), which is a necessary process of plant life.

This results in the following detailed, complex equation of water balance:

$$P = U + S + N + T.$$

The underground and surface components of river flow are determined by an approximate apportionment of its stable part on graphs of daily discharge. As for nonproductive and productive evaporation, summarized data on these elements are not available for the time being; the calculation is therefore carried out on the basis of total evaporation (E).

A very important element of the water balance is the quantity of water which is absorbed by the soil in a year, or the gross wetting of the soil, W. It is equal to precipitation minus surface flow—water irretrievably lost to the soil.

According to the previous equation

$$W = P - S = E + U.$$

In this way, the gross wetting of the soil is expended on evaporation and the recharge of underground water.

The coefficient of the recharge of rivers by underground water (K_U) and the coefficient of evaporation (K_E) are accordingly equal to:

$$K_U = \frac{U}{W} \quad \text{and} \quad K_E = \frac{E}{W}.$$

Consequently:

$$K_U + K_E = 1.$$

It has been established from experiments that the values of K_U and K_E, that is, the part of gross wetting which goes into underground flow and evaporation, remain roughly invariable under considerable variations of wetting. There are good reasons to believe that most of the renewable reserves of underground water enters the river. Below the level of river drainage, the renewable reserve (the volume of surface water which flows directly into the sea, escaping the river) as a rule is not great. This leads to an important conclusion: that the amount of underground water which is intercepted by rivers is for all practical purposes equal to the volume of water that provides the recharge of underground water.

Almost half the precipitation in the USSR finds its way into rivers, and the remainder is evaporated. River flow in the USSR is a little more than one-eighth of the total volume of river flow in the world, which is estimated at 34,880 km^3 (minus 1,750 km^3 which comes in

the form of ice from the Antarctic and Greenland). The depth of runoff
from the river basins in the USSR (their relative water-bearing capacity) is 195 mm, in comparison with an average for the whole world of
263 mm.

Underground and surface flow are not of equal value in economic
terms. A stable underground flow is of great value, since utilization
of it does not require special regulation. This kind of river flow is
about one-fifth of the total; the remaining is surface (runoff) flow,
which is characterized by instability. It is not possible as a rule to
use it for economic purposes without regulating it. The gross wetting
of the topsoil is a very valuable element of the water balance for the
economy, since it ensures the growth of vegetation and the recharge
of underground water. In this way the dispersion of precipitation as
soil moisture is not a "loss" as it is sometimes considered to be. Of
the gross wetting, which amounts to 5,140 km³ in a year, 17 percent
goes to the recharge of underground waters which are drained by rivers, and 83 percent to evaporation. Hence the coefficient of the recharge of rivers by underground waters (K_U) is 0.17 for the USSR as
a whole, while the coefficient of evaporation (K_E) is 0.83 (Table 1).

Table 1. Annual Water Balance of the USSR

Elements of the balance	Volume km³	Depth mm
Precipitation	8,480	390
Total river flow	4,220	195
Underground (stable) flow	880	40
Surface (runoff) flow	3,340	154
Gross wetting of the soil	5,140	236
Evaporation	4,260	196

Source: Data from M. I. L'vovich et al., 1961.

Since most of the groundwater is drained by rivers, it must be estimated that its renewable reserve is not less than 880 km³ a year.
Further research will show how much of the renewable reserve is not
drained by rivers and goes directly into the sea. In any case, when
planning the volume of underground water which may be used annually
in water management, for the time being calculations must be based
on a figure less than 880 km³, because irregular temporary supplies
enter into this volume—dispersed waters and mineralized waters—
which have no practical importance as sources of water supply.

As has been said above, the ratio of the productive and nonproductive sections of evaporation for large territories has still not been determined. On the basis of experimental investigations it has been established only for different types of areas. In the forest-steppe zone (the Kamennaya Steppe) and on the arable land which is given over to cereal crops, only a third of the moisture which evaporates is lost through transpiration. On high-yield fields which are protected by belts of trees, the productive evaporation increases to 50 percent of the total. The percentage of productive evaporation in forests is comparatively high. It can be supposed from a very rough calculation that of the 4,260 km^3 of water expended through evaporation, the productive part amounts to 1,800 to 2,000 km^3.

The elements of the water balance taken over the whole country are very unequally distributed and in general are subject to the conditions which govern the different zones (L'vovich, 1957). Water in the forest zone is particularly plentiful and suitable for use, except in regions where there are large areas of permafrost and also in the western part of the forest-steppe zone. Here there is the highest proportion of naturally regulated river flow of underground origin (U), relatively little surface flow (S), and abundant recharge of underground waters (K_U). The gross wetting of the topsoil (W), where the wetting is not very great and does not create a surplus, ensures a highly productive growth of vegetation. In the steppes and semidesert the structure of the water balance is least favorable. Here the very unstable surface flow is almost the only source of water (Table 2).

In a comparison of water reserves with demand, the fact that more than 80 percent of river flow makes it way into the economically little developed basins of the Pacific and Arctic Oceans is worthy of note. Only 20 percent of flow drains to the populated basin of the Atlantic Ocean and the inland closed basins. A zone of very limited flow covers about 30 percent of the territory of the USSR; it receives in all about 2 percent of the total resources of surface water. As a result of the unequal distribution of river flow, the southern regions of the USSR are experiencing a shortage of water as agriculture and industry develop.

In recent years, in connection with the tremendous growth of industry, a shortage of water has developed even in regions with a comparatively secure water supply such as the Donets Basin, the industrial Urals, the Bashkir and Tatar oil basins, and the Kuznetsk Basin. The number of such regions is steadily rising.

The disparity between resources of surface water and need has led to interbasin transfer of river waters from regions well supplied with water to those which are not. Originally such transfers occurred on a comparatively small scale, for example, the water supply of Moscow by means of the Moscow-Volga canal. Recently it has taken place in an increasingly large volume and over greater distances. The Sever-

Table 2. Examples of Water Balance in Different Geographical Zones and Subzones (in mm)

Zone and subzone	Basin	Precipitation P	Total R	Flow Underground U	Flow Surface S	Evaporation E	Gross Wetting W	Coefficients K_U	K_E	K_R [a]
Tundra	Shchuch'ya	450	340	34	306	110	144	0.24	0.76	0.76
	Amguema	400	296	15	281	104	119	0.14	0.86	0.74
Permafrost taiga	Vilyui	300	117	13	104	183	196	0.07	0.93	0.39
	Olenek	350	177	14	163	173	187	0.08	0.82	0.50
Taiga without permafrost	Pinega	490	302	106	196	188	294	0.36	0.64	0.62
	Vym'	510	350	140	210	160	300	0.47	0.53	0.69
Mixed forest	Berezina	600	183	73	110	417	490	0.15	0.85	0.31
	Klyaz'ma	500	158	63	95	342	405	0.16	0.84	0.32
Forest-steppe	Psel	500	82	16	66	418	434	0.04	0.96	0.16
	Oka	530	167	50	117	363	413	0.12	0.88	0.32
	Medveditsa	370	66	20	46	304	324	0.06	0.94	0.18
Steppe	Ingulets	435	28	3	25	407	410	0.01	0.99	0.06
	Sal	370	19	3	16	351	354	0.01	0.99	0.05
	Malyi Uzen'	250	42	0.4	42	208	208	0.00	1.00	0.17
Semidesert	Turgai	175	10	0	10	165	165	0.00	1.00	0.06
	Sary-Su	175	5	0	5	170	170	0.00	1.00	0.03

[a] Coefficient of flow—relation of total flow to precipitation.

skii Donets-Donbas canal is being built to supply water to the Donets Basin, the Kara-Kum canal has been built, and the construction of the Irtysh-Karaganda and Dnepr-Krym-Kerch' canals is under way. Interbasin transfers will take place in even greater volume in the future. For instance, there is a plan to discharge part of the waters of the Pechora and the Vychegda into the Kama.

The extremely irregular geographical distribution of the resources of river flow is aggravated by its unfavorable seasonal variation. Over the greater part of the USSR spring runoff occurs. At the time

of the spring high water, which lasts from about one and a half to
three months (on very large rivers up to four months), between 50 and
100 percent of the volume of annual flow is carried away by the rivers.
In the middle of summer, on the other hand, flows drop sharply; the
rivers of the left bank of the Volga, Northern Kazakhstan, and a number of other regions dry up in summer, and many rivers of Eastern Siberia freeze to the bottom in winter. However, the distribution of
flow according to season does have its favorable features, particularly with regard to long-term use of water resources. For instance,
in most of the rivers of Eastern Siberia and the Far East, there is a
summer flow at a time when the flow in many rivers of Western Siberia
and the European territory of the Soviet Union is not very great. In
the future, when an integrated power system has been created for the
country, this will doubtless be used as an important regulatory factor.
With a very unequal seasonal distribution of flow in different regions,
the integration of all the power systems will permit the generation of
hydroelectric energy to be regulated throughout the USSR as a whole.

   The country is provided least of all with winter river flow, since
the majority of the rivers of the USSR are in the zone of hard winters,
when the rivers are fed only by groundwater.

   Water resources are very advantageously and opportunely distributed throughout a number of mountainous regions, especially the
Caucacus and Central Asia, where glacial conditions in the high
mountains ensure summer flow, which is used for irrigation in the
piedmont plains. The abundance of warmth and water creates conditions for the development of intensive agriculture.

   Besides the irregular seasonal flow, especially in the south and in
the central belt of the Soviet Union, there are variations in flow from
year to year. There is no strict periodicity, but a succession of cycles
of low-water and high-water years are recorded. In different regions
of the Soviet Union the cycles do not occur simultaneously: often an
increase of flow in the European part of the USSR and Western Siberia
will coincide with a decrease in Eastern Siberia. In particular there
was a sharp decrease of flow in the east and center of the European
territory of the USSR, Western Siberia, and the Kazakhstan Steppes
during the 1930s, while river flow in Eastern Siberia on the whole
increased.

   Almost all branches of the economy which require water need a regular supply of it from year to year. Great fluctuations in annual flow,
therefore, particularly in southern regions, make it necessary to regulate the flow over the years. This is achieved by means of reservoirs
in which the water accumulates during high-water years and from which
water is taken during low-water years. However, during high-water
cycles it is impossible to retain the whole high-water flow; part of it
is discharged through the spillways of the hydroelectric stations. In
general, the lower the capacity of the reservoir, the greater the dis-

charge. But even with well-regulated rivers, not more than half the average annual flow can be retained. Thus the whole series of reservoirs on the Volga are able to retain about 70 to 80 km^3 of water, which is only about half the volume of the average spring high water on the lower Volga.

The occurrence of ice on rivers has an important influence on the use of water resources. On shipping rivers ice curtails navigation for from two to three, to six to eight months. On sections of rivers where there are many rapids and on mountain rivers, the ice piles up and interferes with the production of hydroenergy and the provision of water supplies.

The amount of sediment carried by the rivers of the USSR is not great. Some rivers in the Caucasus and Central Asia are exceptions. The sediment load of the water in the greater part of the rivers does not exceed 250 grams per cubic meter (g/m^3). In these mountainous regions it reaches 4,000 g/m^3 and more. The total flow of suspended sediment of rivers in the USSR is about 580 million tons a year. Almost half this amount occurs in the rivers of the basins of the Caspian and Aral Seas and of other closed lakes of Central Asia. The bed load is very tentatively defined as a tenth of this quantity (Lopatin, 1952). The sedimentation of river waters is no small encumbrance, since it is necessary to settle it out before use and because it causes silting of reservoirs and canals.

For 84 percent of the territory of the USSR, the water in its natural state is of good quality and is not highly mineralized (less than 500 to 800 miligrams per liter), with a prevalence of carbonated ions. The water of rivers occupying 3 percent of the country, chiefly in the south and southeast of the European part of the USSR and in Central Asia, are sulphate. Roughly half these rivers possess significant mineralization (more than 1,000 mg/l). Waters with chloride concentrations are characteristic of the rivers in about 7 percent of the USSR in the area around the northern shore of the Caspian Sea [*Prikaspiya*], northern Kazakhstan, and southern regions of Western Siberia. Roughly two-thirds of the rivers with chloride concentrations have a high mineralization (from 1,000 to 3,000—5,000 mg/l). The total annual flow of dissolved substances of all rivers of the USSR amounts to approximately 335 million tons (Alekin, 1952).

For economic purposes not only are river flow and lake waters used, but also the water areas themselves—rivers and lakes. The total length of rivers of the USSR of more than 10 km is over 3 million km. There are over 330,000 lakes and reservoirs with a surface area of more than 10 hectares, including about 65,000 ponds and reservoirs.

At the present time 43 large reservoirs attached to hydroelectric stations have been created, with a total volume of 262 km^3, a usable volume of 162 km^3 and a surface area of about 70,000 km^2. In addition, 18 reservoirs are being constructed with a volume of 403 km^3, a usable volume of 148 km^3 and a surface area of 2,489 km^2. Something more than 40,000 km^2 of land is inundated by all the reservoirs, both existing and under construction.* (Avakyan and Sharapov, 1960).

Use of the Resources of River Flow

It is difficult to find a branch of industry which does not use river water. It is used in the production of electric power and in the irrigation of fields; large cities could not survive without a river water supply; and, finally, rivers are used for the movement of passenger and freight vessels and for the floating of timber (Table 3).

Table 3. The Utilization of Water Resources in the USSR

Use	1913	1940	1955	1958	1965[a]
Hydroenergy					
Production of hydroenergy, billion kilowatt hours	0.04	5.1	23.1	46.5	100.0
Significance of hydroenergy, in total production of electrical energy, percentage	2.0	10.5	13.6	20.0	20.0
Navigation					
Length of inland waterways in operation, thousand km	64.6	107.3	132.0	133.4	152.0
Length of artificial waterways, thousand km	3.1	4.6	5.6	9.7	15.1
Reclamation					
Actual watered lands, million hectares, approx.	3.5	6.1	7.0	8.0[b]	10.6
Drained lands, million hectares, approx.	2.8	5.9	8.2	8.4[c]	12.4

Source: Data from S. L. Vendrov and G. P. Kalinin, 1959.

[a] As planned
[b] In 1959
[c] In 1956

---

*These are the figures which appeared in the document translated, though the data on surface area appear to be questionable.

Rough estimates indicate that the gross consumption of water by cities and industry is 22—25 km^3 per year, of which 3—4 km^3 cannot be reused and about 20 km^3 are discharged annually into rivers. About 120 km^3 of water per year are taken from rivers for irrigation, of which approximately 40—50 km^3 go back into the rivers. The gross consumption of water in all branches of the national economy at the present time is approximately 200 km^3 a year. In relation to total river flow this is less than 6 percent, but in relation to the stable portion of the flow (the underground recharge of rivers and the flow which is regulated by lakes and reservoirs) it is 18 to 20 percent. The greatest amount of water, particularly in industry, is used in the European part of the Soviet Union. But it is precisely here that the resources of river flow are limited; the economic development of the different regions has reached such a level that the local flow of rivers in their natural condition can no longer meet water needs.

The shortage of water is caused not only by unfavorable geographical distribution of river flow. It is also associated with wastefulness, which is particularly evident in unjustified norms of water consumption, insufficient use of recirculating water supply systems, low efficiency in the operation of irrigation systems, and exaggerated watering norms.

The shortcomings of water management are attributable to poor coordination of water consumption by different branches of the economy and by enterprises. The distribution of economic activities frequently takes place without sufficient thought for the availability of water, particularly with regard to the long-term development of the enterprise. The further development of some activities has therefore required costly water management measures and this has placed a heavy burden on the cost of industrial production.

One of the greatest defects of water management is the pollution of water sources by sewage, which leads to a virtually complete deterioration in water quality—no less an evil and maybe even a greater one, than quantitative depletion. Water pollution has taken on catastrophic dimensions in places, and the struggle to combat this evil is becoming increasingly important. The waters of the Volga, Kama, Oka, Belaya, Ural, the Severskii Donets, and other rivers have lost or are losing their high natural properties. As a result of the discharge of industrial wastes, unpleasant colors and odors have appeared, the hardness of the water has increased, and its chemical composition has deteriorated. And this is not surprising, seeing that during the last forty years the quantity of sewage discharged into rivers has increased almost twenty times, and since industrial wastes contain such harmful substances as oil and oil products, sulphides, various acids, chlorides, spirits, phenols, cyanides, and dyes. The discharge of domestic wastes results in the bacteriological pollution of rivers and bodies of water.

The deterioration of the natural properties of river water causes considerable harm to the national economy. When millions of cubic

meters of industrial and domestic wastes are discharged into the upper reaches of rivers, the water in the middle and lower reaches becomes unsuitable even for industrial water supply, not to speak of
drinking. As a result of river pollution, irrigated pastures have been
destroyed and watering places have been spoiled. Disease and the
poisoning of cattle and waterfowl have been observed, and spoilage
of industrial products and massive fishkills have occurred.

In recent years important changes have taken place in the distribution of water consumers in the USSR; the proportion of water use in
eastern regions has increased. In particular there has been an increase in hydroelectricity, river transport, and industry. This trend
is going to continue.

Preliminary estimates show that with existing standards of water
consumption, in twenty years there may be a need for $650-700$ km^3 of
water per year, and most of this will be in areas poorly supplied with
water. Not less than $300-320$ km^3 of water will be used for industrial
purposes alone in the well-populated part of the USSR.

The growth of industrial demand for water is associated not only
with the total increase in the volume of production but with the increase of water use per unit of new kinds of products. For example,
the cotton factories use about $250-300$ cubic meters of water per ton
of textile, while the kapron fiber factories use 5,000 cubic meters.
Still more water is used in the manufacture of some other synthetic
fibers. About 2,000 cubic meters of water are used in the production
of one ton of synthetic rubber. Some branches of nonferrous metallurgy
are heavy water users, for example, nickel works, which use 4,000
cubic meters of water per ton of output. Up to 35 m^3 of water are used
in the refinement of one ton of crude oil, and so on. New water-
consuming branches of industry are growing faster than the others,
and the increase in the demand of industry for water is therefore out-
stripping the growth of the total volume of industrial production. However, there is a reserve here which is insufficiently exploited—the
adoption of water reuse systems by industrial enterprises, which in
most cases reduce the amount of water used and prevent the pollution
of rivers with wastes.

Considering the increase in the industrial capacity of the national
economy, it may be presumed that the use of water in the production
of electricity at thermal electric power stations will reach something
on the order of 400 km^3 a year in fifteen to twenty years, that is, to
increase about eight times over that of 1960. However, if all thermal
electric stations were to use water reuse systems, the irretrievable
expenditure of water would be in all about 25 to 30 km^3 a year. And
this is no small amount considering that it represents the water use
of only one branch of the economy.

Speaking at the Plenum of the Central Committee of the Communist
Party of the Soviet Union in January, 1961, N. S. Khrushchev empha-

sized: "We can get an additional one to one and a half billion poods of grain, and more if necessary, on lands which are irrigated. This means that we will be able to satisfy 30 to 40 percent of the needs of the country with a guaranteed grain supply from lands under irrigation; that is, to obtain the yield irrespective of drought and other unfavorable natural phenomena." Having responded to the question, "Do we have such lands?" in the affirmative, Mr. Khrushchev remarked that obviously "it is wisest to invest in irrigation in those areas which will give the highest return on the investment.

"Such areas are Central Asia, including parts of the Golodnaya Steppe, the southern Russian Federation, southern Ukraine, Georgia, Azerbaidzhan, and Armenia."[1]

The development of irrigation involves additional use of water, though this use will expand more slowly than will the area of land under irrigation. But irrigated agriculture may expand with the present rate of water consumption because of important, as yet unused, reserves. The efficiency of present-day irrigation systems is low. Much water is wasted in irrigation canals, irrigation norms are overstated, and a considerable quantity of water goes back into the rivers. In prospect is the task of achieving a coefficient of water use in irrigation systems which approaches unity (included among the beneficial uses would be the leaching out of waterlogged soils). This would permit the amount of water which is used currently to irrigate an area at least two and a half times as large.

These examples show that the time has come to change to new methods of planned use of water resources. Planning must be carried out on a long-term basis and not be confined to meeting needs which have just arisen. It must be comprehensive, that is to say, the water needs of all branches of the economy and culture and all forms of water resources should be taken into consideration.

In the future, difficulties caused by the limitations of the water resources may be successfully overcome if all stages of water management are highly coordinated, from the locating of branches of the national economy to the actual exploitation of water resources, ensuring in the process their conservation and sustained yield. Economics plays an important role in the solution of water problems. Modern techniques permit water to be obtained at any place in any quantity, and of a high quality besides. However, in some cases capital investments which are made for these purposes may place a heavy burden on the cost of production. The important principle of economics—a quick return on expenditure—applies fully to water management and must on no account be ignored.

---

1. N. S. Khrushchev, *The Improvement of Public Welfare and the Problems of Increasing Agricultural Production* (Moscow, 1961), p. 15.

Alterations in the Water Balance of Areas
and in the River Flow

River flow is altered in the process of use. It is regulated by reservoirs. It is reduced as a result of withdrawal. These changes are
brought about by hydrotechnical means. However, as mentioned earlier, change in river flow also occurs in the early stage of its formation, on the slopes of the river basin, as a result of agriculture and
different land improvement measures. The volume of these activities
grows uninterruptedly while methods for carrying them out are improving. For this reason the structure of the water balance does not remain constant. It is evident from this that the elements of the water
balance are conditioned not only by cyclical variations of natural
origin but by changes brought about by man's economic activities.

The more frequent cyclical fluctuations in river flow are superim-
posed on the slow changes that occur over the centuries, swinging
the balance one way or the other for long periods of time. These prolonged changes make the average level of a given element in the water
balance unstable. Recent research has shown that moisture conditions
in the Northern Hemisphere are tending generally to decline (Shnitnikov, 1957). A study of this process should be developed, and if confirmed it should be taken into consideration in the planning of water
management.

In the 1890s V. V. Dokuchaev (1892), A. A. Izmail'skii (1893), and
A. I. Voeikov (1894) showed that the water balance of the steppes had
changed as a result of ploughing and primitive methods of agriculture.
Science at that time could not evaluate the extent of the changes which
had taken place, but the trend was correctly diagnosed (an increase
in peak surface flows, a decline in the recharge of underground waters
by midsummer flows, and a general increase in annual flows).

Studies undertaken in the last decade have shown that the general
trend of changes in the water balance and flow has altered under the
influence of modern, more productive agriculture. With intensive agriculture there is a decrease of surface (high-water) flow and a certain
increase in underground (midsummer) flow, with a decline in total annual flow. The reasons for such changes are more modern methods
and mechanization of agriculture and increases in crop yield.

One of the most effective measures that have changed the water
balance in places has been the wide adoption of autumn ploughing,
which began in the thirties. Before the collectivization of agriculture,
this method of working the soil was hardly used, but at the present
time it is widely distributed over the steppe and forest-steppe zones.
Whereas in the past the spring runoff from the fields was formed on
packed soil under the stubble, now it develops on loosened soil,
which has a much higher infiltration capacity. An increase in the
ability of the topsoil to absorb moisture is achieved by a combination

of the correct cultivation of the soil, correct crop rotation, and fertilization. All these measures result in an increase of gross wetting of
the soil and a decrease of surface flow. The ploughing of virgin and
disused lands contributes to this. The water balance and flow may
also be changed substantially by regulating the grazing of cattle and
improving natural meadows.

In zones of insufficient rainfall, protective forest plantations have
a major modifying influence, in that they foster the accumulation of
snow on fields and help to increase the recharge of underground waters
and reduce evaporation; and, as a result, they bring about a decrease
in the coefficient of transpiration. The latter property of field-protecting plantations helps to ensure that every drop of water may produce
better plant growth. In this way the efficiency of use of soil moisture
is increased. The total effect of protective plantations is to increase
yield. Forest plantations also hold back and absorb downhill runoff
and as a consequence, reduce erosion. Their influence on river flow
is expressed in lower high-water flow and higher midsummer flow,
with a reduction in total flow.

An important factor in altering the water balance is reclamation,
that is, drainage and irrigation. On irrigated areas a radical transformation of the water balance occurs. Even such large rivers as the
Syr-Dar'ya are affected.

More work on field-protecting forest plantations is envisaged in
the new program of the Communist Party of the Soviet Union. It has
been established by research and innumerable experiments that correctly planned and carefully cultivated systems of forest belts effectively alter the climate of the air close to the ground and the water
balance of the area. In the steppe and forest-steppe zones there has
been a very real increase of 20 to 30 percent in the yield of grain
crops under the influence of mature forest belts. This result is
achieved by a checkerboard arrangement with fields of the right size,
ranging roughly from 100 to 200 hectares according to the dryness of
the climate. The protective action of the forest belts depends on
their height and is limited to a comparatively small radius. It extends
for a distance not exceeding twenty-five to thirty times the height of
the forest plantation. Consequently, if the height of the forest belts
is, say, 10 meters, their protective action would be to all intents and
purposes imperceptible in the center of an interbelt field with an area
of 500 by 500 meters. Therefore the proposal to create large interbelt fields cannot be considered justifiable. As for the water-regulating
effect of the forest belts, this is confined to the slope below the trees.

Experience and calculation show that with proper placing and the
correct width of forest belts, it is possible to create an effective network of protective plantations which take up 3 to 6 percent of the
arable area. A higher percentage is necessary only in more parched
areas where dry winds and dust storms are frequent, and in badly

eroded districts. In planning, it is necessary to try to extend the forest belts beyond the boundaries of the fields, but this is not always possible. In any event, a reduction in the area of arable land of 3 to 6 percent for the sake of an increase in yield of 20 to 30 percent is perfectly reasonable. The loss of gross returns from the area occupied by forest belts is exceeded five to ten times by the increase in yield from the remaining territory.

In order to obtain quicker results, it is necessary to select species of trees for the forest belts so that a large proportion of them are fast-growing. In the majority of cases the forest belts should be open, or of such a pattern that the air circulates freely.

The direct use of protective plantations for water management is to reduce surface flow and, consequently, river floods, and also to increase the recharge of underground waters. A large part of the forests of the forest zone perform just such a role. The water-regulating role of forests and their influence on the water balance and flow are very important. It is enough to say that in the taiga every 10,000 km^2 of forest increases the recharge of rivers with underground waters by 0.7 to 0.8 km^3 a year. In the hardwood forest subzone this amount is reduced to 0.3 to 0.5 km^3. The destruction of forests and their conversion into areas of low productivity lead to a reduction of the water-regulating capacity of the land. Similar results occur from the industrial cutting of forests with the use of heavy tractors and also from the grazing of cattle in forests, which reduces the high water-regulating properties of the forest topsoil (L'vovich, 1958).

Under present conditions of forest management, of forest conservation and logging, the water-regulating activity of forests in general throughout the country seems to be declining. In this connection urgent measures should be taken to improve the system of water-conserving forests which was created in the USSR twenty-five years ago and which played a positive role at one time. The scientific basis for this system proceeds from the assumption that the water-conserving properties of forests are incompatible with their exploitation. This premise served as the basis for prohibiting timber cutting as the primary use in restricted forest belts along rivers and other forests of the first group, where felling is permitted only for the care and maintenance of the forest, and is in no way connected with industrial logging. Such restricted forests are about 5 percent of the total forested land in the USSR. For example, in the Volga Basin above Gor'kii, they occupy 6 percent of the area, above the city of Rybinsk, 10 to 12 percent, and in the Moscow River Basin, 20 percent. In forests of the other group, ordinary industrial logging is carried out with some or no limitations. In these forests, as a result of significant damage done to the soil by hauling tractors, extensive logging over large areas, and cluttering the ground with debris, as a rule the natural regeneration of the timber is not assured, and the forested area is reduced. Even where the forest does regenerate, its water-regulating properties decline sharply.

The decline in the water-regulating role of forests is by no means an unavoidable result of their exploitation. If the logging is carried out rationally, within the limits of the average annual increase of trees and by ensuring regeneration, the forests fully retain their positive role in the moisture cycle.

The prohibition on industrial logging in forests adjoining rivers is justified only for a narrow zone in which the roots of the trees protect the banks from stream erosion and wave action, and also in the basins of gullies and streams which enter directly into the river. Most of the river flow is formed over the whole drainage area, and in this respect there is no difference between forests along the rivers and those which are far from them. They all have water-conserving importance and all must be conserved and exploited by rational methods.

Legislation to protect the water-conserving action of forests must be aimed not at prohibiting logging in a comparatively small part of the forest and permitting it without restriction in the remaining large part, but at organizing correct, cultivated forest management which would ensure the regeneration of forests of high productivity potential and allow for a more equal distribution of mature forests throughout the whole area of the basins at any period of the logging turnover. It is also necessary to regulate logging methods, forbidding the cluttering of the clearings and the use, particularly in summer on unfrozen ground and on slopes, of heavy hauling tractors. The hauling of timber should be carried out by aerial winches or other methods harmless to the soil, and removal should be by ice, sleeper, and cable-suspension ways. In general the technology of the exploitation and regeneration of forests should be developed in such a way that the water-regulating properties of forest associations should not in any way be reduced.

No generalities can be prescribed on this important issue. Felling regulations should vary according to zonal and local conditions. For example, in the mixed forest belt, where less than half the area is forested, the destruction of large tracts of forest in order to put the land to some other use should not be allowed. Exceptions may be allowed only in those cases where the area on which felling has taken place is earmarked for high-yield agriculture after the necessary land-improvement work has been carried out. In the taiga, reduction of the forest is permissible on the condition that the total forest cover is not reduced below 50 percent of the area; in this way the remaining forests are distributed over not too large tracts. In the steppes and forest-steppe zones the percentage of forested land must be increased by field-protecting and antierosion forest plantations. In forests where felling may cause erosion, it is necessary to have the cutting areas in belts across the slopes. Drainage operations must be carried out in felled areas which have become waterlogged. Strict felling conditions should be introduced in mountain forests, especially where there is poor topsoil. A prohibition on timber cutting as a prime use should be maintained in recreational forests in urban and resort districts. There should be a prohibition on the grazing of cattle in forests.

The organization of a new system of water-conserving forests must be brought about in the near future. The measures which have been outlined will provide for greater efficiency in forest management, together with the preservation of the forest resources of the USSR and of their water-conserving activity. Limited planned felling in parts of forests which have been associated up till now with the first group will permit an increase in yield because of the accumulation in them of overmature timber, and will lead to regeneration of the forests.

Alteration of the water balance occurs usually as a result of land-improvement measures aimed at solving other economic problems, mainly concerned with agriculture and forest management. They have a positive influence on the water balance.

Because of its importance, the water requirements of agriculture naturally enjoy an advantage. However, there is a need to manage the water balance not only in the interests of agriculture and forest management, but of water management as well. In the majority of cases these interests coincide. The water balance of a highly productive area is more favorable than the water balance of an unproductive area. The topsoil of highly productive, arable land, meadows, and woods is characterized by high water-regulating properties. In dry regions both farm and water management are involved in reducing surface flow as much as possible and in translating it into soil moisture. It follows that increased productivity of arable land, meadows, and forests will improve the water balance and river flow.

There is only one element of the water balance in which water management is concerned more than agriculture, and that is underground flow which is running so deep that the capillary border does not reach the root-inhabited stratum. Water management needs this flow as a means of regulating the rivers supplementing the influence of reservoirs.

As has been indicated, there are about 880 km^3 of naturally regulated river water of underground origin in the USSR. To this should be added a further 200 to 250 km^3 of flow which is regulated by lakes. Thus there are 1,100 km^3 of river flow which do not need regulation. No doubt in the future it will be necessary to regulate also the remaining part of surface flow, which is about 3,150 km^3. If this is brought about by means of reservoirs, an excessively large territory will have to be flooded—about 100 million hectares of useful land.

It is obvious that, along with reservoirs, the water-regulating properties of forests and cultivated land must be used to the utmost.

In cases where the problem of improving the recharge of groundwater is not solved by agrotechnical or forest-improvement methods, a solution will have to be sought through the application of new—for example physical-chemical—methods. These methods will, it seems, greatly increase the permeability to water not only of the topsoil but of substantial layers of subsoil.

Back in the 1930s B. V. Polyakov (1939), when making hydrological and water management estimates on the Volga-Don Canal project and on plans for irrigation beyond the Volga, based his calculations on a quantity of flow which was 10 to 15 percent less than the observed amount on the grounds that the increased productivity of agriculture must lead to increased use of water and decreased high-water flow. Taking as a guideline the arrangements that were made at that time to reform agriculture, M. I. L'vovich, in his work of 1952, estimated the expected decrease of river flow in comparison with the flow prior to 1930 at an average of 14 percent for the whole Don basin, 6 to 20 percent for different tributaries of the Don, 7 percent for the Dnepr, and 2 percent for the Volga. Proceeding from these observations, L. T. Fedorov (1952) estimated the decrease in the average volume of spring flow of the Oka at 23 percent, of the Sviyaga at 37 percent, of the Karpovka (Volgogradskaya oblast') at 40 percent, of the Bol'shoi Uzen' at 44 percent, and of the Tsimla at 60 percent. S. L. Vendrov (1953) made a thorough calculation of the change of flow on the Don and came to the conclusion that from 1931 to 1957 the flow had decreased 10 percent, as compared with the period 1881 to 1930. A. S. Shklyaev (1955) by three independent methods determined the decrease in the average flow of the Oka during the years 1931 to 1941 in comparison with the period 1885 to 1930. It was 8 percent. M. I. L'vovich (1960) estimated the decrease in flow occurring at the start of the 1960s in comparison with the period prior to 1950, as follows: for the Don, 9 to 12 percent; for the Voronezh, 9 percent; Khoper, 12 percent; Medveditsa, 15 percent; Chir, 20 percent; Severskii Donets, 8 percent; Sal, 20 to 30 percent. G. V. Nazarov (1960) as a result of two independent methods estimated the decrease in flow of the Malyi and Bol'shoi Uzen' for the years 1950 to 1956 at 20 to 22 percent, compared with the period before the collectivization of agriculture (1909 to 1932), and at 30 to 40 percent for the beginning of the 1960s. In the future, as agriculture develops, the flow of these rivers will, it seems, decrease by 50 percent. I. A. Kuznik (1958) advanced correction factors for the quantity of flow, observed earlier, of the rivers of the middle and lower Volga basin, as follows: for the left bank, in the north, 0.85; for the left bank, in the south, 0.80; and for the right bank of the Volga, 0.85.

In the future, with the growth in agricultural productivity, the change of flow will become more significant. For instance, according to rough calculations made by the Institute of Geography of the Acad-

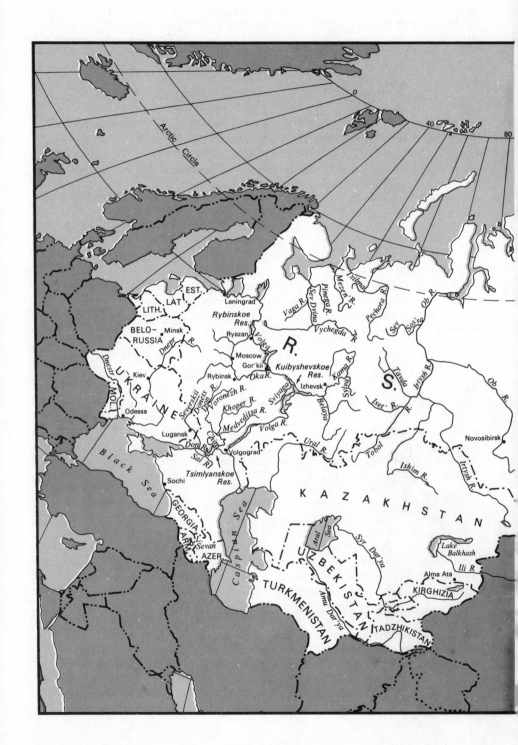

Principal River Systems of the USSR

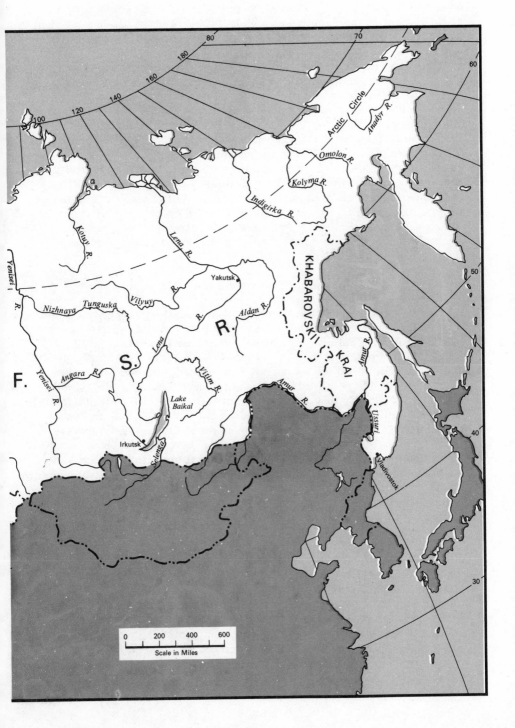

University of Wisconsin Cartographic Laboratory

emy of Sciences of the USSR, the flow of rivers which are formed wholly in the steppes and forest-steppe regions will decrease by 35 to 50 percent in the second half of the 1970s. Decreases in flow even of such a large river as the Don may be expected from 29 km³ (before 1950) to 21 km³ a year, that is, by almost 30 percent.

Thus even an incomplete survey of present data on changes in river flow provides an indication of a definite trend of change in the ratios of the elements of the water balance. These changes must be taken into consideration in planning the utilization of water resources and in implementing hydrological and water management calculations. It cannot be considered right, therefore, that almost all hydroelectric stations are planned and built without regard for the fact that the volume of river water tends to decrease as agricultural productivity increases. In planning these installations it has been assumed that the flow of rivers under identical climatic conditions has been, and will be, unchanged. The productivity of some hydroelectric stations, which have been built on the basis of this false premise, must be expected to turn out to be lower than was envisaged in the plans.

Methods of Hydrologic Calculation

A great deficiency in the planning of hydrotechnical constructions, especially dams and bridges, is the use of formalistic statistical methods of hydrological calculation. In calculating maximum flow, on which the choice of the size of overflow weirs and bridges depends, it is customary to take as a base a statistically computed measurement (maximum flow) of high water, which may recur once in 10,000 years (a probability of 0.01 percent), once in 1,000 years (1.0 percent), or once in 100 years (1 percent), and so on; but the actual choice of probability is not substantiated. The criteria of probability and the types of probability curves which serve for the computation of calculated flows of water do not have any physical significance, are subordinated to the law of large numbers, and in fact cannot be substantiated. As a result, installations are built that are far too big, unnecessarily raising the cost of construction and requiring an excessive use of building materials and metals.

For example, in the plan for the Volgogradskaya hydroelectric station, the dimensions of the spillway of the dam were determined on the basis of a statistically calculated maximum flow of water of 76,000 cubic meters per second. Meanwhile, the maximum flow of water in the Volga, observed over nearly 250 years, has never exceeded 60,000 cubic meters per second. Studies indicate that under exceptionally favorable conditions for spring runoff, the highest (catastrophic) maximum flow cannot be substantially more than the observed quantity. When it is considered that eight large reservoirs

that have been, or are being, constructed on the Volga with a total
usable volume of 75 km^3 (which is 30 percent of the volume of the
greatest high water on the lower Volga), it is quite clear that the calculated daily maximum flow of water not only need not be exceeded,
but may even be reduced. If, in the operation of hydroelectric stations, prognoses of high water are used (which, especially in the case
of large rivers, have a high degree of accuracy), it is possible through
the manipulation of storage to adopt a calculated maximum flow significantly lower than the daily flow. Thus there are reasons to think
that the maximum estimated flow which was used in the planning of
the Volgogradskaya hydroelectric station is much too high. The dimensions of the dam spillway are correspondingly exaggerated. The
same applies to other hydroelectric stations. For example, the Pirogov-
skaya and Akulovskaya dams on the Moscow–Volga Canal, which are
intended to let through a maximum flow that may recur once in 10,000
years, have not once been opened during the whole twenty years of
their existence. The floodgates of the Rybinskaya hydroelectric station dam, which has been in existence since 1942, were opened only
once, in 1955, and then only to let through 25 percent of the calculated maximum flow, although the maximum in that year was the highest for the upper Volga for seventy-five years.

These examples indicate that in hydrotechnical construction there
is considerable excess capacity, created as a result of formalistic
statistical methods of hydrological calculation. There are ways that
have been tested to replace these methods with better substantiated
genetic methods. They are based on a physical analysis of the possible maximum flows of water. Unfortunately, this important problem
is underestimated in water management. Hydrological institutions
give it little attention, while hydrotechnical and water management
personnel do not make the appropriate demands of science and do not
make use of what science has achieved.

Our extensive, small reservoir economy also suffers from a number
of shortcomings. Hydrological and water management estimates of
small reservoirs are often poorly substantiated. A formalistic use of
the method of calculation by methods of analogy, which exists for this
purpose, frequently results in the small reservoirs that have been constructed being without water or, on the other hand, in the calculated
maximum flows being underestimated and the dams being destroyed by
floods. To this must be added the low quality of construction. Dams
are frequently built without spillways, and break, or else spillways
are made without regard for the most elementary technical rules and
are washed away. In a number of cases small reservoirs in the steppes
and forest-steppe zones have suffered intensive siltation, as much as
4 to 6 percent and more of their original capacity in one year. Such
ponds, after ten to fifteen years, are already losing their importance.
If measures to protect their watersheds from erosion are carried out,

their life may be extended tenfold and more. Small reservoirs are quite inadequately used for fish-breeding, and where attempts are being made in this direction, the fish frequently do badly because of pollution of the water with sewage. It is gratifying to note that in the last four to five years local water authorities have begun to give more attention to correcting the small reservoir economy.

One of the most important tasks for the subsequent development of water management is to develop new methods of hydrologic calculation, which would provide for economy in hydrotechnical constructions and water management measures, and for a quick return on capital outlay with a full guarantee of the durability of the structures and of their operational safety (L'vovich, 1959b).

Conservation of Water Resources

With the growth of the national economy, greater demands are being made on the quality and quantity of water. At the present time, water consumption in the USSR has reached a stage where the conservation of water resources has become a very great problem, and the further development of the whole national economy depends upon its being resolved successfully.

Water conservation is regulated by the appropriate directives— ordinances of Party Congresses and decrees of higher government agencies. At the basis of these directives lie the instructions and thoughts of V. I. Lenin. Speaking on 11 April 1921, to the communist faction of the All-Union Central Council of Trade Unions on concessions, Lenin said: "In order to preserve the sources of our raw materials we must strive to fulfill and observe scientific and technical principles. In the matter of timber production, for instance, it is necessary to see that forest management is correctly carried out; in oil production, be alert to the problem of water contamination. In this way, scientific and technical rules are observed and rational methods of exploitation used."[2]

Recalling Lenin's instructions that the conservation of natural wealth must occur simultaneously with its exploitation, we are forced to observe that of late the conservation of river and underground water resources has lagged behind the scientific and technical principles which operate in production.

Until very recently the regulation of river flow was associated with the management of the water regime of reservoirs, while much too little attention was given to measures on the watersheds. Questions of different measures and scientific and technical principles concern-

_____

2. V. I. Lenin, *Collected Works*, vol. 32, p. 286.

ing the conservation of water resources in different natural zones and regions have been quite inadequately studied. Work in this sphere has been poorly coordinated with measures to protect other forms of natural wealth.

A number of organizational and legislative measures to improve and develop water management have recently been implemented. An important step in this direction was the decree of the Council of Ministers of the USSR of 22 April 1960,[3] on the basis of which the republic state committees on water management were set up, provision was made for the creation of scientific institutes for a comprehensive study of water resources, and the introduction of a number of other improvements concerning water use were introduced.

The organization of a State Committee of the Council of Ministers of the RSFSR on water management and of similar committees in other Union Republics has great significance. Departments of water management have been opened in the State Planning Committee of the USSR and in the State Economic Council of the USSR. The passage on 28 October 1960 of the Law on the Protection of Nature in the RSFSR,[4] which provides for the conservation of all water sources (surface and groundwater, soil moisture), and the creation of analogous laws in the majority of Union Republics are of major importance. The work which was begun in 1960 to draw up a general outline for the development of water management has opened up great new vistas in this field.

Thus, the organizational prerequisites for the development of water management have now been created in accordance with the program to build communism in our country.

As has already been pointed out, the conservation of water resources falls into two parts: measures to improve the water regime on the watersheds and the conservation of resources of river (stream) flow. They are physically interrelated, but at the same time each pursues its own objectives and is carried out by its own methods. The first part is closely connected with agriculture, and the second with, primarily, industrial production, public utilities, and, in part, with irrigation. Regulation of the surface flow results in changes in the water balance of the earth surface, and regulation of river flow leads to a restructuring of the water management balance. Both parts have the same purpose—the correct exploitation of water resources, based on the principle of preserving them. In order to achieve this it is necessary:

---

3. On Measures to Regulate Use and Increase Conservation of Water Resources of the USSR, *Collected Legislative Acts*, Moscow, 1961.

4. *Collected Legislative Acts*, Moscow, 1961.

1. to plan the use of water resources with, as a rule, consideration for their renewable portion;
2. to study the influence which exploitation of one water source
   has on others, which requires a comprehensive and coordinated
   approach to the solution of water management problems;
3. in the course of exploitation to ensure the renewal and, as far
   as possible, an expanded renewal of water resources;
4. together with the main uses for water, to encourage greater use
   for collateral, but also important, purposes (for example, fish-
   breeding in ponds and reservoirs created for power);
5. to plan the use of water resources on a scientific and long-term
   basis;
6. to base decisions regarding the economic objectives of water
   on the principle of the quickest return on expenditure.

The principle of conserving water resources from quantitative depletion is embodied in these points.

Another very important problem is the preservation of water quality.
During the next twenty years the amount of sewage discharged into
rivers and other bodies of water will increase several times over,
even if a significant proportion of industrial enterprises changes to
a recirculating water supply system. The purification and disinfec-
tion of all sewage by treatment plants requires an annual expenditure
of many millions and is therefore a complicated problem in both the
technical and economic sense.

The following ways to reduce expenditure on treatment of sewage
are possible.

Municipal sewage, even after the most perfect treatment methods,
is not completely free of harmful substances. In this connection, the
use of sewage on agricultural sewage farms deserves the most serious attention (Levitskii, 1957; A. I. L'vovich, 1957). This method is
used for the treatment of about one-half of all sewage, including two-
thirds of communal and one-fifth of industrial wastes. It avoids the
disposal of this amount of sewage into rivers and other bodies of
water and at the same time provides for an increase in agricultural
production of not less than 4 to 5 billion rubles a year. In this way
municipal sewage is turned into a means of irrigating and fertilizing
agricultural crops. As experience indicates, in particular on some of
the state farms near Moscow, the yield of agricultural crops in fields
that have been irrigated in this way is increased three or four times.
Agricultural enterprises which use sewage are amongst the most
profitable. The expense of constructing irrigation systems is recovered in three or four years. Not less than 10 million tons of fertilizer,
contained in the annual volume of municipal sewage suitable for irrigation, may be used in this way. Mainly feed crops should be grown
on fields irrigated with sewage, and a meat-dairy industry developed

on this base. It is precisely an increase of this type of production that is needed by the cities around which the development of these sewage farms is necessary and feasible.

Associated with the problem of using sewage for agricultural irrigation is the development of sewage management in cities.

It is advisable to apply prophylactic treatment to industrial wastes that are unsuitable for agricultural sewage farms. All forms of production should be switched to a technological process which would not let out a single drop of wastes that contain valuable substances and at the same time are water pollutants. The additional complication of the technological process will in many cases be repaid by economies at the treatment plants and the sale of extracted substances. The oil industry alone loses several hundred thousand tons of oil and oil products per year in waste discharge; great losses are borne by the pulp and paper mills, which discharge a sulphate alkaline solution from which it is possible to get ethyl alcohol, albuminous yeast, and alcohol residues. One could cite many more such examples. On the whole the national economy, by not effecting a rational use of sewage, suffers annual losses which can be reckoned in hundreds of millions of rubles. It is obvious that in the future many enterprises must be developed as combines, reworking all substances which can be isolated during the main technological process.

At the present time measures to deal with the pollution of rivers and lakes are based on the passive principle of the self-purification of water and the gradual dilution of harmful substances. The concentration limit for each substance in river water has been determined on this basis. Water does purify itself; however, these standards of permissible concentrations of harmful substances require reconsideration, especially since they are frequently applied only nominally. The high quotas allowed, without regard for the damage which is caused by the accumulation and interaction of different poisonous substances, have in many cases encouraged the concentration of factories and plants on the large rivers. With this kind of situation, harmful substances are discharged in great quantities. Little enough is done about treatment, not to mention utilization of the wastes. At the present time the limits of permissible pollution have been reached on the large rivers and this impedes or even prevents the construction of new enterprises and the expansion of the industrial potential of existing factories and plants.

Thus, in the problem of protecting surface waters from pollution, the question of dealing with the pollution of rivers and bodies of water in a scientific and effective way must take far from last place.

A recirculating water supply system has opened up considerable opportunities for dealing with the pollution of rivers and other bodies of water, although it has not yet been widely adopted. Only isolated enterprises use the same water two or three times. One example is the

Saratov Oil Refinery, which uses wastes containing oil several times over. The opportunities contained in a recirculating water supply system are considerable. For instance, eight cubic meters of water are used for one ton of extracted and concentrated copper ore, but a recirculating water supply system uses a quarter as much. For smelting one ton of cast iron and converting it into rolled metal, the corresponding figures are 170 to 200 cubic meters and about 20 cubic meters; for a ton of nickel, it is correspondingly 4,000 cubic meters and 600 cubic meters; rubber, 2,100 cubic meters and 165 cubic meters. Use of these hidden reserves could give water management many cubic kilometers of "additional" water. At the same time the adoption of a recirculating water supply system is one way to combat the pollution of rivers and other bodies of water.

Problems for Science and the Application of Scientific Knowledge

Broader, creative scientific research and comprehensive planning are needed for the development of water management.

Priority should be given to the following: a study of the water balance and the changes it undergoes and the development of the most effective methods of regulating the water balance of the earth's surface by integrated measures for forest, land, and water management; a search for new ways of regulating the water balance through soil management; the development of reliable methods of protecting water resources from qualitative depletion; and the development of more economic standards and methods of hydrologic calculation. Experimental studies of the water-regulating action of the topsoil in different physio-geographic and management conditions are needed.

A number of problems already resolved by science are being taken into account much too slowly by planning and management organizations. Methods which have been worked out for differentiated study of the water balance, for forecasting changes in water balance and river flow as a result of agricultural activity, for effective field-protecting forest cultivation, are all instances of these, as are also the scientific principles which have been worked out for a new improved system of water-conserving forests, for treating sewage through use on sewage farms, and so on. The results of research providing for a fuller and more effective use of water resources are as yet inadequately applied in production. And at the same time water management makes insufficient demands on science by not taking full advantage of its potentialities.

A major organizational task is to improve cooperation between scientists and water management personnel. Experience shows that the more contact there is between them, the greater the progress.

It appears to us that a radical improvement in water management could be achieved by the organization of a planning bureau or institute to work out long-range programs for dealing with large, complex water management problems, taking into account the interests of all branches of the national economy. This organization must not undertake the specific planning of individual water management measures, but must work on general problems. It must project the principal trends of water resource use, coordinate the interests of all branches of the national economy connected with water consumption, and outline future plans for water use. In common with scientific bodies, such an organization might be able to undertake research assignments as a basis for specific planning in different areas of water management— irrigation, power, water transport, water supply. A new type of organization of this kind would be able to play a leading role in working out a general outline for the complex long-range use of water resources.

BIBLIOGRAPHY

Alekin, O. A. *Gidrokhimiya* [Water chemistry]. Leningrad: Gidro-meteoizdat, 1952.

Armand, D. L. *Fiziko-geograficheskie osnovy proektirovaniya seti polezashchitnykh lesnykh polos* [Physio-geographical bases for planning a system of field-protective forest belts]. Moscow: Izdatel'stvo Akademii Nauk SSSR, 1961.

Avakyan, A. B., and Sharapov, V. A. "O klassifikatsii vodokhranilishch gidroelektrostanstii SSSR" [On the classification of the reservoirs of hydroelectric stations of the USSR]. *Izvestiya vsesoyuznogo geograficheskogo obshchestva*, 1960, Vol. 92, No. 6.

Budyko, M. I., and Gerasimov, I. P. *Teplovoi i vodnyi balans zemnoi poverkhnosti, obshchaya teoriya fizicheskoi geografii i problema preobrazovaniya prirody* [The thermal and water balance of the earth's surface, a general theory of physical geography and the problem of transforming nature]. Leningrad, 1959. [Papers presented at the third conference of the Geographical Society of the USSR; speeches on "The water-thermal regime of the earth's surface."]

Dokuchaev, V. V. *Nashi stepi prezhde i teper'* [Our steppes yesterday and today]. St. Petersburg, 1892. Also *Izbrannye sochineniya* [Collected works]. Vol. 2. Moscow: Sel'khozgiz, 1949.

Fedorov, L. T. "Issledovanie i raschet maksimal'nykh raskhodov snegovykh polovodii rek Evropeiskoi chasti SSSR" [The study and calculation of maximum flows of snow floods of the rivers of the European part of the USSR]. In *Problemy regulirovaniya rechnogo*

50   N. T. Kuznetsov & M. I. L'vovich

stoka [Problems of regulating river flow]. Moscow: Izdatel'stvo
Akademii Nauk SSSR, 1952.
Gerasimov, I. P., and Glazovskaya, M. A. *Osnovy pochvovedeniya i
geografii pochv* [The principles of soil science and the geography
of soils]. Moscow: Geografgiz, 1960.
Glushkov, V. G. *Voprosy teorii i metody gidrologicheskikh issle-
dovanii* [Questions of the theory and methods of hydrological re-
search]. Moscow: Izdatel'stvo Akademii Nauk SSSR, 1961.
Grigor'ev, A. A. *Rezhim tepla i vlagi i geograficheskaya zonal'nost'*
[Heat and moisture conditions and geographic zones]. Leningrad,
1959. [Papers presented at the third conference of the Geographical Society of the USSR; speeches on "The water-thermal regime of
the earth's surface"].
Izmail'skii, A. A. *Kak vysokhla nasha step'* [How our steppes have
become arid]. Poltava, 1893. Also, *Izbrannye sochineniya* [Col-
lected works]. Moscow: Sel'khozgiz, 1949.
Kuznik, I. A. *Obosnovanie gidrologicheskikh raschetov pri proektiro-
vanii vodokhozyaistvennykh meropriyatii v Povolzh'e* [The basis
for hydrological calculations in the planning of water management
measures along the Volga]. Saratov, 1958.
Levitskii, A. M. "Ispol'zovanie stocknykh vod v sel'skom khozyaistve"
[The utilization of sewage in agriculture]. In *Soveshchanie po
ispol'zovaniyu i obezvrezhivaniyu stochnykh vod na zemledel'-
cheskikh polyakh orosheniya* [Conference on the utilization and
treatment of sewage on sewage farms]. Moscow, 1957.
Lopatin, G. V. *Nanosy rek SSSR (Obrazovanie i perenos)* [The sediment of the rivers of the USSR (formation and transportation)].
Moscow: Geografgiz, 1952.
L'vovich, A. I. "Osnovnye polozheniya ustroistva i proektirovaniya
zemledel'cheskikh polei orosheniya" [Basic principles for the construction and planning of sewage farms]. In *Soveshchanie po
ispol'zovaniyu i obezvrezhivaniyu stochnykh vod na zemledel'-
cheskikh polyakh orosheniya* [Conference on the utilization and
treatment of sewage on sewage farms]. Moscow, 1957.
L'vovich, M. I. "O metodike raschetov izmenii pitaniya rek podzem-
nymi vodami" [On methods for calculating changes in the recharge
of rivers from underground water]. *Doklady Akademii Nauk SSSR*
[Speeches of the Academy of Science of the USSR], 1950a, Vol. 75,
No. 1.
———. "Medotika paschetov ozhidaemykh izmenenii rezhima rek
pod vliyaniem osushchestvleniya plana lesonasazhdenii" [Methods
of calculating anticipated changes in the regime of rivers affected
by the program of afforestation]. *Doklady Akademii Nauk SSSR*
[Speeches of the Academy of Sciences of the USSR], 1950b, Vol. 75,
No. 2.
———. "O preobrazovanii stoka rek stepnykh i lesostepnykh raionov

Evropeiskoi chasti SSSR" [On changes in river flow in the steppe and forest-steppe regions of the European part of the USSR]. *Izvestiya Akademii Nauk SSSR, seriya geografii* [Transactions of the Academy of Sciences of the USSR, geographical series], 1952, No. 5.

————. "Effektivnoct' zapretnykh vodookhrannykh polos lesa vdol' rek i problema ikh ekspluatatsii" [The effectiveness of restricted water-protective forest belts along rivers and the problem of their exploitation]. *Izvestiya Vsesoyuznogo Geograficheskogo Obsh-chestva* [Transactions of the All-Union Geographical Society], 1958, Vol. 90, No. 5.

————. *Vodnyi balans sushi* [The water balance of the land]. Leningrad, 1959a. [Papers presented at the third conference of the Geographical Society of the USSR; speeches on "The water-thermal regime of the earth's surface"].

————. "Kompleksnyi geograficheskii metod v gidrologii i zadachi ego razvitiya" [Complex geographical method in hydrology and the objective of its development]. *Trudy III Vsesoyuznogo gidrologicheskogo c'ezda* [Transactions of the third All-Union Hydrological Conference]. Vol. 7. Leningrad, 1959b.

————. "Izmeneniya rechnogo stoka pod vliyaniem zemdedeliya" [Changes in river flow as a result of agriculture]. In *Kolebaniya i izmeneniya rechnogo stoka* [Fluctuations and changes in river flow]. Moscow: Izdatel'stvo Akademii Nauk SSSR, 1960.

L'vovich, M. I.; Bass, S. V.; Grin, N. M.; et al. "Vodnyi balans SSSR i perspektivy ero preobrazovaniya" [The water balance of the USSR and prospects for transforming it]. *Izvestiya Akademii Nauk SSSR, seriya geografii* [Transactions of the Academy of Sciences of the USSR, geographical series], No. 6 (1961).

Molchanov, A. A. *Gidrologicheskaya rol' lesa* [The hydrological role of forests]. Moscow: Izdatel'stvo Akademii Nauk SSSR, 1960.

Nazarov, G. V. "Analiz estestvennykh i antropogennykh faktorov stoka v Yuzhnom Zavolzh'e" [A study of the natural and human factors of drainage in Southern Zavolzh'e]. In *Kolebaniya i izmeneniya rechnogo stoka* [Fluctuations and changes in river flow]. Moscow: Izdatel'stvo Akademii Nauk SSSR, 1960.

Polyakov, B. V. "Vliyanie agrotekhnicheskikh meropriyatii na stok" [The influence of agrotechnical measures on flow]. *Meteorologiya i gidrologiya* [Meteorology and hydrology], 1939, No. 4.

Shklyaev, A. S. "K voprosu o vliyanii khozyaistvennoi deyatel'nosti cheloveka na stok basseina reki Oki do goroda Kalugi" [The influence of human economic activity on the drainage of the Oka river basin above the city of Kaluga]. *Uchenye zapiski Permskogo gosudarstvennogo universiteta* [Scientific transactions of Perm state university], 1955, Vol. 9, No. 1.

Shnitnikov, A. V. "Izmenchivost' obshchei uvlazhnennosti materikov

Severnogo polushariya" [Fluctuations of the general moisture con-
ditions of the continents of the northern hemisphere]. Moscow-
Leningrad: Izdatel'stvo Akademii Nauk SSSR, 1957. *Zapiski
Geograficheskogo Obshchestva SSSR*, novaya seriya, Vol. 16
[Transactions of the Geographical Society of the USSR, new series,
vol. 16].

Vendrov, S. L., and Kalinin, G. P. *Resursy poverkhnostnykh vod SSSR,
ikh ispol'zovanie i izuchenie* [Surface water resources of the USSR,
their utilization and study]. Leningrad, 1959. [Papers presented
at the third conference of the Geographical Society of the USSR;
speeches on "The role of geography in the study, utilization, conservation and renewal of the natural resources of the USSR"].

Voeikov, A. I. *Vozdeistvie cheloveka na prirodu. Izbrannye stat'i.*
[The influence of man on nature. Collected articles.] Moscow,
1894.

Vyzgo, G. S. "O kompleksnom ispol'sovanii vodnykh resursov" [On
the complex use of water resources]. *Elektricheskie stantsii*
[Electric stations], 1961, No. 1.

The Law's Response to Conflicting Demands for Water

The United States and the Soviet Union

Peter N. Davis

Introduction

The industrialized nations of the world are confronted with increasingly large demands on their limited supplies of water from a variety
of users. These demands frequently are concentrated in location and
often are more or less incompatible. Major consumptive withdrawals
are made for industrial, municipal, and irrigation purposes. In addition, large volumes of water must be provided for industrial processes
and cooling purposes and to maintain flows for waste dilution and
hydroelectric power. Furthermore, water levels must be maintained
for navigation and recreational activities. Not only is water lost from
watercourses and groundwater supplies by consumptive diversions—
by irrigation in particular—but its quality is greatly altered and often
substantially degraded by sewage, industrial effluent, irrigation drainage, and runoff carrying agricultural wastes and chemicals. In years
to come thermal additions to watercourses from steam and nuclear
generating stations may develop into a serious and widespread problem.

Frequently various water uses conflict with each other. For ex-

---

*An earlier version of this paper was prepared for the Proceedings
of the First International Conference on Water Law, Mendoza, Argen-
tina, Aug. 29 to Sept. 2, 1968. See P. N. Davis, "Soviet and American
Water Law: Two Approaches to a Common Problem," *Annales Juris
Aquarum* 1 (1968): 283.

ample, pollution increases the cost and difficulty of purifying water
for public water supplies; hydroelectric power generation requires a
peak-and-valley flow pattern which may be incompatible with navigation; and, on smaller streams, large consumptive withdrawals may
preclude withdrawals for other purposes at nearby locations.

Today these problems are complex and widespread. But the law
had to cope with similar problems, at a more localized and simpler
level, in earlier days. Thus, the law concerning allocation and protection of water has had many years to develop.

Comparison of Soviet and American Water Law

The United States of America and the Soviet Union, two leading industrial nations having strikingly similar water problems, rely upon
totally different concepts for resolving these problems. In essence,
American water law has been occupied primarily with resolving conflicts among users in a market economy, while Soviet water law reflects an emphasis on planning which seeks to accomplish programmed
economic growth. American law assumes that an efficient economy
will result from the interaction and accumulation of individual economic decisions, while Soviet law assumes that an efficient economy
will be achieved through state direction of economic development.
These differences in water law are the result of the differences in
economic structures and philosophies, in the logic of economic decision-making, and in legal tradition.

1. American Water Law

The older of these approaches to water allocation law is found in
the United States. Within some of its fifty states may be found the
water law of the two great international legal traditions, common law
riparian rights (in twenty-seven states east of the Missouri River
and the District of Columbia) and civil law water rights (in Louisiana).[1]
In recent years, two of these eastern states have enacted permit systems which appear to have supplanted common-law riparian rights,[2]
and a few others have adopted permit systems which have partially

---

1. The civil law of Louisiana concerning water will not be discussed in this paper because it has not contributed to legal thinking
outside that state. For an extensive discussion of water law in Louisiana, see M. E. Borton and H. H. Ellis, *Some Legal Aspects of
Water Use in Louisiana*, Agricultural Extension Service Bull. 537
(Baton Rouge: Louisiana State University, 1960).

2. See the Iowa and Minnesota statutes cited in note 22, below.

replaced riparianism. In addition, the seventeen states west of the
Missouri River, Alaska, and recently an eastern state, Mississippi,
have adopted a different water allocation system, prior appropriation.
Hawaii has developed a unique water allocation system which is not
discussed in this paper.[3] That doctrine has been implemented in all
of these states by extensive statutory permit systems.

The common thread running through the American legal traditions of
riparian rights and prior appropriation is a set of rules and principles
for settling conflicts between water users. Typical conflicts to be
resolved in the eastern states were lower mills flooding out upper
mills and upstream diversions greatly reducing flows to downstream
users. The coequal sharing rule of riparianism was evolved to deal
with these problems. In the West, miners and irrigators had to be
assured of a dependable water supply safe from the depredations of
later diverters. The absolute water right with a priority based on time
of first use was developed to assure users a continuing water supply.

In recent years, an extensive array of arrangements for regulating
use has developed in the federal and state governments. The purpose
of that regulation is to offset the deficiencies of private water allocation law, to coordinate federal and state water resources projects,
and to promote comprehensive planning and management of water resources development. The two basic American water allocation doctrines and the major types of regulatory legislation will be examined
in turn.

a. *The Riparian Doctrine of the Eastern States.* The origins of
the riparian doctrine followed in most of the eastern states are un-
known.[4] In the beginning, all American jurisdictions, except Louisiana, adopted the common law of England to govern their everyday affairs. But the English water law of the time was confused and unclear.[5]
While scholars generally believe that the riparian doctrine came to

---

3. For an extensive discussion of water law in Hawaii, see W. A.
Hutchins, *Hawaiian System of Water Rights* (Honolulu: Board of
Water Supply, 1946).

4. The eastern states are the thirty-one states extending eastward
from and including the tier of states along the west bank of the Mississippi River. Common law riparian rights are no longer operative in
Iowa, Minnesota, and Mississippi. Louisiana was always a civil law
state.

For a more extensive discussion of the riparian doctrine, see P. N.
Davis, "Australian and American Water Allocation Systems Compared,"
B. C. Ind. & Com. L. Rev. 9 (1968): 647, 676—88.

5. See T. E. Lauer, "The Common Law Background of the Riparian
Doctrine," *Mo. L. Rev.* 28 (1963): 60.

the United States either from France[6] or from England,[7] recent research suggests that the doctrine probably was formulated first in the United States and later went to England.[8] Drawing upon early English, American, and perhaps French authorities, Mr. Justice Story was the first to propound the riparian doctrine as we know it today in *Tyler v. Wilkinson*[9] in 1827.

The riparian doctrine states that each proprietor whose land abuts upon a watercourse is entitled to have its waters come down to him unaltered in quantity or quality, subject to the coequal right of each proprietor on the watercourse to do the same. Each riparian may take water for domestic purposes without regard to the effect of such diversions on the quantity of water continuing downstream or on the uses made by others. Furthermore, each riparian is entitled to make a reasonable use of those waters. What constitutes a reasonable use is determined by the circumstances of each case, taking into account such things as the size and flow characteristics of the watercourse, the nature of the uses and the sizes of diversions of the affected riparians, and the location of these uses. The rule of "reasonable use" applies to all nondomestic uses, such as for mills and generating stations, and diverting water for manufacturing and irrigation. Generally speaking, only riparian proprietors, persons whose lands abut on the watercourse, are entitled to make use of its waters. The location of such use usually must be on the proprietor's own land and within the watershed. The right to use water is an appurtenance to the land abutting upon the watercourse and exists forever. It cannot be lost by nonuse of the water and can be exercised at any time.

It is clear at once that each riparian's right is measured by and in relation to the coequal rights of the other riparians and that the measure of the right can change over a period of time as new uses are initiated and old ones are abandoned. Riparianism is a concept which works best when the demands for water are much less than the supply available. Hence, the doctrine was well suited to the pioneer economy in the humid eastern states.

The growth of the eastern economy and the increasing demands for

---

6. See S. C. Wiel, "Comparative Development of the Law of Watercourses in the Common Law and the Civil Law," *Calif. L. Rev.* 6 (1918): 245, 342; S. C. Wiel, "Waters: American Law and French Authority," *Harv. L. Rev.* 37 (1919): 133.

7. See A. A. Maass and H. B. Zobel, "Anglo-American Water Law: Who Appropriated the Riparian Doctrine?," *Pub. Policy Yr. Bk. Harv. Sch. Pub. Admin.* 10 (1960): 120.

8. Unpublished research by H. H. Ellis, J. P. DeBraal & K. Koepke, (U.S. Dept. of Agric., Law Sch., Madison Wis., 1965–1970).

9. 4 Mason 397, 24 Fed. Cas. 472 (No. 14,312) (C.C.D.R.I. 1827).

water have put a strain on riparianism, at least in densely industrialized areas. Rather than engage in expensive and complicated litigation, water users faced with threats to their water supplies have
resorted to various legal devices to firm up their water rights. Most
common, no doubt, are informal sharing arrangements between water
users. If extensive capital investment is involved, users may formalize their arrangements by contract. In other instances, especially
on smaller streams, certain large water users may purchase the water
rights of other riparians. Sometimes special legislation is sought
and enacted to protect certain favored industries. For example, several states long ago enacted statutes prohibiting newer mills from interfering with the operation of older mills.[10] In most states, electric
power companies and cooperatives (whose rates are regulated by the
states) are given power to acquire compulsorily (condemn) water rights
and water power sites. State governments, municipalities, and other
governmental bodies have power to condemn water rights in the same
fashion as they condemn land needed for various public purposes.
(Compensation is paid for such rights acquired by condemnation.)
Another method by which industries can acquire water and bypass potential conflicts with other users is to buy it from municipal water
utilities.

All this is state law. The federal government has no constitutional
power to legislate on matters dealing with property rights or relations
between persons. Construction of the extensive water resources projects by the federal government is based on its constitutional authority
to regulate interstate commerce, one aspect of which is navigation.
So far as water rights themselves are concerned, the federal government has no power; all authority lies with the states.

Riparianism and the patchwork of legal devices associated with it
are the predominant body of law and practice in the humid eastern
states. It does not purport to be a logically consistent body of law;
rather it is a pragmatic set of *ad hoc* rules and practices developed as
needs arose. Generally, that is how the common law has always developed.

While the riparian doctrine appears to have been generally satisfactory for the past 150 years, in recent years scholars in the field
have advocated substantial modifications in the doctrine to cope with
problems anticipated in the not distant future. As a result, a few
states have enacted statutes empowering them to issue permits to
water users, and thereby to regulate water allocation. Iowa, Minnesota, and Mississippi are especially notable for their comprehensive

---

10. See Del. Code Ann. tit. 23, §1901 (1953); Mass. Gen. Laws
Ann. ch. 253, §2 (1959); Va. Code Ann. 1950 §§62.1–116, −122, −124
(1968); Wis. Stat. §31.32 (1969).

permit systems.[11] These statutes will be discussed shortly. First, the water law of western United States, which is distinctly different from the law of the East, should be examined.

b. *The Prior Appropriation Doctrine of the Western States.* After the 1848 gold rush, when miners began to mine gold by primitive alluvial methods in the arid California mountains, they found it necessary to acquire dependable water supplies. Both mining claims and water supplies were taken on a "first come, first served" basis.[12] Such water rights were enforced against later appropriators by custom and, when necessary, by force.[13] Such customary rights, established by the rough-and-ready justice which prevailed in that wilderness, received judicial recognition by the California courts in 1855 as the prior appropriation doctrine.[14] The doctrine quickly spread throughout the West.[15] While it was a doctrine first established only by custom and judicial decision, its principal features eventually were incorporated into diversion permit statutes. They have governed water rights in all of the western states to this day.[16]

Prior appropriation rests on the maxim "first in time, first in right." The first landowner to establish a right to divert water is the last person to be cut off in time of shortage. Thus, when water supplies are inadequate, the most junior right is cut off first, and thereafter rights are cut off in inverse order of seniority until the quantity of water to be diverted again equals the available supply.

---

11. See notes 21 and 22, below.

12. For a more extensive discussion of prior appropriation, see Davis, "Australian and American Water Allocation Systems," pp. 688–97.

13. S. C. Wiel, *Water Rights in the Western States* (3rd ed., 1911), vol. 1, pp. 68–73.

14. Irwin v. Phillips, 5 Cal. 140 (1855).

15. Two other theories have been suggested for the origin of the prior appropriation doctrine. During the early part of the nineteenth century, in parts of the Pacific Southwest colonized by the Spanish and Mexicans, irrigation from community *acequias* (canals) was practiced and was operated under a system of water rights under civil law which was similar to prior appropriation. See Clough v. Wing, 2 Ariz. 371, 17 P. 453 (1888). The Mormons settled Utah in 1848 and developed their agriculture by irrigation, employing a system of appropriate rights. See C. S. Kinney, *Law of Irrigation Water Rights*, 2d ed. (San Francisco: Bender-Moss, 1912), vol. 1, §243. These may have been parallel developments of law.

16. The western states are the seventeen states in conterminous United States extending westward from but not including the tier of states along the west bank of the Mississippi River, and Alaska.

Rights are established by giving notice of intent to divert, and, within a reasonable time, by applying the water to a beneficial use. Today, such notice is given to the state agency administering the prior appropriation permit system. A permit is issued by the agency authorizing the permittee to proceed with the diversion works and to apply the water to a beneficial use. A beneficial use is defined as an application of water which brings an economic benefit to the appropriator; the use must involve actual physical control over the water by diversion or retention. When the water has been applied to a beneficial use, the right is perfected, with the date and order of seniority or priority established by the date of notice, and a permanent license is then issued.

The appropriative right is based on actual use. Therefore, the use must be continuous; the appropriative right can be lost after a period of nonuse, usually of a few years duration. Because the right is not related to ownership of land abutting on the stream, but on physical appropriation of water, the water may be put to use anywhere.

The prior appropriation permit systems enacted by all the western states formalize these principles and provide for the registration and adjudication of water rights. They do not significantly alter the basic concepts of the doctrine. Unfortunately, they do not remedy one of the principal defects of prior appropriation, the rule that no one can reserve or appropriate water for use within the stream; that use is held not to constitute an application of water to beneficial use. Hence, in most western states, neither the state nor private persons may appropriate water to maintain stream flows or levels for preservation of wildlife habitat or scenic areas, or for creation of recreational facilities. However, a few states have enacted statutes permitting the state to appropriate for such purposes water not previously appropriated.[17] But, in sizable areas of many states, such statutes would be of little help, because there remains no unappropriated water.

In many areas irrigators have found it beneficial to band together to construct and operate jointly owned storage reservoirs and distribution canals. The precise legal mechanisms for those projects vary. Generally the irrigators surrender their prior appropriation water rights to an association in return for stock representing a share in the joint enterprise and a right to receive water from the association. The irrigation district, as the association is often called, exercises the water rights surrendered to it and supplies the water to which it is thereby entitled to the owners or members of the district.

---

17. Special appropriations have been made by legislation. Idaho Code Ann. §§67–4301, –4304 (1949); Ore. Rev. Stat. §§538.110–.300 (1969). However, no general authorization for state appropriation of water for recreational purposes appears to have been enacted in any state.

There are very few ways for a latecomer to obtain water under the prior appropriation doctrine. Usually he must purchase the water right of an existing appropriator. But often that water right may be exercised only at the original location of the diversion because of the difficulties in securing administrative or judicial approval for a transfer of location. This problem arises because the law of many states requires that the water supplies to other appropriators not be adversely affected by the change in location of use. Adverse effects upon some users are difficult to avoid in areas where a watercourse is being heavily utilized. Another method available in urban areas for obtaining water and for avoiding legal difficulties is the same as in the East, that is, the purchase of water from a municipal water utility. In the West as in the East, municipal water utilities usually have been given power to condemn water rights for public water supplies. But in some states, even municipal utilities may have difficulty in securing permission to change the location of diversion. On occasion, this restriction has severely limited the effectiveness of the condemnation power.

Because the water supplies in both the eastern and western states are now clearly seen as being limited, and because the riparian and prior appropriation doctrines are not designed to anticipate allocation problems before they arise or to determine the most beneficial development of water, some form of planning seems to be required.

c. *Planning and Management of Water Resources.* Development of water resources in a highly industrialized economy with its heavy water demands cannot be allowed to proceed at random. Some form of economic rationality must be injected into the process regardless of the economic system followed in a particular country. This need has been felt in the United States in recent years, because it has been learned that the market economy does not result in an economically efficient allocation of water resources or take into account all private or public interests in them. In fact, in some areas of development, notably in irrigation, power, navigation, and flood control, there has been for several decades a strong effort to achieve economically efficient development. The entire reclamation program of the Bureau of Reclamation in the western United States since the turn of the century has involved central planning of irrigation and power projects. The program of navigation improvements, flood control, and electric power production of the Corps of Engineers in its areas of influence in states east of the Rocky Mountains and along the Pacific Coast has been more or less centrally planned. The Tennessee Valley Authority has pursued a notable program of unified development of a single river basin for general economic growth. The Federal Power Commission, in its regulation of hydroelectric projects throughout the United States, has required all projects to meet a standard calling for the "best comprehensive development" of the particular river system.

True, those various federal activities have not been well coordinated at times and planning often has not been comprehensive, but a significant effort has been made. Better coordination of federal activities is expected in the future as a result of the formation of the Water Resources Council, which consists of representatives of the federal agencies active in water resources development.

In recent years, there has been a growing opinion that both the law for resolving water rights conflicts and the hodgepodge of planning of particular projects by various federal, state, and local government regulatory and operating agencies are inadequate for the complicated water resources problems which lie ahead. Attempts have been made to fill the gaps on two fronts.

The first is the development of mechanisms for more comprehensive planning and development of water resources programs. In 1965, Congress enacted the Water Resources Planning Act[18] which provides for the establishment of river basin commissions. Their major function is broad planning and coordination of activities by federal and state agencies in each river basin. Five of an eventual sixteen such commissions have already been created and preliminary studies have begun. Earlier, in 1962, a quite unique commission was established. Under an enabling interstate compact, a river basin commission with both planning and management functions was established for the Delaware river basin.[19] It is hoped that in years to come these river basin commissions will provide a satisfactory mechanism for coordinating the planning of water resources projects and directing efforts for the most efficient and practical solutions to water problems.

The second effort to fill the gaps in existing law and practice is an attempt to allocate water among all users and to anticipate and satisfy the needs of as many users as possible. Several eastern states have enacted water use permit statutes to allocate water among users.[20] The purpose of these statutory allocation procedures is to avoid the water rights conflicts and litigation which are sure to arise under existing laws and to provide a mechanism to implement whatever degree of water resource planning is considered desirable. These state statutes appear to supplant the existing riparian law for determining water rights. Mississippi has adopted the prior appropriation system of the western states.[21] Its statute gives all persons using

---

18. Water Resources Planning Act of 1965, 79 Stat. 329, 42 U.S.C.A. §§1962—1962d-3 (1970).

19. Delaware River Basin Compact, 75 Stat. 688 (1961).

20. For a more extensive discussion of eastern permit systems, see Davis, "Australian and American Water Allocation Systems," pp. 697—705.

21. Miss. Code Ann. §§5956-01—5956-30 (Supp. 1968). For a discussion of the experience under this Act, see W. H. Champion, "Prior

water at the time of enactment in 1956 an equal priority and gives all
subsequent applicants for permits more junior priorities according to
the date of application. The other eastern states enacting permit
systems—the statutes in Iowa and Minnesota are the most comprehensive[22]—do not create priorities between older and newer users.
All users are treated equally. Should it become necessary, the administering state agencies apparently have authority to resolve water
use conflicts. It is assumed that these agencies will choose not to
grant applications for permits when all the water in a particular stream
has already been allocated to older users. That policy would avoid
overallocation of water supplies. If that policy is followed, the
agency will then have to decide whether it will refuse to renew an
older user's permit in order to effect a shift of water to a newer user
whose proposed use would be more beneficial to the public interest.
Such choices will be hard to make, will involve planning, and may
subject the agency to strong political pressures. Up to now, however, such hard choices have not arisen, so it cannot be ascertained
what policies the agencies will actually follow.

In addition to providing a new water rights allocation procedure,
the eastern water permit statutes frequently allow the agencies to
establish minimum stream flows.[23] These flows may not be invaded
by diversions for consumptive uses. They are designed to maintain
water levels and flows needed for the exercise of public rights, such
as boating, fishing, and swimming, and for the preservation of fish
and wildlife habitat and scenic amenities. The minimum stream flow
provisions make it possible for the state to preserve and enhance
some of the qualities of living which are part of our heritage and
which can be endangered by indiscriminate alterations of the environment caused by industrial and population growth.

d. *Pollution Control*. One further matter must be discussed. Use
of water resources is not confined to consumptive and nonconsumptive
diversions. The quality of water is just as important as its quantity,
especially in modern times when so many industrial, municipal, and
agricultural users of land and water are discharging their wastes into
watercourses and groundwater aquifers. If we are to avoid poisoning

---

Appropriation in Mississippi—A Statutory Analysis," *Miss. L. J.* 39
(1967): 1.

22. Iowa Code Ann. ch. 455A (Supp. 1970); Minn. Stat. Ann. §§105.41–
.47 (1964, Supp. 1971). For a discussion of the experience under the
Iowa Act, see N. W. Hines, "Decade of Experience Under the Iowa
Water Permit System," *Nat. Res. J.* 7 (1967): 499; *Nat. Res. J.* 8
(1968): 23.

23. See, for example, Iowa Code Ann. §§455A.1, .22 (Supp. 1970);
Miss. Code Ann. §§5956-02(i), -04(c), (d) (Supp. 1968).

ourselves and all life dependent on our water resources, we must control pollution of those resources. The technological and financial problems of treating waste discharges are enormous; both the quantity and complexity of pollutants to be treated is huge. But the technological means are available for treating most of these wastes. Laws and administrative procedures must be established to make sure that these means are used.

The common law has proven to be inadequate to control pollution. Under the "reasonable use" rule of riparian law, one of the rights of a riparian proprietor is to discharge wastes into the watercourse abutting his land, provided (1) the use is reasonable with respect to uses made by other riparians,[24] and (2) a private or public nuisance is not created.[25] That law is very difficult to use by injured riparians because of the necessity to prove a causal relation, the expense of litigation, and the reluctance of courts sometimes to grant injunctive relief against municipalities and large industries even when pollution is clearly established.[26]

The necessity for regulating pollution has been recognized in the United States for many years, but in all but a few states, little was done until very recently. Under the aegis of the federal government through regulation of pollution in interstate waters, especially under the Water Quality Act of 1965,[27] all fifty states have enacted adequate legislation for the control of water pollution in their respective territories. All state water pollution control agencies have established stream water quality standards for use as a basis for regulation, and most are initiating vigorous abatement programs. These state agencies frequently are independent of the agencies which administer the water

---

24. See, for example, Clifton Iron Co. v. Dye, 87 Ala. 468, 6 So. 192 (1889); Parker v. American Woolen Co. j 195 Mass. 591, 81 N.E. 468 (1907); Packwood v. Mendota Coal & Coke Co., 84 Wash. 47, 146 P. 163 (1915).

25. See, for example, Pennsylvania R.R. v. Sagamore Coal Co., 281 Pa. 233, 126 A. 386 (1924); Winchell v. City of Waukesha, 110 Wis. 101, 85 N.W. 668 (1901).

26. See, for example, Thomas v. Village of Clear Lake, 270 Wis. 630, 72 N.W.2d 541 (1955).

27. Water Quality Act of 1965, 79 Stat. 903, as amended 33 U.S.C.A. §§1151—1160 (1970). In 1970, the Corps of Engineers began designing a comprehensive regulatory program of waste discharge into navigable waters of the United States. Under an old statute permits are required for discharges of refuse into those waters. Rivers and Harbors Act of 1899, 30 Stat. 1152, 33 U.S.C.A. §§407, 411, 413 (1970). See B. Schorr, "Federal Pollution Fighters Devise New Ways to Use Old Laws in Curbing Industrial Wastes," *Wall St. J.*, 10 December 1970.

rights permit systems. Experience will determine whether the two
should be merged.

To bring about a reduction in water pollution more quickly, the federal and state governments have established grant-in-aid programs
for constructing municipal sewage treatment plants. The grants provided under these programs supplement locally secured funds. Industrial polluters, however, are expected to pay for their own treatment
facilities. Restoring water quality to adequate levels throughout the
nation will be a long process, but the massive effort needed has begun. Whether the state regulatory programs will be prosecuted vigor-
ously or quickly enough remains to be seen.

e. *Summary of American Water Law.* American water law is made
up of several elements, parts of which were developed as the need
arose. The elements may be summarized as follows:

(1) Court-made law governing the water rights of landowners with
respect to each other, the riparian doctrine in the eastern states
and the prior appropriation doctrine in the western states;
(2) Water use permit systems in a few eastern states to replace the
riparian doctrine, and in all western states to implement the
prior appropriation doctrine;
(3) Several large water resource development programs by various
agencies of the federal government and by a few state governments which may or may not be coordinated with each other;
(4) Recent attempts at comprehensive planning and management of
water resources projects through the device of river basin commissions; and
(5) A massive nationwide program to reduce water pollution by a
coordinated effort between federal and state water pollution
control agencies.

Typical of American thinking toward economic development generally
is the idea that the interaction and accumulation of economic decisions made by private individuals best serves the public interest. The
proper role of government is regarded as being remedial and supplementary to the activities of the private sector; government should step
in only where private activity is unsuitable, inadequate, or unrespon-
sive to the public interest. American water law reflects this attitude.
That is why planning by the federal and state governments of water
resources development and management is only now getting attention.
It was only recently that the need for such planning and for more significant state intervention was felt.

2. *Soviet Water Law*

In the Soviet Union the government dominates the development and
management of the economy generally, including water resources.

Soviet water law reflects the government's primary and predominant role in economic planning, investment, operation, and management.

O. S. Kolbasov's book, herein translated, is a valuable contribution to the literature. His discussions of Soviet water law of the mid-1960s are not only helpful to our understanding of the pertinent Soviet law, but also highlight water allocation problems common to all industrialized nations and suggest some solutions. Since it is the only comprehensive description of Soviet water law available in the English language, this discussion is confined to the points discussed by Kolbasov. There are one or two matters on which more information would be helpful. They will be mentioned as they are reached.

The Soviet water law system is based on two fundamentals. First, water is owned exclusively by the State.[28] The ownership of water was vested in the State after the 1917 Revolution. Moreover, like other forms of real property in the Soviet Union, property in the water itself may not be alienated. Only the use right in the water may be assigned.[29] In this regard the law in the United States and England is the same: only the right to the use and enjoyment of water, not the water itself, may be transferred.

Second, users are allowed to develop water resources only according to the overall plan for the national economy. That plan is formulated to promote the use of water for maximum benefit and for the full satisfaction of diverse needs for water.[30] The priorities established by the overall plan and the emphasis given to its various elements during implementation in the past apparently have often promoted industrial development to the detriment of water resources conservation. The law gives first priority to public and domestic water supplies,[31] and lesser priorities to other uses, such as industrial water supplies, hydroelectric power generation, navigation, timber-rafting, irrigation, fishing, and waste disposal. Detailed economic planning for a national economy is, of course, a complex matter. With respect to water, the plan must take into account the needs of various users, anticipated needs for water in the future, the availability of water at various locations, the interrelationships between various types of uses, and the overall set of economic and social values concerning waters and neighboring lands. In addition to making plans for development of water as part of the overall economic development of the country, the State must make corresponding plans for managing the water which it

---

28. Constitution of the USSR, Article 6 (1963); Principles of Water Law of the USSR and the Union Republics of 10 December 1970, Article 3.

29. Principles of Water Law of the USSR (1970), Article 3.

30. O. S. Kolbasov, *Legislation on Water Use in the USSR* (Moscow: Juridical Literature, 1965), p. 107.

31. Ibid., pp. 107–8, 141–42.

has developed. Because of conflicting economic and political demands, the priorities established for water use apparently many times
have taken second place to the priorities for economic development.
That is, of course, a phenomenon not unique to the Soviet Union but
is common to all nations.

The concept of comprehensive planning must be translated into a
set of laws, regulations, and rules governing development and management of water resources. They should establish priorities between
uses and provide procedures for resolving the conflicts between uses
which inevitably arise in the operation of a complex river system.
However, Soviet water law of the mid-1960s, as described by Kolbasov,
does not appear to be adequate for resolving such conflicts. There
does not seem to be any unified set of rules governing all water use
activities. Instead, there appear to be several sets of rules, one for
each type of water use—industrial water supplies, municipal water
supplies, irrigation, navigation, hydroelectric power, fishing, timber-
rafting, and pollution. These sets of rules seem to be conceptually
independent with very little relationship between them.[32] Planning
and management does not seem to have been organized in a way that
recognizes that water is a common resource, that it is and should be
used by various types of water users.

One general principle does seem fairly explicit. In planning and
operating a water resource project, other uses of the water resource
should not be interfered with.[33] In this way, the planning procedures
do recognize the interdependencies of water uses. Thus, water intakes
must have fish protection devices approved by the appropriate fishery
agency, and structures placed in shipping waterways must have the
approval of the appropriate river transport concern.[34] Hydroelectric
power authorities must operate their dams to maintain reservoir levels
within guidelines established to protect navigation, irrigation, and
flood control uses.[35] Industrial enterprises must construct and operate waste treatment facilities which meet the standards set by the
water pollution control agencies.[36] Nonetheless, it is the failure to
incorporate adequately the noninterference principle into planning procedures which appears to be the major defect of Soviet water law.

The inability of the previous law governing water resources to cope
with the conflicting and urgent demands of economic development has
led to a renewed effort in the Soviet Union to protect its water resources. This has resulted in new national legislation. The Principles

---

32. Ibid., pp. 127–28, 170, 198.
33. Ibid., pp. 117, 144.
34. Ibid., pp. 117, 175–76, 180–81.
35. Ibid., pp. 166, 181–82.
36. Ibid., pp. 208–9.

of Water Law of the USSR, enacted by the Supreme Soviet in December
1970, laid down general principles designed to deal more effectively
with the problems of multiple use of water. Generally speaking, the
Principles require that the siting of new facilities and the operation
of all existing and new facilities must take into account other uses
of the same water supply.[37] Implementation of the general principles
by specific legislation and regulations is left to the constituent Republics.[38] Apparently in response to considerable concern about the
growing water pollution problem throughout the Soviet Union, the Principles establish a policy of conservation of water, protection from
pollution, and protection from depletion by excess diversions.[39] While
the Principles do not appear to establish any policies on multiple
("complex") use startlingly different than those discussed by Kolbasov,
the fact that these policies have now been incorporated in national
legislation should have some impact on the attitudes of the planning
agencies and operating authorities. The emphasis on conservation of
water resources and abatement of water pollution seems to represent
a strong change of emphasis from the former attitude of exploitive
development which Kolbasov decried.

There seem to be very few effective sanctions to enforce noninterference regulations if they are not complied with.[40] Presumably this
is because, in the vast majority of cases, compliance is provided for
in the construction and operating plans. One gets the impression that
such deviations from compliance as occur are resolved by *ad hoc* nego-
tiations between the agencies. Presumably, such deviations either
were relatively rare occurrences or were considered to be of relatively
little importance so that until recently very little need was felt for
developing methods to handle them. But such breakdowns in the planning procedure can result in many incidents of misallocation of water
or conflicts between users. Perhaps that is why Kolbasov asserts
that there has developed very little law defining the relationships between uses and between users and that the situation should be rem-
edied.[41]

Kolbasov cites a few examples of breakdowns in the planning process. He tells of a collective farm which constructed fish-breeding

---

37. Principles of Water Law of the USSR, Articles 10, 17, 33.
38. Ibid., Articles 2, 5—8. Participation by public organizations,
such as trade unions, youth organizations, and conservation groups,
and by citizens is provided for; see Article 9.
39. Ibid., Articles 37—40.
40. Kolbasov, *Legislation on Water Use in the USSR*, pp. 118,
171, 214; except in the case of water used for public water supplies,
pp. 148—49, 207—8.
41. Ibid., pp. 127—28, 170, 198.

ponds in 1947. These ponds, which raised fish for sale, were supplied by a small river. Thirteen years later, in 1960, another collective farm which was located upstream from the first also constructed
ponds. The new ponds were supplied from the same river. There was
not enough water in the river to supply both ponds; so the lower collective farm lost its water supply even though its use of the water was
much older. This dispute was never settled because Soviet law does
not address itself to the problem of allocating water in strictly local
bodies of water.[42] This is precisely the type of situation that the common law and civil law are designed to regulate. It is surprising that
the Soviet law apparently has not worked out a set of rules to be followed when conflicts arise in spite of or in the absence of planned
allocations of water.

In another situation, a different characteristic of Soviet water law
is illustrated. This example has to do with the locus of decision-
making. A set of rules for operating reservoirs has been established
in several of the Republics. These rules require establishment of maximum and minimum water levels and of release criteria to meet the
needs of all users as far as possible. On the basis of these criteria,
particular operating rules are set up for each reservoir.[43] Kolbasov
cites an example of a reservoir operated by an electric power authority
which drew down the water level below the minimum required for navigation. Boats of the river transport group were stranded. This decision by the electric power authority was contrary to the operating
rules established for the reservoir and was made over the vehement
protests of the river transport authority, because there were extremely
heavy demands for power on the grid system. The river transport
authority had no recourse and navigation was not restored until the
power shortage abated.[44]

Whoever operates a water resource facility determines how this
function is to be performed. Apparently, reservoirs are operated by
power authorities in the Soviet Union. In the United States, by contrast, government reservoirs are operated by agencies whose primary
concerns are with navigation and flood control or with irrigation.
Private power dams are licensed by the federal and state governments,
and their operating rules are regulated by those governments in the
public interest. Especially at the state level, electric power is not

---

42. Ibid., p. 198.
43. Regulations on the Use of the Water Resources of Reservoirs
of the RSFSR; Basic Provisions of the Rules for the Use of the Water
Resources of a Reservoir (Dispatching Rules for Flow Regulation)
(RSFSR); discussed by Kolbasov, *Legislation on Water Use in the USSR,*
pp. 166–68.
44. Kolbasov, *Legislation on Water Use in the USSR,* pp. 170, 182.

the predominant interest of the regulatory bodies. The result is the
creation of a somewhat different set of priorities for operating reservoirs than in the Soviet Union. This difference would be most apparent in emergency or drought situations, as in Kolbasov's example.

Apparently some urgent need for better coordination of conflicting
uses has been felt in the past. In 1960, the Council of Ministers of
the USSR promulgated a decree requiring the Union Republics to organize special agencies for the use and conservation of surface and
underground water.[45] These agencies were instructed to inventory
water resources, develop long-range plans for their use and conservation, prepare operational plans for the "complex" use of water throughout river basins and at reservoirs, supervise rational use of water by
enterprises, and control pollution. Further, the decree required that
the national economic plans reflect the need for rational use of water
and for eliminating pollution. It established a special group within
the central planning agency to implement such planning and coordination.

Kolbasov only alludes to the work of the Republic agencies established under the 1960 decree to implement this program and does
not specifically describe their activities. Nor does he state whether
all of the Republics have formed such agencies. Perhaps, in 1965, it
was too early for him to obtain the necessary data on their activities.
But time has passed and these agencies have now had almost a decade to do significant work. The work of these Republic agencies and
of the coordinating group in the central planning agency ought to have
had great impact on the planning and operation of water resources
projects. They are agencies which could define the relationships both
between uses and between users and could fill the profound gap in the
law which Kolbasov deplores.[46] Their work should be described.

The 1970 Principles of Water Law of the USSR recognize the necessity to provide means for resolving disputes between water users.
The Principles provide that disputes are to be resolved under the administrative procedures established by national and Republic legislation.[47] That means, one presumes, that the implementing legislation
and procedures have been or will be provided. Furthermore, the Principles provide for criminal and administrative liability for violations

---

45. On Measures to Regulate Use and Increase Conservation of
Water Resources of the USSR, Decree of 22 April 1960; *Collected Decrees of the USSR*, 1960, No. 9, Article 67 (Council of Ministers of
the USSR).

46. Kolbasov, *Legislation on Water Use in the USSR*, pp. 127–28,
171, 182, 198.

47. Principles of Water Law of the USSR (1970), Article 35.

of specified types of multiple use, conservation, or pollution abatement regulations,[48] provide for discontinuance of authority to use water in such circumstances,[49] and require reimbursement for losses resulting from such violations.[50]

In summary, Soviet water law is based on the concept that water is a resource to be used for national economic development. The relationship between users and between types of uses at any particular location is to be determined both by the economic needs of the area and by the national economic plan which that water resource will serve. But until 1970, no conceptual framework for defining the relationships both between users and between uses had been established to guide such planning. While conflicts between users and uses may develop only occasionally, the planning procedure should be designed so that major conflicts will be anticipated and either avoided or resolved before the water uses are initiated. The recent legislation establishing agencies for water use and protection appears to have been designed to provide the necessary cross-linkage between various groups planning for the growth of particular industries or portions of the economy. The new 1970 Principles of Water Law specifically recognize the necessity for planning for multiple use of water resources and for providing means for resolving disputes among water users.

Discussion

The complexities of the modern industrial and urban economy have placed new pressures on the water law systems of the United States and the Soviet Union. The object of law and government administration in both countries is to promote development of water resources while creating a balance between various water users. In the United States, the economic system of individualized decision-making has had the expected result of developing conflicts between incompatible water uses. The law's response to this problem has been to evolve methods for resolving these conflicts by court-made rules of law, statutes for particular situations, and the purchase and sale of water rights. As water demands intensified in modern times, an unexpected result of the interplay between individualized decision-making and case-by-case rule-making has occurred, namely, an economically inefficient allocation of water. To deal with this new problem, law and government have evolved a corrective influence in the form of various

---

48. Ibid., Article 46.
49. Ibid., Article 18.
50. Ibid., Article 46.

degrees of regulation of water use. First, this involved a rationalizing
of proposals initiated by the individual water users by administrative
regulation. Second, units of government have initiated planned projects and have made grants-in-aid designed to influence activity in
predetermined directions. Furthermore, several states have taken
initial steps to create permit systems for the regulation of water rights
which will enable those states to plan future water resources development to the extent deemed necessary. This more comprehensive effort
will supplement the particularized planning that has accompanied various water resources projects in the past. The major reliance for decision-making in water resources development in the United States
continues to rest on the initiative of the private sector, but its activities are likely to be regulated more closely than before. While
such regulation is relatively new in the water resources field, it is
well accepted in other fields of economic activity, such as the control
of urban development by zoning and urban planning, regulation of
public utilities and transportation companies, and the antitrust regulation. Therefore, planning of water resources development is not a
radical departure from the American legal and administrative tradition.

The Soviet Union also has as its chief object of water law and
government administration the promotion of development of water resources while creating a balance between various water users. Its
primary mechanism for achieving this, however, is decision-making
by comprehensive state planning. Law and government administration
have had to deal with the expected result of this mechanism, namely,
a lack of bureaucratic coordination and a lack of sensitivity to particularized conflicts between water uses. This problem has been at-
tacked by improved planning techniques and internal procedures for
resolving conflicts, both before and after the fact. An unexpected by-
product of these techniques and procedures is the realization that
economically inefficient allocations of water and conflicts between
users will occur in spite of the best efforts of the planners to avoid
them. The reliance on planning also leaves unsettled any conflicts
which involve users outside the planning process. The corrective response of law and government ought to be the development of general
rules to govern such situations. A corrective response apparently has
been initiated as a consequence of the recently developed concern
for conservation of water resources.

The use of rules is strikingly different in the United States and in
the Soviet Union and reflects differences in economic philosophy.
Those affected play different roles in the decision-making process in
the two countries. In the United States, each water user is an independent entity making its own decisions. These decisions are based
on the needs of the particular water user, as influenced by the general
rules of law governing the relationships between users. Only in the
case of actual conflict must a resolution be effected, either by nego-

tiation between the parties or by a lawsuit. But these rules of law have a very great influence on the decisions made by each water user, because they are the basis for any negotiated compromise or any court decision. Within this general framework of law, even where the influence of state planning may be felt strongly through a water rights permit system or other forms of state regulation, most of the basic decisions about overall water resources development are syntheses of individual decisions by independent water users. For that reason, the general rules of law must be and are known to water users.

In the Soviet Union, water resource development decisions largely are made by the planning organizations. Usually, the planning of different industries or sectors of the economy is done by different planning groups. The plans are interrelated only to the extent that the planners consult each other. This they evidently do, although with respect to utilization of water resources the consultation apparently has been deficient. Conceptually, the planning organizations are all creatures of one decision-maker, the State. To the extent that mechanisms can be designed to implement that conceptual unity, the agglomeration of individual planning decisions will have an actual unity. Mismatching of plans is the result of inadequate mechanisms to actualize the conceptual unity.

The concept of the unity of the decision-maker must affect the process by which overall water resource decisions are made. Planners would not assume that the summation of their individual decisions would lead to the most beneficial overall result; they would feel constrained and required to consult each other. A conscious attempt would be made to coordinate planning at all levels. When conflicts occurred, they would be resolved by negotiation within the planning structure. That process resembles the internal decision-making process within government departments or industrial organizations with which everyone is so familiar, but on a larger scale. Rules of thumb for resolving conflicts may or may not be evolved, they may or may not be followed consistently, they may or may not be the same throughout the planning agency, and they certainly do not become rules of law. Nonetheless, they are very important for understanding how decisions are made, how conflicts are resolved, and what priorities are established. This is, in the last analysis, the role of law in society. When such rules of thumb are the predominant influence in overall decision-making, as they seem to be in Soviet water law, they must be examined to obtain a proper understanding of the functioning of the system and of the law in the real world. They must be made known if they are to be useful in future decision-making.

The use of rules of thumb for decision-making is the very antithesis of good planning. Planners need some general notions about the most desirable relationships between uses and between users of water to guide them in making day-to-day planning decisions. Operators of facilities want them for the same reason. Without such notions, decision-making will be idiosyncratic, unpredictable, and unreliable. Planners and operators of an enterprise will not know what its relationship is supposed to be with other enterprises of the same or different types. They will not know how to act in the event of an emergency or other contingency not envisaged by the plan. Other water users might suffer unnecessary harm as a result of decisions made in ignorance of an agreed upon relationship between users, and undesired side effects could occur. If, contrary to the impression Kolbasov creates, general rules concerning interrelationships between water users do exist and are used by the planning and operating agencies, they should be made explicit. With enactment of the 1970 Principles of Water Law by the Supreme Soviet of the USSR, and with the adoption of Republic legislation and regulations, the need for a more rational conceptual framework on which to base planning and operating decisions ought to be filled.

Conclusion

In the face of increasing demands for water from burgeoning industrial and population growth, both the United States and the Soviet Union have given increasing attention to allocating water resources, planning their development and management, and protecting their quality. Their legal and institutional arrangements necessarily reflect the growing complexity of interrelationships between users. As time goes on, the inexorable growth of demands on limited water supplies will force the improvement of techniques for planning water resources development and adjusting conflicts between users.

Because of the similarity of water problems in the United States and the Soviet Union, and despite the great differences in the economic philosophies in the two countries, each has evolved techniques for planning water resources development which may be useful to the other. In addition, the techniques for resolving water use conflicts developed in the United States may be adaptable to the Soviet system for the resolution of the unexpected conflicts of water use which inevitably arise in spite of the best efforts of planners. Those techniques need not be regarded as being so intimately tied to the political systems of each country that they cannot be borrowed from one and adapted for use in the other.

We should look to the experience of other nations and adopt their ideas when they are suitable to our own conditions. We should look not merely at the bare bones of the legal systems expressed in statutes, administrative regulations, and court decisions. The working of the law is an active process. To understand fully what law really means to people, we must see how law is applied and how it affects them in practice. In the water resources field, we must examine how the rules of law are applied by administrators and to what extent the water user follows those rules in making his day-to-day decisions. If a statute or court-made rule is not followed in practice, it is not the law which governs the user. What water users actually do is the law which in reality controls the situation. Thus, in trying to understand our own legal systems, and those of other nations, we must look not only at statutes and court decisions, but behind them to the law as it is applied in practice. This essay has tried to do this by discussing water law as it actually functions and affects decision-making in the United States and the Soviet Union.

Kolbasov's *Legislation on Water Use in the USSR* from the Perspective of Recent Trends in Soviet Law

Zigurds L. Zile

Soviet legal reforms of the post-Stalin era have sought both to elevate the overall "legal culture" and to improve the substance of individual laws. The significance of Kolbasov's book can be better assessed against the backdrop of this dual trend.

The efforts to elevate the legal culture in general can be seen, above all, in the gradual reorganization, rationalization, and systematization of the legal system. The publication of normative acts (mainly statutes and executive decrees), judicial decisions, and the periodic and monographic legal literature has become more orderly and complete than at any time since the 1920s. Soviet lawmakers with the help of jurists have begun to sweep their Augean stables of the accumulations of obsolete and contradictory enactments of bygone days. Many comprehensive laws or codes covering well-defined segments of law (such as criminal and civil law and procedure, court organization, family law, and so on) which had served the country for several decades have been rewritten, and codification is planned for other segments, some of them never before expressed in codified form. Soviet law of water use, which is the topic of Kolbasov's book, is an area in which original codification of principles has just been achieved.[1]

Substantive improvements are found throughout the legal system. The earlier revisions expunged some of the most noxious survivals of

---

1. Principles of Water Law of the USSR and the Union Republics of 10 December 1970, *Vedomosti Verkhovnogo soveta SSSR* 1970, No. 50, Text 566. (See Appendix, p. 221.)

Stalin's rule and thereby somewhat enhanced the individual citizen's
legal position vis-à-vis the state. The reforms of criminal law and
procedure were the standouts of the early phase. They had the most
immediate impact on the lives of Soviet citizens and, because of their
potentially far-reaching political implications, attracted much attention abroad. However, the substantive improvements in Soviet law
have not been confined to these flashier aspects of governing the
country. They have equally extended to areas of law which, although
less newsworthy now, may become increasingly significant for the development of the Soviet Union in the long run. The law governing the
various aspects of Soviet economic and social life has been extensively modified and here and there greatly expanded to meet the conditions of the 1950s, '60s, and now the '70s. These revisions over
the past fifteen years or so have restructured the planning and contractual relations between the state economic enterprises, the status
and management of the collective farms, the distribution of consumer
goods, and regional and urban planning, to cite but a few examples.
In addition, the proper utilization and conservation of the natural environment has been the object of a mass of new legislation, rule-
making, and literature. Kolbasov's book can also be viewed as representing this recent concern.

The rest of this essay deals with two background questions raised
by the preceding paragraphs: (1) the style of Soviet codification and
legal scholarship and (2) the state of Soviet nature conservation law.

The Style of Soviet Codification
and Legal Scholarship

The first chapter of Kolbasov's book is directly addressed to the
codification issue. His preoccupation with the conceptual framework
of the law of water use, which may strike an American reader as be-
labored and fruitless, is a characteristic warm-up exercise for codi-
fiers. Since the Soviet legal system aspires to be a codified system,
it must live up to the standards of such a system. In short, it must
not only have its law reduced to written sources but must also have it
organized in doctrinally distinct and internally consistent segments.
The boundaries between these segments and the points of their potential contact must be thought out with care. This naturally encourages
conceptual, compartmentalized thinking at the expense of a pragmatic,
result-oriented search for solutions to real-life problems. Consequently, a Soviet jurist is led to sharpen his legalistic skills and ne-
glect the nonlegal element of the situations with which he deals.

However, Soviet legalism is not exclusively attributable to the
exigencies and thought patterns of a codified system. The insipid
Soviet legal literature reflects the relative underdevelopment of Soviet

social science research and teaching. Soviet sociology and political
science are still quite rudimentary. The specialized areas of political and administrative behavior, which are highly relevant to law, are
almost totally ignored. The significant contributions of economics
are pretty well confined to the mathematical side of economic planning. All Soviet scholarship containing social science elements is
stifled by a lack of freedom to generate and communicate knowledge
and ideas. It is hemmed in by the ideological frames of reference.
Its factual findings and theoretical postulates must not assail directly
or put in doubt the proclaimed fundamental truths of the Soviet system.
    The repression of the intellect and its corollary, the barrenness of
Soviet social science and legal scholarship, are the result of many
ideas and forces, with a special mention going to Stalin, whose program of economic development and social and political transformation
could tolerate neither empirical inquiries into the processes of change
nor dispassionate weighing of alternative courses of action. Stalin's
political dictates devitalized the active social sciences and put an
end to a flourishing, social science oriented school of law which had
reached its peak in the late 1920s. For these reasons, there is almost
total discontinuity between the present Soviet legal scholarship and
that of the 1920s. In sharp contrast to today's exclusiveness and
conceptualism of Soviet law, the legalistic element in law was de-
emphasized in the 1920s. In fact, law as a distinct discipline was
regarded as imminently withering away, as being swallowed up by
economics and sociology. Forty years later, the almost opposite situation prevails. Law or "legal science," as the Soviet writings put
it, is not only regarded as a distinct discipline but treated as almost
self-sufficient. While the Soviet jurists are cognizant of the instru-
mental role of law, they mostly deal with its actual operation in a
passing manner. When questions of "law in action" arise, the problems are as a rule imperfectly identified and their causes and solutions superficially analyzed.
    Kolbasov's book, as Soviet law treatises go, is among the better
ones in blending doctrinal description and analysis with references
to the context in which legal principles and rules are implemented
and translated into action. In the special chapters, Chapters 2—4,
Kolbasov constantly makes it a point to identify the principal objectives of the legal regulations in question and occasionally to suggest
explanations of why certain provisions might or might not work. Such
assessments are supported in part by the citation of actual experience.
Unfortunately, these examples are too sketchy and too far apart to permit a reader to form a judgment on the efficacy of the regulatory devices under discussion. In particular, one is inclined to doubt the
effectiveness of those legal provisions which presuppose a more or
less perfect coordination of the interests and activities of the several
state-affiliated water users and state administrative agencies. The

illustrations of difficulties adduced by Kolbasiv only reinforce these
doubts. The disadvantages of not having reliable empirical evidence
are painfully evident.

Kolbasov's book also brings out another aspect of Soviet codification—the question of the constitutional allocation of the relevant
governmental powers and responsibilities in these matters.

The Soviet Union is a federal state. According to the USSR Constitution of 1936, as since amended, the federal (union) government has
extensive powers to control the various aspects of Soviet life. Some
of these powers are exclusive, some concurrent. The important point
is that nothing seems to be clearly reserved to the fifteen Union (constituent) Republics. However, in many areas of concurrent powers the
federal government does not choose to make laws and, consequently,
the unpreempted field can be occupied by union-republic legislation.
This, as Kolbasov indicates, has largely been true with respect to the
law of water use. When Kolbasov wrote his book, there was no basic
federal statute as yet on the subject, and republic legislation had
taken the form of disjointed laws, executive decrees, and departmental
regulations. But "since attempts already made to codify water law
throughout the Union Republics [had] not led to the creation of an integrated and well-coordinated system of norms,"[2] the focus was shift-
ing on federal action.

When the awaited federal action came in 1970, it did not produce
a single comprehensive code of the law of water use. Enactment of
such a code would not have been a proper exercise of the federal legislative power, by reason of a peculiarly balanced concurrent competence
over the subject matter. Article 14 of the Constitution of the USSR provides:

> The jurisdiction of the Union of Soviet Socialist Republics, as
> represented by its higher organs of state power and organs of state
> administration, covers: . . .
> (c) definition of the basic principles of land tenure and of the
> use of mineral wealth, forests, and waters.

In other words, the federal government may promulgate a law on water
use that sketches in the regulatory contours and supplies a list of
basic do's and don'ts but must leave the details to the individual republics.

The Principles of Water Law of the USSR and the Union Republics
of December 10, 1970, were adopted in ostensible conformity with this
constitutional scheme. The relatively short law (forty-six articles)
was, indeed, cast in general terms, leaving much room for interstitial

---

2. Oleg S. Kolbasov, *Legislation on Water Use in the USSR* (Moscow: Juridical Literature, 1965). See p. 111, below.

legislation. In this instance, however, the Principles announced that much of the implementing detail might be filled in by the federal government rather than the governments of the Union Republics (for example, Articles 2 and 5).

This smacks of a bootstrap operation. The federal government empowered to enact only general principles seems to be taking the position that one of these principles authorizes it to enact more detailed laws and regulations. It is another matter, of course, whether the federation will, in fact, attempt to exercise this arrogated power. In most other areas in which the exercise of federal powers has been constitutionally confined to the prescription of general principles, federal attempts at particularization have not been widespread, albeit the level of generality of the guiding principles themselves has varied.

While an attempt on the part of the federal government to invade a field such as water use by detailed prescriptions would appear unconstitutional, the question of constitutionality would probably not be raised. The likelihood of such a test is excluded, first of all, by Soviet political realities. The Soviet system is dominated by a centralist outlook. Despite the recognized distinction between the federation's competence to legislate *in extenso* and its competence to prescribe only broad guidelines, there is no clear notion of powers reserved to the individual republics. In the policy-making process of the one and only Communist Party, the country is essentially treated as unitary. In the second place, the constitution itself upholds the principle of the federal legislators' supremacy. In the absence of judicial review, the federal legislature, that is, the Supreme Soviet of the USSR itself (acting through its Presidium), is the ultimate arbiter of the constitutionality of its own actions.[3] Third, when all-out federal action is deemed necessary and politically feasible but seems to run into constitutional obstacles, a constitutional amendment can be adopted as easily as a conflicting law.

The State of Soviet Nature Conservation Law

During its drive toward economic (technological) maturity, the Soviet system disregarded the impact of modernization on the quality of the country's natural environment. Indeed, as I mentioned earlier, the entire question of the social costs of Stalin's programs was beyond the pale of inquiry and debate. It was Stalin's death that roughly coincided with and, thus, symbolically marked the passing of the old Bolsheviks and an end to the single-minded, sustained industrialization and simultaneously inaugurated a limited reconsideration of Soviet

---

3. USSR Constitution of 1936, art. 49 (B).

development. It devolved upon Khrushchev to preside over the process of redefinition of the objectives and the operational style of future development. The responses of the Khrushchevian leadership to this challenge were often erratic, swinging between benevolence and harshness, balanced economic plans and crash programs, pragmatism and ideological revivalism. Nonetheless, Khrushchev will be remembered for his recognition of the fact that amidst the struggles for higher economic indexes and for communist purity there should be room for a modicum of personal enjoyment. There was a noticeable turn toward the better life here and now. Greater personal security was promised by the abolition of mass terror and the refurbishing of the tarnished image of socialist legality. This was accompanied by a rising level of well-being through more substantial material rewards and a more pleasant physical environment.

The physical environment had suffered to excess over the previous thirty-five years and was continuing to deteriorate in the face of voracious heavy industry. Urban housing was in a horrible state. By 1950, with the wartime destruction subtracted from the already meager fund, only about fifty square feet of living space was available to each urban resident, and the average residential density stood at almost three and one-half persons per room. The cities themselves had sprung up and grown haphazardly, also for the convenience of industry. Preservation and establishment of greenery within the cities was neglected. The concern about recreational needs and fresh air reservoirs was minimal. The prediction of Larin, one of the early Soviet economic planners, that Soviet industrial plants would give off "no smoke, soot, noise or smells"[4] had not been fulfilled. In fact, air pollution had become serious in many industrial centers and was getting worse.

Those who sought to escape the urban centers for a respite in the surrounding areas found nature badly marred. Woods that had once ringed many cities had been largely destroyed during the postwar reconstruction wave when the law's criterion was not prudent forest management but proximity of timber to processing and building sites. Some of the remaining nearby forests were decaying under the influence of noxious industrial funes. Woodlots and groves of trees not logged or poisoned were increasingly trampled down by recreation-seeking city dwellers or overgrazed by their goats and cows. Bodies of water, especially rivers flowing through or in close proximity to cities, were in various stages of silting and pollution. Fish and wildlife suffered, in part because of the impairment of their habitat, in part because of irresponsible harvesting.

---

4. Iu. Larin, "Zhilishchnyi vopros v rekonstruktivnyi period" [Housing question in the period of reconstruction], *Sovetskoe stroitel'-stvo* 1931, No. 5—6, pp. 140, 152.

Even away from the densely populated centers, in places where the vastness of nature seemed overwhelming, damage was done on a scale that made one doubt the inexhaustibility of nature's gifts. Forest fires reminiscent of the logging disasters of the nineteenth-century American Midwest destroyed millions of acres of standing timber. Spectacular regional developments considered among the greatest Soviet achievements later revealed a spectacular debit side. Thus the Volga Basin project, which yielded electric energy, water for municipal and industrial uses, and improved waterways, was accomplished at a great cost to the Caspian Sea fisheries and navigation. The results of the tampering with the natural flow of the Volga were aggravated by the destruction of forests within the basin. From 1930 to 1956 the level of the Caspian Sea fell by more than seven feet. The sea retreated from the shores from 12 to 20 (in some places, 40) miles, and the total area of the sea decreased from about 170,000 to 150,000 square miles. There were also entire regions in the Soviet Union subjected to heavy erosion and gullying by runoff. In the Saratov region alone (a relatively small region straddling the Lower Volga) the area of eroded lands came to exceed 1,750,000 acres.

The rising concern about the fate of the natural environment, as evidenced in the Soviet scientific literature, mass media, and the law since the mid-1950s, has by no means reversed the previous course. While some of the most pernicious practices have been halted or at least curtailed, other abuses go on practically unchecked. Neither a rationally designed, social-cost calculus nor a reliable enforcement mechanism is yet in operation. The ploughing up of the steppes pursuant to Khrushchev's "virgin lands" program created a new, grave risk of a massive dust bowl. The damage caused by wind erosion has already been significant; a belated effort to plant shelter belts aims to forestall worse consequences. The disruption of the ecological balance of the steppes has endangered numerous species of wildlife. The newly built, grandiose paper mills on Lake Baikal which discharge huge quantities of industrial effluent imperil this unique body of water.

But what distinguishes the post-Stalin era is the spreading awareness of the perils of industrialization and urbanization and considerable opportunities for voicing the conservationist point of view. This was very much in evidence during the Lake Baikal debate of the late 1960s. To be sure, the Soviet system still does not speak with one voice in favor of nature conservation. Certainly, the state is still "both the police and the policed."[5] But there now is a voice that challenges the viewpoint of the industrial technocrats, a voice that

---

5. Demitri B. Shimkin, "Resource Development and Utilization in the Soviet Economy" in *Natural Resources and International Development*, ed. Marion Clawson (Baltimore: Johns Hopkins, 1964), pp. 155, 185.

reminds one hand of the state to restrain the misdeeds of the other. In short, conservation sentiments within the Soviet system are more evident and are gaining position relative to competing sentiments.

A recently published report of a quaint research project poignantly sums up the history of Soviet conservation. It appears that at the end of the 1920s, a study group had counted and categorized the bunches of flowers carried by individuals into Moscow through the city's railroad stations. The group found that half the flowers brought in were wild flowers. It is not entirely clear what purpose this research was to serve, and there is no evidence that the findings were ever used in either policy-making or policy execution. The research seems to have been inspired by a concern for a balanced development, for a growth of material well-being without destruction of the quality of the country's natural environment. However, it was precisely at the time that the worship of technology was nearing its peak. The solicitude for wild flowers and like human values espoused by the socialist romantics had no place in the country's plans for roughly the next three decades. Significantly, the flower count was repeated in the 1950s. The follow-up showed that no wild flowers were brought in from the environs of Moscow at all. This lead the researchers to conclude that, as a result of systematic, unchecked picking by the urban vacationers and picnickers, the wild flowers indigenous to the flora around Moscow had completely disappeared.[6]

The vanishing wild flower is a relatively trivial cost item on the debit side of the development ledger. It mainly symbolizes the fate of the countless components of the biosphere: rivers, lakes, species of wildlife, upturned steppes, and even the air man breathes. It also underscores, in the same token way, the fact that the Soviet Union in its drive toward economic maturity did not act significantly better, if better at all, than other societies passing through comparable stages of economic growth. Despite the lessons found in the experience of such other societies and a state power that had gained supremacy on the promise of development without recklessness and predation, the Soviet Union essentially took the same low road. The achievements of the Soviet system eventually came to be measured almost exclusively in tons of steel, barrels of oil, and yards of cloth.

The outpouring of concern beginning in the mid-1950s took diverse forms. The Council of Ministers of the USSR issued several decrees seeking improvements in forest management, fish and wildlife protection, conservation of water resources, and geological exploration. In none of the cases was the executive action clearly based on preexist-

---

6. Konstantin N. Blagosklonov, Aleksandr A. Inozemtsev, and Vadim N. Tikhomirov, *Okrana prirody* [Protection of nature] (Moscow: Higher School, 1967), p. 18

ing enabling legislation. Moreover, some of the rather detailed provisions of the decrees seemed to go beyond the constitutionally dele-
gated federal power of "definition of the basic principles ... of the
use of mineral wealth, forests and waters." But, as we said, it is an
idle exercise to analyze Soviet normative acts in these terms. If
there was fault to be found with the new enactments, it was on substantive rather than constitutional grounds. The decrees by and large
did not introduce significant innovations into the existing federal and
republic (especially the RSFSR) laws, decrees, and regulations. Their
main significance lay in the fact that the federal Council of Ministers
emphatically restated the essence of the dormant provisions of several conservation laws at this time.

A similar activity was observable at the republic level. Between
1956 and 1960, the influential RSFSR alone issued no less than nineteen executive decrees on nature conservation, and its new Criminal
Code of 1960 included ten articles (Arts. 98, 99, 163–166, 168, 169,
223, and 230) punishing sundry offenses against the natural environment. Also in 1960, the RSFSR enacted a comprehensive law "On Nature Conservation."[7] The process was pretty much repeated in the
smaller republics. In fact, by 1963, the Supreme Soviets of all fifteen
Union Republics had enacted broad nature conservation statutes.

The flurry of law-making was accompanied by conservation propa-
ganda through the communications media, schools, and mass organizations (trade unions, youth leagues, and scientific groups). In addition, special conservation societies were organized and, in some
cases, entrusted with quasi-public functions. Thus the All-Russian
Collaborative Society for Protection of Nature and Maintenance of
Greenery in Populated Places (which claimed a membership of 3,500,000
in 1962) was charged by Article 16 of the RSFSR Law of October 27,
1960, with the "guidance of all social effort in the area of nature conservation." The social effort includes, among other things, the operation of societal inspectorates, submission of proposals for legislative
and executive action, and celebration of "awareness periods" such as
"Forest Month," "Garden Week" and "Bird Day."

It was also at this time that the first serious effort was made to introduce examination of the problems of nature conservation into the
curricula of educational institutions. It appears that previously one
single specialized course on nature conservation had been taught in
the entire country—by the Biology and Soils Faculty of Moscow University—since 1948. The law faculties got into the act in 1960–61
when Legal Protection of Nature was first taught at Moscow University

---

7. Law of 27 October 1960 (RSFSR), *Vedomosti Verkhovnogo
soveta RSFSR,* 1960, No. 40, Text 586, transl. in *Current Digest of
the Soviet Press,* 30 November 1960, p. 3.

as a segment of a course on Soviet Land Law. The first textbook on
the law of protection of nature was published in 1962,[8] two years after
what appears to have been the first contemporary law review article
on the subject.[9]

Although conservation sentiments have clearly been on the upswing,
the Soviet Union's environmental troubles are far from over. Several
reasons for this suggest themselves.

First, the Soviet approach to the natural environment is still mainly
preservationist and regulatory in outlook. That is, the tendency in
both conservation law and practice still is to focus on the fate of isolated conservation categories, such as forests, minerals, waters, and
wildlife. Accordingly, some individual segments of nature are singled
out for total protection, for example, nature preserves, vanishing wildlife species, and so on. Other segments must suffer encroachments,
but an attempt is made to keep the latter within prescribed bounds.
There is an increasing ecological awareness among the Soviet conser-
vationists, but it is not widely applied. The practice still does not
treat the natural environment as a web of interdependencies and does
not adequately relate the quality of the environment to the biological
and psychological needs of man. The statements of high policy still
too often regard the natural environment as but a necessary ingredient
in further economic development. The various links of nature are too
lightly classified into useful and useless. Certain predatory animals,
for example, are destroyed without any compunction. According to a
recent report, wolves are almost extinct in the European part of the
Soviet Union, and their number in the forests of Siberia and the Far
Eastern territories has been reduced to a mere 9,000. The chemical
assault on weeds and insects is still in its early phase. By contrast,
carp and lamprey are freely stocked in various bodies of water for the
sole purpose of increasing the protein yield of the fisheries. The virgin lands program perhaps constitutes the most massive recent disturbance of the ecological balance in the Soviet Union, with still un-
foreseeable implications. This disturbance not only threatens some
wildlife species with extinction but also fosters the multiplication of
successional species. For example, in the virgin lands of Southern
Kazakhstan there used to be only an average of 10,000 nests per spar-
row colony. By 1961, after several years of ploughing the steppes,
the average size of a colony had reached 42,500 nests. If it is re-

8. Elena N. Kolotinskaya, *Pravovaya okhrana prirody v SSSR*
[Legal protection of nature in the USSR] (Moscow: Moscow University,
1962).

9. N. D. Kazantsev, "O pravovom regulirovanii okhrany prirody" [On
the legal regulation of protection of nature], *Vestnik Moskovskogo
universiteta: Pravo* 1960, No. 1, p. 5.

membered that each bird consumes about 6.6 pounds of grain per season, another minus must be added to the bold program. Likewise, the
Lake Baikal problem is far from solved. An aware Soviet commentator
concedes that purification devices required by law have been installed
by the pulp plants on the lake's shores. "However," he points out,

> in order to destroy Lake Baikal it is by no means necessary to
> dump completely unpurified water into it....After all, even where
> the purification installations have been built at the most modern
> technical level and are operated by highly skilled personnel, the
> effluent differs very greatly from the natural body of water, for
> even the so-called "final purification" intercepts no more than
> 97% of the impurities. Therefore, the "purified" effluent of the
> Baikalsk Pulp Plant is still far from being the same as Lake Baikal's
> water. The designers themselves admit that, at best, the water
> will have a completely different composition of salts and that this
> alone is enough to destroy part of the lake's unique population.

> ...Lake Baikal is a complex living organism, and the laws of the
> movement of the water in its depths are by no means manifest yet.
> Thus, the designers are taking on themselves a great deal too much
> in asserting that it is safe to dump purified effluent into Lake
> Baikal.[10]

Second, the sources of Soviet conservation standards are found
mainly in republic statutes, decrees, and regulations. This is not, on
surface, particularly undesirable. The geographic variations of the
Soviet Union are too immense to allow the application of entirely uniform rules throughout its territory. The problem is of quite another
kind. Republic law, without the backing of the authority of federal
"guiding principles," falters when challenged by federally managed
economic empires. Hence the clamor of Soviet legal writers for a
clear statement of principled commitment to the environmental cause
at the federal level. In fact, some existing federal laws are thought
actually to detract from the effectiveness of those republic laws which
the republics are willing to enforce. Thus, under a 1961 USSR law
curtailing the scope of administrative liability, administrative forfeitures can be collected only from individuals and not from enterprises, institutions, and organizations. This means that agencies
enforcing conservation laws must do more than merely show a violation by an entity; they must, as in a criminal case, identify the official
responsible for the particular infringement. It seems, however, that

---

10. *Literaturnaya gazeta*, 20 December 1967, transl. in *Current
Digest of the Soviet Press*, 10 January 1968, p. 12.

administrative and criminal prosecutions of plant directors, engineers, and like officials are too infrequent to amount to an effective deterrent. Civil liability, the third form of sanction, is an imperfect substitute for administrative forfeitures charged against enterprises. Civil damages may amount to little more than payment for misappropriated resources at a state price.

Third, the regulatory mechanism on which the present Soviet conservation relies is inadequate under conditions of rising demands and pressures on the natural environment. Conservation responsibilities are scattered among a host of agencies which operate disjointly and often at cross-purposes. Most of these agencies are assigned primary economic tasks as well as environmental policing functions. In the competition between them, the economic tasks seem to gain an easy upper hand. Thus the principal job of the Ministry of Agriculture is to increase and improve agricultural production. At the same time, one of its departments, the Chief Administration for the Protection of Nature, Nature Preserves, and Hunting, is charged with seeing that conservation standards are complied with in the process. However, the problems of Soviet agricultural output being what they are, the voice of the Chief Administration is little heeded. Other examples can be cited. The Ministry of Land Reclamation and Water Management includes the Chief Administration for the Integrated Use of Water Resources and the State Inspectorate for the Protection of Sources of Water which is responsible for interdepartmental administration, use, and protection of waters. But in this ministry, too, the environmental policing functions are subordinate to its economic tasks: the development of irrigation, drainage, and other measures of land melioration. As Kolbasov has observed in a recent article, in the execution of these tasks, the ministry and its component and inferior agencies themselves are making use of waters on a large scale and "are not only unable to monitor the appropriateness of the use of water resources in all the other branches of the economy, but stand in need of control themselves."[11] In short, the difficulties in enforcing conservation standards, because of the fact that control over the activities of one governmental agency is exercised by another coordinate agency of the same government, are compounded by a situation in which a proposed course of action of a department head committed to objective A is expected to be effectively scrutinized and, if need be, vetoed by a subordinate official charged with the pursuit of objective B.

---

11. Oleg S. Kolbasov, "Pravovaya okhrana prirody v SSSR [Legal protection of nature in the USSR], *Sovetskoe gosudarstvo i pravo*, 1968, No. 9, pp. 41–45, transl. in *Soviet Law and Government*, Spring 1968, pp. 17–21.

Certain key industries seem to be so powerful as to defy external control and shed most pretensions of self-policing. By way of illustration, Soviet specialists have demonstrated that the pollution-causing water-cooled systems of the petrochemical industry can be easily replaced by air-cooled systems. Furthermore, the air-cooled systems are said to use much less water, occupy less space, and be cheaper to build and much cheaper to operate.

Although in the past ten years or more, this problem has been examined and discussed by various departments and establishments, so far there have been no practical results. Despite their clear advantage, the introduction of air-cooled systems in industry is being unjustifiably delayed. New projects are being designed incorporating the old cooling systems with all their inherent faults. The Ministry of Petroleum Processing and Petrochemical Industry and the Ministry of Chemical Industry have shown a certain amount of interest in the problem and have worked out the measures designed to promote a wide-scale introduction of air-cooled systems, but these useful intentions are unsatisfactorily implemented.[12]

The final and main reason has to do with the nature of the Soviet system itself. Because of its breadth, this point can be said to encompass all three preceding reasons. The Soviets, despite a perpetual glorification of "self-criticism," are less than candid about their problems and are apt to assess them in contradictory terms. Thus a recent textbook on nature conservation dogmatically asserts that "the socialist form of the economy does not admit of destruction and annihilation of natural resources" and that "no special measures of nature conservation are needed," yet in the same breath concedes that "correct utilization of nature has not yet been achieved in every sector of the national economy" and that one still encounters "unsocialist, predatory attitudes toward the national wealth."[13] Kolbasov sees no conflict between nature conservation and the interests of the development of agriculture, industry, and sources of power.[14] "However," he goes on to say,

the present state of conservation in the country provides reason for concern. Along with the growth in the productive forces of our society, an impairment of natural conditions is occurring in a number of regions. Considerable damage to nature is caused by mistakes in planning the location of productive forces, by violation of

12. Moscow Radio, 31 January 1968.
13. Blagosklonov et al., *Okhrana prirody*, p. 43.
14. Kolbasov, "Legal Protection of Nature in the USSR," p. 18.

conservation requirements in the building and exploitation of industrial and other economic entities, and also as the result of violation of conservation requirements by individual citizens in their
use of forests and waters in the course of hunting and fishing.[15]

Such a view of things assumes that the "inner logic" of the Soviet
system ensures ideally balanced development and that deviations from
the straight path are caused by factors extraneous to the system. The
whole complex of the pernicious side effects brought about by the
processes of industrialization and urbanization is somehow but a
dance of shadows on the wall of the cave, while the unsullied socialist reality glistens behind the Soviet man's back. This logic conveniently deflects the search for causes from the top decision-makers
or factors over which they have little or no control to the lower eche-
lon officials responsible for policy execution. Instead of explaining
the damage to the natural environment in terms of party-sanctioned
priorities, in terms of a deliberate sacrifice of the natural resources
to an industrial-technological base, the Soviet writers pin the blame
on planners-technicians and economic managers for mislocating plants,
failing to install purification devices, and so on. The not-so-invisible
hand of Soviet socialism by definition guarantees equilibrium between,
for instance, fishermen's catches and cannery capacity. If fish come
to be dumped on collective farm fields as fertilizer, the fault is sought
only with men and not definitions.
      American legal order grew in the nineteenth century "to protect and
promote the release of individual creative energy to the greatest extent compatible with the broad sharing of opportunity for such expres-
sion." It sought to "give men more liberty by increasing the practical
range of choices open to them and minimizing the limiting force of
circumstances."[16] Private property, contract, and associations occupied a central place in the legal order. Private property was defined
"in terms of a legally assured measure of autonomy for private decision makers against the public power."[17] "...[T]he development of
contract meant increasing the scope of individual discretion in the
management of resources"[18] and, subsequently, a concern with "the
business corporation and its financial techniques."[19] By contrast, Soviet legal order grew in the first half of the twentieth century to estab-

      15. Ibid., p. 20.
      16. J. Willard Hurst, *Law and the Conditions of Freedom in the
Nineteenth-Century United States* (Madison: University of Wisconsin,
1956), p. 6.
      17. Ibid., p. 9.
      18. Ibid., p. 14
      19. Ibid., p. 15.

lish and safeguard state property and to legitimize and maintain the power of a self-perpetuating elite to define economic priorities and to implement their choices through comprehensive economic planning. The American legal order and its companion, market economy, have been blamed for the heavy social cost of environmental deterioration, a cost item imperfectly expressed in the market calculus. Conversely, the Soviet legal order and its companion, command economy, have been thought to possess the capacity to avoid similar costly side effects. Since the Soviet way has failed in this respect, the causal connection between the American way and environmental deterioration is in doubt.

A more likely explanation for the dual failure may be found in those sentiments, "instincts," ideas, and forces that drive human societies to modernize in the first place, and in the shortest time possible. The temper of modernization neglects almost anything that does not contribute to rapid capital formation or to the supply of technical personnel and a suitable labor force. Even after economic (technological) maturity has been reached and the stage of high mass consumption entered into, the initial emphasis is on individual gratification through gadgetry and leisure. The outlook remains industrial, albeit with production for consumption gaining relative to production for further production. The gadgets and leisure time increase the mobility of the people and the frequency of their encounters with the diverse parts of the natural environment. A growing concern about the impending exhaustion of particular natural resources required by industry is now reinforced by a perception of environmental damage directly inimical to the interests of individuals as consumers. The two combine to produce a change in the society's economic behavior. New sentiments are formed, new ideas articulated. Other "instincts" become dominant and other forces are set in motion. In the United States, the democratic legislative process and the creativity of the courts thereupon gradually invest the government with powers to deal with environmental problems. In the Soviet Union, environmental considerations become a weightier input into the decision-making process of the ruling elite. The powers it has always had in fact, but which have lain dormant, are revived and deployed along the environmental front.

According to Walt Rostow's analysis of the "stages of economic growth," the United States reached economic (technological) maturity by about 1900, while the Soviet Union got there some fifty years later, in 1950.[20] In both cases, this point in development was followed by manifestations of acute concern about the natural environment. The conservation mood and accomplishments of Theodore Roosevelt's ad-

---

20. Walt Rostow, *The States of Economic Growth: A Non-Communist Manifesto* (Cambridge, Cambridge University, 1960), p. 59.

ministration in the first decade of this century were closely paral-
leled by those of Khrushchevian rule half a century thereafter. In both
cases, basic public policies were declared and important conservation
laws adopted (in the case of the Soviet Union, these being, to a large
extent, restatements of preexisting, quiescent legal principles). But
it took some four or five decades more for the United States to become,
if you will, environment obsessed. It may take the Soviet Union a
shorter time span to get that way, thanks mainly to an almost unlimited
opportunity for appropriation of technology and for observation of the
environmental crises elsewhere. However, the Soviet list of high priority items other than environmental quality is a long one: roads, urban housing, agriculture, better quality consumer goods, and many
more. There is little fat in the economy. With the exception of military and space programs, no other significant sectors of the economy
permit reallocation of resources in favor of protection and preservation
of the natural environment. Some recent actions taken by the Soviets,
while entirely consistent with standards of economic behavior during
an early stage of high mass consumption, do not augur well for the
environment. I have in mind here the efforts to expand the output and
application of pesticides, fungicides, herbicides, and mineral fertilizers in farming, aggressive exploitation of ocean fisheries, stepped-
up production of automobiles, global competition over the SST, and
others.

    In all probability, then, the Soviet socialist system will continue
its economic development through its current stage with continuing
high, although somewhat leveling, social costs in terms of the quality
of the natural environment.

Legislation on
Water Use in the USSR

Problems of Perfecting
Soviet Legislation
on the Use of Water Resources

O. S. Kolbasov

Preface

Together with planning and the implementation of necessary economic-
technical measures, great importance is now attached to the legal
regulation of the use of the water resources of the USSR, to the strict
observance of the rules for the use of different water bodies and underground waters, and to perfecting the law of water use. The problem
of a rational utilization of water resources has proved to be not only
a scientific-technical and economic problem, but it has also acquired
a distinct juridical character.

In the present work, in addition to considering some general theoretical questions of Soviet water law, a summary and analysis of water use legislation is undertaken on a more or less generalized level.
Through a discussion of a selected range of questions, the shortcomings of the practical application of the law of water use are identified,
and measures to remedy them are proposed. In addition and in particular the quality of the legislation itself, its social effectiveness, and
ways and methods of perfecting it are illuminated.

An analysis of water use law is a necessary step in a study of the
legal regulation of water resources and of their correct utilization and
conservation, as a very important natural resource of the Soviet Union.
Interest in studying this question was determined, on the one hand, by
the great economic importance of water resources, and, on the other
hand, by the desire to overcome the lag in the scientific elaboration
of the problems of the legal regulation of water use in the USSR.

It must be said that questions of the rational use and conservation
of water resources are immediate not only for the USSR, but for most
countries of the world. With the aim of studying world water resources

and investigating ways and methods for their rational use and conservation, a general program for the International Hydrological Decade
proposed for 1965—75 was worked out at an intergovernmental meeting
of experts, which took place at UNESCO headquarters in April 1964.
The forthcoming International Hydrological Decade is regarded as an
unparalleled model of scientific cooperation which will have important
practical consequences.

Chapter 1

Concept and Basic Principles of the Law of Water Use

1. *Concept and Law of Water Use*

In order to regulate water use relationships in a legal system and thus to ensure their development in the desired direction, it is necessary to know that water use is something that is covered by the regulatory function of Soviet law; that is to say, the concept of water use should be defined. This need is all the more evident if it is recognized that, according to Soviet law, not all cases of the use of water are juridically recognized as water use. Some instances of water utilization are related to water use and others are not, depending on the conditions under which use of water is carried out. But neither the legislation nor the juridical literature contains any exact definition of the concept of water use.

For example, the existing laws on agricultural water use in the Central Asian and Transcaucasian Union Republics only refer to the concept of water use without indicating its distinguishing features.

In the work of L. I. Dembo, there is a chapter on "The Law of Water Use in the USSR and its Forms,"[1] but water use is discussed here as if it were something that went without saying, as the use of water in general. A similar attitude is contained, too, in later works on water law where different questions of water use are considered, but the concept itself is not defined in juridical literature.

---

1. L. I. Dembo, *Fundamental Problems of Soviet Water Law* (Leningrad, 1948), pp. 86–104.

An analysis of existing water legislation and the practice of its application convince one that Soviet law relates to water use only those cases of use in which water appears as a natural object—the object of the right of exclusive state ownership.[2] Water use is the use of water in its natural condition in seas, lakes, rivers, and so on, and also of water, the natural state and location of which is changed as a result of human industrial activity (reservoirs, canals, and so on) but which, nevertheless, has not ceased to be a constituent part of the natural environment available for economic utilization.[3]

The use of water which does not form part of the water resources of the USSR is not juridically recognized as water use, and is either entirely unregulated by law or is regulated in another capacity (as selling, delivery, material services, and so on) under civil or administrative law, but not under water law. The use of water which has lost the quality of a natural wealth, having been detached from its natural

---

2. For concepts of natural wealth, natural resources and commodities, and for differences in their legal governance in the USSR, see O. S. Kolbasov's "Nature as the Object of Legal Protection" in the collection *Legal Questions of the Protection of Nature in the USSR* (Moscow: State Juridical Publishing House, 1963).

3. It is sometimes said that the water resources of reservoirs and canals cannot be considered as natural objects, but should be looked upon as a commodity, since human labor has been applied to them. In this connection suggestions have been made concerning the establishment of a monetary valuation of the water resources of reservoirs and canals. For example, *Izvestiya*, 4 May 1964, under the heading "The Price of Water," published a letter from the Chairman of the Tatarbunarskoe Vosstanie Collective Farm of the Odesskaya Oblast, V. Z. Tur, with a commentary by a special correspondent of the newspaper, A. Yanov. The authors of the articles consider that water in the canals of state irrigation systems is a commodity output of the management of the irrigation systems and should be sold for a fee. Such opinions are unacceptable for they do not take into consideration that natural objects to which human labor has been applied become a commodity only when they have been detached from the natural medium. The water resources of reservoirs and canals, although they are to a certain extent the product of human labor, have not been isolated from the natural surroundings and remain natural, that is, a noncommodity object. They are not excluded from the natural water cycle and are not isolated from interaction with groundwater and surface flow. As regards the expenditure of labor, this is only necessary expenditure for the improvement of natural conditions, like expenditure on artificial reforestation and the improvement of natural fish reserves, the animal world, and so on.

surroundings as the result of the application of labor, is considered
to be the use of a commodity (raw materials, consumer products), but
is not recognized as water use.

So, between the use of water from a natural body of water and the
use of water from the city water supply there exist both economic and
juridical differences caused by the differences in the objects of use.
In the first instance, use of water is the use of natural wealth with
the observance of the requirements of Soviet water law. In the second instance, the use of water is none other than the use of communal
services for a fee, regulated under civil law.

Thus, not every use of water is recognized as water use. Only the
use of water as a substance of nature, as one of the natural resources
that are the object of the law of exclusive ownership of the Soviet State,
is considered to be water use.

Water use, because of its economic-technical character, is extraor-
dinarily versatile. Water, as distinct from land, may be directly consumed. L. I. Dembo correctly noted that the use of water consists
either in the consumption of water for different domestic and agricultural needs (for drinking, watering, irrigation, and so on) or in the use
of flowing water and bodies of water as means of communication, as
a motive force, or as the natural environment for the animal world (for
purposes of transport, water operating enterprises, fishing, and so on).[4]
It may be added that in recent years the natural reserves of water in
seas, rivers, lakes, and elsewhere are being widely used for the discharge of industrial and domestic sewage and other wastes. However,
for the definition of a legal concept of water use, all this has no significance. Differences in purpose, in technical ways and methods of
using water, are taken into account by the law in the differentiation of
forms of water use and the establishment of rights and obligations for
different categories of water users, but they do not alter the basic
distinctive identification of water use as the use of water resources.

In this context it should be pointed out that such concepts as water
consumption or discharge of sewage into bodies of water must not be
distinguished from water use.

In the opinion of M. Ishimov, in water law the term "water use"
does not always exactly reflect the essence of the use of water resources. "It is known," he writes, "that water in certain sectors of
the national economy (chiefly in the production of agricultural produce,
in the public water supply, and, partially, in industry) is a consumable
natural resource, and in other sectors of the national economy it is a
usable resource (electric power, transport, and so on). Therefore, in
the context of water law, the terms *water consumption* and *water use*
should be employed."[5]

---

4. See Dembo, *Problems of Soviet Water Law*, p. 68.
5. M. Ishimov, "Some Questions of the Law of Water Use in Cities

It is impossible to agree with this judgment, for the simultaneous use of these terms in legislation will only complicate it. However the technical-economic methods of using water resources may differ, in our society it is all from the juridical point of view the use of water resources.

Having defined the concept of water use, it is not difficult to define the law of water use.

The law of water use in the USSR is the sum total of juridical norms by which the use of water resources is regulated as a natural, material wealth which is the exclusive property of the Soviet state, that is, those norms which stipulate the conditions and procedure of water use for the different needs of the population and the national economy. The law of water use is a component of one of the institutes of Soviet law. In addition, it is also considered to be the subjective right of enterprises, institutions, organizations, and citizens, that is to say, the opportunity granted to them by the law to use the water resources with the observance of established conditions and requirements.

2. *Forms of Water Use*

Specific ways and means of using water resources in private life, industry, agriculture, for transport, and so on, which have changed through history, depend on the level of economic development of the society and on the application of new achievements in science and technology. As the economy grows, more and more reserves of water resources are utilized and diverse water resources are developed. All this complicates public water use relationships, and for their proper legal regulation a classification of forms of water use should be established.

L. I. Dembo was the first to try to produce a classification of forms of water use. In particular he wrote that "the law of water use varies, both by subject and object and by its substance, depending on its specific purpose, on the type of use, and on the branch of water management. For this reason, water law is a greatly ramified legal institution and is divided into a number of separate forms of water use. In consequence, a classification of forms of water use is important for an analysis of this complicated legal system.

"Forms of water use should be classified according to the subject, the object, and the substance of the law of use itself."[6]

---

of the Uzbek SSR," in *Scientific Works and Reports*, Department of Social Sciences of the Academy of Sciences of the Uzbek SSR (Tashkent, 1962) 5:295.

6. Dembo, *Problems of Soviet Water Law*, p. 86.

To present the issue correctly, it is necessary first of all to specify what the question is—the classification of the law of water use,
or the classification of water use. One would think the classification
of water use should come first, since the forms of the law of water
use follow the forms of water use. This is not clearly reflected in the
writings of L. I. Dembo. He uses the concepts "water use" and "the
law of water use" as though they meant the same thing, although in
fact they do not mean the same.

With regard to the aim of the present work, there is no need to
consider all the possible classifications of forms of water use. We
will therefore only discuss those that have juridical significance,
those through which the legislation binds together the rights and obligations of water users and establishes requirements in the interests
of improving further the use of water resources in the USSR.

L. I. Dembo proposed to classify forms of water use by subject, object, and the substance of the law of water use itself.

In particular, in the classification of the forms of water use by subject, he proposed to distinguish between direct and derivative water
use. He attributed to the first form all cases of the use of water carried out by the Soviet State, as the owner of the water resources, by
means of state enterprises, institutions, and organizations. To the
second form, he attributed all cases of the use of water by public organizations and citizens who are not the owners of the water resources.

In his classification by object, L. I. Dembo identified as forms of
water use communal and agricultural water use, hydropower production, use of water for water transport, for floating timber, for the fishing industry, sports, and so on. But he considered that the classification of forms of water use by the substance of the law of water use
coincided with the classification of branches of water management.

The classification of the forms of water use suggested by L. I.
Dembo has a certain theoretical value, but it cannot satisfy the modern practical requirements of the legal regulation of the use of water
resources in the USSR.

In our view, it is inappropriate to divide kinds of water use by subject into direct and derivative uses. Theoretically, of course, it is
possible to permit the direct use of water resources by their owner.
But in our country this thesis has no practical utility, since with us
the proprietor of the water resources, the Soviet State, is not directly
the effective subject and does not use water. Hence, there is no need
of the State as such in the legal regulation of water use. To consider
that the water use of state enterprises, institutions, and organizations
is direct use by the State itself is, in our view, mistaken.

If one proceeds from the fact that state enterprises, institutions,
and organizations, in using water resources, realize the competence
of the State as owner of these resources, then it is necessary to recognize one of two things. Either the state enterprises, institutions, and

organizations are not the subjects of water use, but are only the agencies of another subject, which is the Soviet State; or the one and the same right of water use must belong to several subjects—to the Soviet State and, in addition, to the state enterprises, institutions, and organizations. L. I. Dembo, however, while asserting that water use by state enterprises, institutions, and organizations is a direct use of water by the State, at the same time recognizes them, and not the State as a whole, to be the subjects of the law of water use. "The state farm," he wrote, "as a state enterprise engaged in agriculture and using land and water, as a juridical person possesses only the right of use; but this right is by its nature direct use on the part of the State, since the state farm is an agency of the State."[7]

A number of inaccuracies can be found in this reasoning. In the first place, if it is admitted that the State uses water by means of enterprises, institutions, and organizations, acting as independent subjects of the law, then such water use cannot be called direct. Second, L. I. Dembo confuses the right of water use with the use itself, saying that "the right is by its nature a direct use." Third, if it is considered that the state farm (or any other enterprise) is an agency of the State and the State is the water user, then logically the state farm should be only an agency of the water user, but not the water user itself. In reality, the state farm is the independent subject of the law of water use, as opposed to the State as owner of the water resources. Relations between the State and the state farm concerning water use are like relations between different subjects. Fourth, the division of forms of water use classified by subject into direct and derivative ought to be reflected in the procedure for granting the right to use water and in the continuing competence of different subjects. In reality, state farms (like other state enterprises) are granted the right to use water in the same manner as collective farms and other cooperative and public organizations are granted this right. In this connection the right of the state farm to the use of water resources is as derivative as is the right of the collective farm. There is no difference either in the continuing competence of the subjects of the direct and derivative right of water use.

Our legislation recognizes both public and state undertakings and organizations to be the independent subjects of the law of water use in relation to the State as a whole and to one another. This position represents the only fair one in conditions of a socialist economic system, where state enterprises and organizations, not being the owners of the means of production and the products used by them, establish relationships on principles of self-sufficiency and possess economic and juridical independence in public production.

7. Ibid., p. 87.

UNIVERSITY OF VICTORIA
LIBRARY
Victoria, B. C.

Thus, the differentiation between direct and derivative water use as forms of water use does not have any legal significance and is not reflected in actual legislation. Much more clearly expressed in the legislation is the differentiation between the use of water resources for state and public needs on the one hand, and for the satisfaction of the individual needs of citizens on the other. And if it is necessary to classify forms of water use by subject, then it would be expedient, in the first place, to subdivide them into water use for state and public needs and water use by citizens.

The classification of forms of water use by object, set out in the work of L. I. Dembo, in essence is a substitute for classification according to branches of water management. In our opinion, in order to classify correctly forms of water use by object, it is necessary to begin by establishing the relationship between qualitative features of the object and the accepted juridical conditions of their use. From this standpoint, it is necessary first of all to distinguish between the use of surface and underground water resources, because the legislation associates with these different objects different conditions for their use. Inasmuch as the more specific features of the objects are taken into account in the legislation, there is a certain degree of classification of forms of water use by object. Thus, use of surface waters is divided into use of running and still waters from natural and artificial water courses, navigable and nonnavigable rivers, fishing and nonfishing bodies of water, and so on. Use of underground waters is divided into use of fresh and mineral waters, cold and hot (so-called hydrothermal resources), and so on.

Classification of the forms of water use according to the substance of the law of water use is not carried out in the legislation and has no basis, since the substance of the law of water use cannot be a classification characteristic, being itself to a significant degree caused by the existing classification of forms of water use. L. I. Dembo nevertheless assumed that such a classification exists, and that it coincides with the classification of branches of water management. However, in his work he cited neither one nor the other classification, and instead he differentiated between forms of water use depending on the basic purpose (economic purpose) of the use.

In fact, during the very early period of the development of Soviet water law, the classification of forms of water use according to purpose (economic purpose) of use was already seen to be one of the main classifications, and at the present time it is of dominant importance. Although modern water law does not indicate directly the paramount importance of this method of classifying forms of water use, actually the establishment by law of the rights and obligations of different water users is especially tied up with the differentiation between forms of water use according to the basic purpose for which the water resources are used. For example, the Supreme Soviets of a number of Union Republics (the Uzbek, Tadzhik, Kirghiz, Kazakh, Armenian, and Azerbaidzhan Republics) adopted laws on agricultural water use, in which they defined the procedure for the use of water resources for the irrigation of fields and for other aspects of agricultural production, as distinct from that governing the use of water resources for industrial, domestic, hydrotechnical, transport, and other purposes. The procedure governing the use of water resources for these purposes is defined in turn in different legislative and departmental acts of the USSR and the Union Republics.

However, in addition to the classification of forms of water use according to basic purpose, classifications according to the subject and object of water use, and also according to other identifications, are reflected to one degree or another in different legislative acts. For example, three kinds of water use are distinguished in the water-land reclamation code of the Belorussian Republic, that is, water use of individual farms and general and special water use. According to this code, the water use of individual farms is considered to be the use of bodies of water which are on the lands used by these farms; general water use is the use of water for domestic needs, agriculture, water transport, public recreation; and special water use is the use of water resources through the construction of headworks or other hydrotechnical facilities.

The Regulations on Water Use in the Georgian SSR of 19 February 1958 (Article 24) sets out the differences between two groups of bodies of water and divides water use into individual water use and collective (joint) water use. Individual water use takes place in those cases where a body of water is used by one subject (such as a state or collective farm, factory, mill, and so on). Water use is considered collective when the same body of water is jointly used by several subjects.

Until there is an all-Union law on the utilization of water resources in the USSR, methods of classifying forms of water use common to all Union Republics will not be established. Because of this, forms of water use in different Union Republics are defined in different ways, which results in an unwarranted lack of coordination in the regulation of water resource use relations. In the interest of achieving a uniform and clear-cut legal regulation of these relations, therefore, it seems necessary to establish common bases for the classification of forms of water use in future Principles of Water Law of the USSR and Union Republics.

3. *Objects of Water Use*

The main characteristics of objects of water use were noted above in the discussion of the concept of water use. It is evident from this that not every use of water is legally recognized as water use.

In the technical-economic sense, the object of water use is water
in the form of a special substance characterized by definite chemical
and physical properties. Juridically, however, it is not a quantity of
water which can be measured in liters, cubic meters, kilometers, and
so on that is assigned for use to the subjects of the law of water use,
but rather it is a water source or body of water containing a changing
or relatively stable quantity of water.

Thus, in cases where water is extracted for domestic or industrial
purposes, a body of water is assigned to be the source of supply with
an indication of the place of water diversion. If underground water is
used, a certain aquifer is allotted to each of the subjects with an indication of the point of water withdrawal. When water is utilized for
hydroelectric purposes, a certain water course, with an indication of
the site of the dam and of the size of the reservoir above it, is allotted
for the use of the subject. For fishing purposes, fishery bodies of water or fishing sections are allotted to subjects of the law of water use.
For other forms of water use, the objects are defined in a similar way.
The establishment of objects of water use for irrigated agriculture is
a little more complicated when water is provided by the large state
irrigation systems from centralized sources. As in other forms of water use, the object here is the body of water which is the source of
the irrigation water supply, on which is indicated the place of diversion into the main irrigation canal. The farm water users, however,
do not use water directly from this body of water but obtain it from
the main canals; and these water courses are, in effect, the objects
of water use in such cases.

Water sources and bodies of water, but not the water itself, are set
aside as objects of water use depending on the particular conditions
prevailing and the legal governance of the water resources of the USSR,
which exist in the form of seas, lakes, rivers and other water bodies,
and are by existing law granted to the subjects for use only.

A water source, body of water or other water object, is not destroyed
by normal use, and when the need for it has passed, or in other circumstances specified by the law, it can be withdrawn from the use of one
subject and transferred to another. (This applies also to other natural
objects which are in the exclusive ownership of the Soviet State and
which are allotted to enterprises, institutions, organizations, and citizens for the right of use only.)

On the other hand, the substance of water cannot be granted for the
right of use, since in the process of being used it is destroyed and
changes its physical state, or changes its spatial position, or is removed by the action of natural forces and leaves the possession of
the subjects naturally. In this case water, as the object of legal relations, displays the same juridical characteristics as other articles of
consumption (such as corn, food, industrial raw materials, and so on).

This is why the substance of water cannot juridically be the object
of water use. For this reason the objects of water use are considered

by the existing legislation to be water sources and bodies of water, which in some legislative acts are called by a single term—water objects.

Few legal scholars have tried to illuminate and analyze the specific features of objects of water use. Only once has the question been raised on the compatibility of so-called consumable water use with the law which makes the water resources of the USSR the exclusive property of the State, and with the ability to own water for the right of use only. This was in the article by A. M. Turubiner, "On the Law of Water Use in the USSR and its Forms." He tried to answer the question by contrasting the concepts "waters" and "water." By "waters" he meant the aggregate of water resources, without, however, elucidating the actual concept of water resources. "From water resources," wrote A. M. Turubiner, "it is necessary to distinguish the 'water' in them, which can be assigned for use as a consumable wealth, being transformed in the process of use into other forms of material wealth."[8] On this basis he concluded that there are two forms of water use—consumable, when the use of "water" occurs without the use of water resources, and nonconsumable, when the use occurs of "waters," that is to say of water resources without the use of water.

In spite of the originality of his thesis, A. M. Turubiner, in our view, is mistaken in claiming that water is assigned for use as a consumable wealth, for, as has been said above, what is consumed in the process of being used cannot be loaned. Consequently, in juridical terms it is not the water which is assigned for use, but water objects, bodies of water, water sources—that is to say, seas, rivers, lakes, streams, springs, underground aquifers, and so on. And although A. M. Turubiner tried to operate with the terms "waters" and "water" in his exposition, he was nevertheless unable to avoid using the terms "body of water" and "water source" in the sense of objects of water use.

In addition, it is not possible either to accept as correct the contraposition of the concepts "waters" and "water," for in both cases we have the same substance of water. It follows, therefore, that the use of these concepts in water law, in the sense given them by A. M. Turubiner, will in no way help to improve the law.

4. Basic Principles of the Law of Water Use

The law of water use, which in the final analysis is one of the institutes of Soviet land law, contains the same basic legal principles which are characteristic of land law as a whole. Side by side with these, there are other principles which fall only within the framework of the law of water use and are basic only to this legal institution.

---

8. *Soviet State and Law*, No. 8 (1963), p. 123.

First, there is the principle of the exclusive right of state ownership of natural objects, which includes water resources.

The exclusiveness of the right of state ownership of water resources
means that in the USSR these resources are owned by one subject
only—the Soviet State. Other subjects can only use the water resources in accordance with the procedure established by the state.

All the juridical norms which regulate relations of water use in the
USSR conform to this basic principle, and the substance of legislative
requirements in this sphere of law is determined thereby.

The principle of the exclusive right of state ownership of water resources long ago received general recognition in the USSR. However,
neither in the Constitution of the USSR nor in any of the acts of water
law is this principle really confirmed. Only in Soviet civil law is it
specifically expressed—initially, in Article 53 of the Civil Code of
the RSFSR (1922); then in the Principles of Civil Law of the USSR and
Union Republics (Article 21, Part 4); and, finally, in the actual Civil
Codes of the Union Republics (in particular, Article 95 of the Civil
Code of the RSFSR, which states that "the land, its minerals, waters
and forests, being the exclusive property of the state, may be allotted
for use only").

Anyone looking up Article 6 of the Constitution of the USSR, which
contains the most general juridical norm on state ownership, will notice at once that it does not emphasize the exclusive character of the
right of state ownership of natural objects. It says only that the land,
its minerals, waters, and forests are national property. But all objects
of state ownership are national property, whereas only natural objects
are the exclusive property of the state. In our view, it would be desirable to establish the right of state ownership in a separate article
of the Constitution which would clearly indicate its exclusive character.

As objects of the law of exclusive ownership of the Soviet State,
water resources are outside the sphere of civil law. They cannot be
placed in the possession of or under the operative management of enterprises, institutions, organizations, or citizens, and can be allotted to
them only for use. The law contains clear instructions to the effect
that when the parties to an agreement aim to establish the right of
ownership of the water resources of another subject, but not of the Soviet State, the transaction is invalid. However, water as a commodity
may be in the ownership of public organizations and citizens.

In juridical literature the idea of the inalienability of water has
been put forward as one of the principles of water law. Specifically,
K. A. Shaibekov, in his article "Principles of Soviet Water Law," wrote:
"From the exclusive character of the right of state ownership of water
comes the principle of its inalienability."[9]

_____

9. *Transactions of the Alma-Ata Juridical Institute* 1 (1955):151.

The impossibility of alienating water resources is, in my opinion, one of the manifestations of the exclusive right of state ownership of water resources in the USSR and cannot be considered an independent principle of water law.

The establishment of the right of exclusive state ownership of water resources and their exclusion from the civil sphere not only makes the alienation of natural reserves of water impossible, but precludes the transfer of the water resources to the operative management of separate state enterprises, institutions, and organizations. By the same token, the unwarranted surrendering of the rights of water use and so on cannot be allowed.

One of the most important principles underlying the legal regulation of water use in the USSR is the concept of development according to plan. This means that Soviet legislation on water use in its regulatory activity operates on the basis of a calculation of needs and the planned distribution of water resources among water users, both as a whole throughout the country and the Union Republics, and throughout the big river basins and other bodies of water. Planning the use of water resources is a part of all economic planning and therefore it is coordinated with plans for the distribution of productive forces and the development of all branches of the national economy.

The planned use of water resources in our country has been made possible by the presence of two circumstances—the exclusive state ownership of water resources and the large-scale socialization of production in all its main branches. In place of the earlier large numbers of small water users in industry, agriculture, transport, and so on, water today is used by large undertakings, whose whole activity is developed according to plan. In this connection, the principle of development according to plan became clearly expressed in Soviet water law after the industrialization of the country and the collectivization of agriculture had been completed.

At the present time, the basic requirements which express and strengthen the principle of development according to plan are established in the decree of the Council of Ministers of the USSR of 22 April 1960, "On Measures to Regulate Use and Increase Conservation of Water Resources of the USSR,"[10] which specified that water balances and a scheme for the use of water resources throughout the main basins of surface and underground waters be worked out.

The principle of development of water use according to plan finds further definition in legislative acts that regulate certain forms of water use.

Closely associated with the principle of development according to plan is the principle of the fullest and most effective use. This em-

---

10. *Collected Decrees of the USSR*, 1960, No. 9, Article 67.

braces the need to use water resources with maximum benefit and for
the full satisfaction of the diverse water needs of people, public production, and so on, through scientifically based limitation and regulation of these needs with the aim of avoiding a shortage of natural reserves of water for present and future generations. However, as it applies to water resources, this principle is chiefly (but not always) revealed in the demand for the complex* use of water resources.

At the present time, the principle of complex use of water resources
is one of the most important principles of the law of water use.

The complex use of water resources implies, first, the use of the
reserves of every body of water or water source as far as possible for
the fulfillment of the whole complex of different requirements of all
interested water users, and, second, the discovery and utilization of
all the useful properties in natural reserves of water.

The principle of the complex use of water resources is expressed
in many legislative acts and, especially in the decree of the Council
of Ministers of the USSR of 22 April 1960, "On Measures to Regulate
Use and Increase Conservation of Water Resources of the USSR." All
the measures which the Council of Ministers of the USSR specified in
this decree aim to regulate the complex use and conservation of water
resources.

The principle of complex use is expressed quite clearly in Article 1
of the Regulations on the Use of the Water Resources of the Reservoirs
of the RSFSR, which says: "The water resources of the reservoirs of
the RSFSR should be used to the maximum national economic effect in
the interests of all water consumers and water users, including interests concerned with the preservation of nature and the use of bodies
of water for cultural-domestic purposes."

Although water resources should be utilized for the satisfaction of
the whole complex of water requirements, nevertheless certain requirements are met first in view of their special importance to man.

Water is so necessary to human life that any obstacle to the satisfaction of public requirements for water would threaten public health
and the well-being of society. Therefore, unlike legislation on land
use, which does not give any special priority to the utilization of land
for the personal needs of citizens, water legislation gives first priority to the use of natural reserves of water of a potable quality in
order to meet the personal needs of the population. The establishment
of first priority for the domestic water supply of the population in relation to other forms of water use entails a number of legal conse-

*The term *kompleksnyi* in this context is translated throughout this
document as "complex." It refers to multiple purpose use of a given
water resource and multiple means of serving those purposes in a comprehensive fashion within an area such as a river basin.

quences, which will be discussed in later chapters of this work. But the idea itself of first priority for domestic water supply so widely affects the legal regulation of the use of water resources that it must be considered as one of the basic principles of the law of water use.

In order to secure through legislation the planned, fullest, and most effective use of water resources, the principle of developing water use for a special purpose is applied. This means that in issuing authorizations for the right of water use, state agencies, in accordance with the plan and with the applications of the water users, must determine for which of the purposes permitted by law the water objects allocated for use should be used. The specific purpose for which the water is used by each water user is subsequently settled by the agencies of water management, which keep a record of the availability and use of water resources and register the water users; and this is taken into account when schemes are drawn up for the use of water resources and water balances, under the current agency regulation for the use of water reserves and also with the establishment of priorities to meet water needs.

Water users have no right to change the use to which the water is put without the permission of the agencies of water management.

Finally, inherent in the law of water use in the USSR are the principles of free and indefinite use of water resources. Natural reserves of water are always allotted for use without charge and, in the overshelming majority of cases, for an indefinite period of time.

A short characterization of the basic principles of the law of water use shows that in the USSR the law of water use responds to the interests of all society, which is building communism. These principles create a legal environment in which all the conditions exist for the development of social productive forces for the well-being of every worker and all the Soviet people.

5. General Characteristics of the Codification of Water Law and its Perspectives

In the existing legislation the norms of the law of water use are distributed throughout numerous legislative acts, passed at different times on different issues. Most of these norms are contained in legislative acts of the Union Republics and in rules, regulations, and instructions issued by Ministries and Departments of the USSR and Union Republics. There would be nothing wrong with this if all the material were well coordinated and consistent. But unfortunately the reverse is the case. The norms contain contradictions, legislation has failed to regulate a number of matters, and so on, which in the final analysis only serves to reduce the effectiveness of legal regulation.

For example, with regard to the use of water resources for the domestic needs of the population, Union law deals largely with the sanitary protection of water mains and sources of water supply. Furthermore, in Union legislation the principle that first priority be given to public needs for drinking water has only been indirectly established. At the same time, there are other important aspects of this form of water use requiring legal settlement (for example, the utilization of underground water of a potable quality for industrial-technical needs) which have not been settled by legislation. In addition, the building norms and regulations governing the construction of water mains issued by the State Committee on Construction of the Council of Ministers of the USSR, and the regulations for the use of communal water supplies issued by the Ministries of Communal Management of the Union Republics, and other departmental normative acts deal partially with only some of these aspects.

The use of the water resources of large reservoirs in some of the Union Republics is governed by special regulations which are approved by the Councils of Ministers of the Republics. For example, the Regulations for the Use of the Water Resources of the Reservoirs and Bodies of Water of the Azerbaidzhan SSR were approved by the decree of the Council of Ministers of the Azerbaidzhan Republic of 8 August 1962, but in some of the other Union Republics similar regulations have been issued as departmental normative acts. For example, in the Russian Federation the Regulations on the Use of the Water Resources of Reservoirs were approved by the former State Committee of the Council of Ministers of the RSFSR on Water Management.

It is impossible to explain by any national factors or local economic conditions the fact that in some Republics this most important normative document is a legislative act, while in others it has the same status as a departmental instruction. One would think that in all the Union Republics, and especially in the Russian Federation where a great number of large reservoirs have been created, the Regulations on the Use of the Water Resources of Reservoirs would have the force of a legislative act. And, if one takes into account that in the future large reservoirs are going to be created, the use of which will affect the economic interests of more than one Union Republic, then it must be acknowledged that such Regulations ought to be issued by the Council of Ministers of the USSR.

Legislation on agricultural water use in the USSR, although more developed than other branches of water law, nevertheless inadequately defines the rights and obligations of water users concerning the rational use of water resources, particularly with regard to water use by collective and state farms directly from bodies of water outside the state irrigation systems.

For many years Soviet water law has developed primarily as legislation on agricultural water use, directed principally toward the regulation of relationships associated with the irrigation of lands and

drainage land improvements. Such is the case of the land-water codes
of the Uzbek and Turkmenian Republics of 1929,[11] the Water-land Improvement Code of the Belorussian Republic of 1928,[12] the Provisional
Regulations on Water Use and the Protection of Irrigation Systems and
Constructions on Them in the Kazakh Autonomous Republic of 1929,[13]
and many other legislative acts of Union Republics on water use passed
in the twenties.

It is true that in the thirties and forties legislative acts were passed
which regulated the use of bodies of water for the needs of river transport, the fishing industry, and domestic water supplies. These were
the Statutes of Inland Water Transport, approved by the decree of the
Council of People's Commissars of the USSR of 24 October 1930;[14] the
decree of the Council of People's Commissars of the USSR of 25 September 1935, "On the Regulation of Fishing and the Protection of
Fish";[15] and the decree of the Central Executive Committee and Council of People's Commissars of the USSR of 17 May 1937, "On the Sanitary Protection of Water Mains and Sources of Water Supply."[16] Nevertheless, legislation on the use of water resources in agriculture con-
tinued to occupy first place. A number of decrees of the Government
of the USSR and specialized laws in a number of Union Republics were
devoted only to agricultural water use (for example, the decree of the
Central Committee of the All-Union Communist Party [Bolsheviks] and
the Council of People's Commissars of the USSR of 23 May 1932, "On
the Struggle with Drought and Irrigation beyond the Volga";[17] the decree of the Council of Ministers of the USSR of 19 March 1949, "On
Measures to Develop Lands Under Irrigation and to Improve the Operation of Irrigation Systems";[18] the decree of the Council of Ministers of
the USSR of 17 August 1950, "On the Transition to a New System of Irrigation in Order to Make Fuller Use of Irrigated Lands and to Improve
the Organization of Agriculture";[19] and others. There were also the
Law on Agricultural Water Use in the Uzbek Republic of 24 March 1941,
and the decrees of the Presidiums of the Supreme Soviets of the Tadzhik

11. *Collected Statutes of the Uzbek SSR*, 1929, No. 72, Article
425; *Collected Decrees of the Turkmenian SSR*, 1929, Nos. 13–14,
Article 134.
12. *Collected Laws of the Belorussian SSR*, 1928, No. 14, Article
118.
13. *Collected Statutes of the RSFSR*, 1929, No. 55, Article 538.
14. *Collected Laws of the USSR*, 1930, No. 55, Article 582.
15. Ibid., No. 50, Article 420.
16. Ibid., No. 35, Article 143.
17. Ibid., 1932, No. 38, Article 232.
18. *Hydrotechnics and Land Improvement*, No. 1 (1949).
19. *Izvestiya*, 18 August 1950.

Republic of 10 September 1943, of the Kazakh Republic of 24 April 1946, and of the Kirghiz Republic of 19 August 1946 on agricultural water use in these Republics).

And only very recently have legislative acts been passed providing for the planned, complex use of water resources in all fields of the national economy, including industry and hydroenergy, and also for the protection of waters from depletion and pollution. For example, the decree of the Council of Ministers of the USSR of 22 April 1960, "On Measures to Regulate Use and Increase Conservation of Water Resources of the USSR,"[20] relates to these acts.

The extraordinary lack of coordination of the norms of water law, its unjustified diversity of character, and the gaps and other short-comings of the legislation on water make its application difficult. As a result, there is an urgent need for codification of the law.

Since the attempts already made to codify water law throughout the Union Republics have not led to the creation of an integrated and well-coordinated system of norms, ensuring a thorough and complete legal regulation of the use of water resources,[21] it has become necessary first of all to codify all-Union water law.

In connection with the search for the best ways and forms for the codification of water law, a lively discussion of this question has developed in juridical literature in recent years. Proposals have been made for the codification of water law, together with legislation on the use of land, minerals, and forests, in a single legislative act which, as the authors of the proposition supposed, is envisaged in paragraph "c" of Article 14 of the Constitution of the USSR.[22] There were proposals concerning the separate codification of land, mineral, forest, and water legislation by the promulgation of all-Union codes for each of these divisions of land law.[23] However, the majority was

---

20. *Collected Decrees of the USSR*, 1960, No. 9, Article 67.

21. See *Theoretical Questions of the Systemization of Soviet Legislation* (Moscow: State Juridical Publishing House, 1962), pp. 424, 430–431.

22. See the speech by V. S. Tadevosyan at the meeting devoted to the discussion of questions of the scientific principles of land-law codification, in *Soviet State and Law*, No. 2 (1956), p. 129.

23. See, for example, N. D. Kazantsev, "The Question of the Codification of Land Law," in the collected speeches, *On the Principles of the Codification of the Land Law of the USSR* (Moscow, 1955), p. 5. Subsequently, N. D. Kazantsev considered more acceptable the promulgation of principles of legislation on the use of land, minerals, forests, and water; see his article, "The Question of the Codification of Land Law of the USSR," in the collection, *Questions of Codification* (Moscow, 1957), p. 171.

inclined to consider that land, mineral, forest and water legislation should be codified separately by the promulgation of the appropriate legislative Principles (on a nationwide scale) and codes (in each Union Republic).[24]

Let us attempt briefly to define the merits and demerits of the proposals which have been put forward.

If all-Union Principles of legislation on the land, its minerals, forests and waters, and the corresponding Republic codes (on land, minerals, forests, waters) are issued, then only a certain degree of consolidation of the legislation will be achieved, and there will remain sufficiently broad scope to enable norms to be set up both in Union Republics and on an all-Union scale. This has both positive and negative aspects.

On the positive side, by such a system of structuring the law very important guarantees are provided, which enable the substance of the legislation to be coordinated with the actual and evolving features of the use of natural resources in different Union Republics and different branches of the national economy. It also guarantees that the Republic authorities are fairly free to make their own laws, which is a necessary feature of the sovereignty of the Union Republics. From this point of view, the promulgation of all-Union codes (but not principles of law) that preclude legislation by the Republics would, of course, be undesirable.

However, these positive features will be apparent before any kind of reasonable correlation can be observed between the Union Principles of legislation (being as it were above the law) and land, mineral, forest, and water law itself.

From the meaning of the term *principles*, it may be supposed that these will contain only the most general provisions of the different branches of the law, while the codes will include legal norms of a specific nature. This does not preclude enactment of laws of the USSR and Union Republics, of decrees of the Councils of Ministers of the USSR and of Union Republics, and also of other legislative acts, on an all-Union and Republic scale on questions of use of land, minerals, forests and waters. With time, besides the Union principles and Republic codes, there will appear many separate legislative acts on these questions which will weaken the positive features of codifi-

_____

24. See, in *Questions of Codification*, the articles of I. V. Pavlov, p. 147; N. D. Kazantsev, p. 171; G. A. Aksenenok, p. 183; A. A. Ruskol, p. 207; G. N. Polyanskaya, p. 230; and also the following works: *Theoretical Questions of the Systemization of Soviet Law*, p. 436; and *Questions of the Codification of Water Law in the USSR and Union Republics* (Moscow: State Juridical Publishing House, 1963), pp. 18, 53, 149.

cation. In our opinion, in order to avoid this it is necessary to specify in the Principles and in the codes a strictly limited range of legislative acts to function in conjunction with the Principles and codes, and to establish that the legislative bodies will, as the need arises, supplement and change them, refraining, however, from passing laws which go beyond this range.

Finally, if the Principles of water law of the USSR (like the Principles of land, mineral, and forest law) contain only the main fundamental provisions, they will duplicate one another to a considerable extent since the provisions for the legal regulation of all natural resources are basically similar (for example, the law of exclusive state ownership, possession with the right of use only, and so on), and an increase in the number of legal norms would not then be justified.

This could be avoided, of course, by passing a single legislative act on the Principles governing the use of natural resources (instead of separate Principles of legislation for land, minerals, forests, and waters). However, such a solution would, in its turn, give rise to another real shortcoming: such a legislative act could not possibly cover the different forms of use of the different kinds of natural resources. Therefore, believing the proposal that water law should be codified by the promulgation of all-Union Principles, and Republic water codes to be the most acceptable one, we suggest that, in the Principles of water law, greater emphasis should be placed upon norms which reflect the special characteristics of the use of water resources. This would make it possible to avoid in the Principles of water law the duplication of norms contained in the Principles of land, mineral, or forest law.

Assuming that a study of the existing legal procedure for the use of water resources might be useful in helping to achieve a scientifically sound set of codified works and bring about their greater effectiveness, let us turn to a discussion of the legal regulation of water use with reference to its basic forms.

To achieve some internal consistency and in order to present the material conveniently, we will divide forms of water use into three groups. In the first group are those forms in which water use is expressed primarily as the withdrawal from water sources of a certain quantity of water for use as a consumable commodity; in the second— forms of water use not associated with the consumption of water; and in the third—water use characterized by the discharge into bodies of water of sewage and other industrial and domestic wastes.

Chapter 2

Legal Regulation of Water Use Associated with Water Consumption

1. *Industrial Water Use*

Modern industry is a large consumer of water. It is difficult to name any form of production or branch of industry which could manage without water as a basic or subsidiary raw material. In some branches of industry the use of water is very great. For example, it is necessary to use eighteen tons of water to refine one ton of petroleum, twenty-five tons of water to smelt a ton of steel, up to six tons of water to manufacture a ton of synthetic fiber, two and one-half tons of water to make a meter of woolen cloth. For this reason the large chemical, metallurgical, pulp and paper, and certain other enterprises have specialized water supply units pertaining to the principal departments of the enterprises. The water supply and sewerage systems in all other industrial enterprises are usually subsidiary departments under the authority of the chief power specialist or the chief mechanical engineer, but they are still a most necessary element of production.

The provision of water for industrial needs occurs mainly in two ways:

First, by allocating for the use of enterprises the natural reserves of water in rivers, lakes, reservoirs, underground aquifers, and so on, which are readily available for industrial use. In these cases one or several enterprises together build their own structures for water intake and conveyance to supply them with the water they need from a natural water source.

Second, by allocating to the enterprises water from the centralized municipal water supply of cities and other centers of population. In these cases, the industrial enterprises do not have to have their own water intake facilities and do not use water directly from natural water sources, but connect their internal water supply facilities to the municipal water mains.

The legal relationships which stem from these two methods of industrial water supply differ juridically and are regulated in different ways.

Industrial enterprises which use water from natural water sources enter directly into legal relations with the owner of the water resources—the Soviet State. These relations have the clearly defined character of legal relations of water use and differ (because of the differences in objects of water use) from legal relations which develop when water is supplied from municipal water mains. In water use from rivers, lakes, reservoirs, and similar water sources, the object of use is the natural resource, which is the exclusive property of the State; whereas the water which is supplied to the industrial undertaking from the city water supply has already used up its economic quality as a natural resource and has become a commercial commodity.

In a comparison of these legal relations with other legal relations which develop in the use of natural resources (such as in the use of forests and minerals), it can be said that the relations involved in the withdrawal of water from natural water sources are similar to the relations which develop in the cutting of standing timber or the exploitation of mineral deposits; while relations which develop in supplying water from city water mains are the same type of relations as those which arise between the recipient of wood and the timber logger who delivers it, or between the recipient of raw ore and the mining enterprise which supplies it. It follows from this that use by industrial enterprises of water from natural water sources is regulated under water law (as one of the institutes of Soviet land law), while use of water from city mains, being part of the raw material of the enterprise, is regulated under civil law.

The main conditions of water use by industrial enterprises (such as the choice of water source, or the location, method, and maximum capacity of water withdrawal) are determined at the stage of planning and installing the water supply of the enterprise. After the plan has been approved, these conditions acquire the force of mandatory requirements and must be observed both when the construction (or reconstruction) of the industrial water supply is under way and when it is in operation. Industrial enterprises do not have the right to change the conditions of water use at their own discretion (in deviation from the plan).

In the planning and construction of water mains which are intended for the industrial water supply of enterprises, the designing and managing organizations must be guided by "The Regulations on the Choice and Approval of Sites for the Construction of Industrial Enterprises,"

by "Norms and Technical Conditions for Planning the External Water
Supply of Industrial Enterprises and Associated Settlements" (NiTU
126—55), by "Fire Prevention Norms for the Structural Planning of Industrial Enterprises and Populated Areas" (N 102—58), and by other
laws and departmental normative acts on questions of industrial water
supply.

Under the existing system, the choice of the source of water supply of an industrial enterprise is based only on considerations of a
technical and economic nature. The legislation does not stipulate
any specific and strictly mandatory requirements whatever for the
selection of source of water supply. Since all the water resources in
the USSR are the exclusive property of the State and the majority of
them are in free public use, legal obstacles to the choice of a source
of water supply do not arise in practice. However, to utilize a source
of water supply for industrial purposes, it is necessary to comply with
the requirements for the rational, and especially the complex, use of
water resources, as well as meet the technical-economic needs of the
plan.

Unlike relationships arising from land use and the use of minerals
and forests—where the legislation provides for the allocation of sections of land, mineral deposits, and forests and the issuance of legal
documents (such as acts, contracts, notes, orders, and so on) to
users—the allocation of water resources for the use of industrial enterprises is not defined by law. Allocation of water resources for use
is not made and legal documents are not issued to water users, except in cases of use of underground water.[1] But if it is taken into account that the main conditions of water use are determined when the
plan for industrial water supply is approved, and that the use of water
with the observance of these conditions is sanctioned by an act of
the state commission which authorizes the operation of the water supply facility, then approval of the plan and the authorization for the
operation of the water supply may be considered to be equivalent
juridically to the allocation of water resources for use. These actions
contain the will of the State, in consequence of which the industrial
enterprise receives permission to use the selected water source.

The procedure for authorizing the operation of the water supply
systems of industrial enterprises, like other installations, is regulated by the decree of the Council of Ministers of the USSR of 15 September 1962, "On the Procedure for Authorizing the Operation of Completed Enterprises, Buildings, and Installations."[2]

The date for putting a newly constructed or reconstructed water

---

1. For the procedure for allocating underground waters for use,
see Section 3 of this chapter, below.
2. *Collected Decrees of the USSR*, 1962, No. 17, Article 136.

supply system of an industrial enterprise into operation is considered
to be the date of signing the act by the state examining commission
responsible for authorizing the operation of the water supply.

Newly constructed enterprises have a right to use the selected
water source. The construction plans of these enterprises provide for
water to be supplied from natural water sources, as a rule, as soon as
the enterprise begins to function after the act has been passed authorizing its operation. If the productive capacity of the enterprise is put
into operation by stages, the right of water use starts from the moment
that operation of the first stage (that is, a group of technically integrated departments) is authorized. In the case of enterprises which
previously acquired water for productive needs from communal-domestic
water supplies and then switched to natural water sources for their supply, the right to use the water source begins as soon as operation of
the principal water intake installations of the industrial water supply
is authorized.

When water is withdrawn from sources in general use, industrial
enterprises must not violate the interests of other water users. In this
connection, "Norms and Technical Conditions for Planning the External
Water Supply of Industrial Enterprises and Associated Settlements"
(NiTU 126—55) obliges planners and owners of water supplies to build
riparian structures for river water intake (such as wells, dikes, dams,
pumps) and also gravity feeding mains, tunnels, and headworks in
order to ensure the least possible constraint of the river and to avoid
a transformation of its channel. Where navigation is carried out on
the body of water which is used as a source of supply, the construction of the planned water-intake installations and their location must
be agreed upon with the river transport agencies.

If water for industrial needs is extracted from fishery waters, the
industrial enterprises—the water users—are obliged to take measures
to protect the fish. According to Article 12 of the Regulations for the
Protection of Fish and the Control of Fishing in Waters of the USSR,
approved by the decree of the Council of Ministers of the USSR of 15
September 1958,[3] water may be withdrawn from fishery waters for the
needs of enterprises and for irrigation only if special devices are installed, in agreement with the agencies of fish protection, to prevent
the fish from getting into the water intake structures.

From the general legal principle of complex use of water resources,
it emerges that, when the same body of water is used jointly, all the
water users are mutually obliged to consider the interests of their co-
users. Therefore, if an industrial enterprise is a water user, it is
obliged not to infringe on the interests of other water users and, in its
turn, has the right to demand consideration of its interests by other

3. *Collected Decrees of the USSR*, 1958, No. 16, Article 127.

water users and to insist on the removal of any obstacle to its use of
the water or cause of deterioration in conditions of use.

Use of water from natural sources by industrial enterprises for productive needs is not subject to a time limit and is free of charge.

The maximum quantity of water which can be extracted from a water
source in a unit of time by means of water supply installations is determined when the construction or reconstruction of the industrial undertaking is planned. The plan must take into account the productive
capacity of the enterprise being constructed (or reconstructed), the
features of the chosen method of production, the need for water for
fire suppression measures, and the necessity to keep a certain reserve
of water supply capacity with a view to future increases in the productive capacity of the undertaking. Consequently, the technical capa-
bilities of the enterprise to withdraw water for industrial needs are
usually higher than its actual requirements. But this does not mean
that every enterprise has to withdraw the maximum quantity of water
of which it is technically capable. It should withdraw only as much
water as it needs to maintain normal production.

However, the legislation does not establish either standards of
water consumption for industrial needs or the obligation of the enterprise to use the water carefully. In practice, individual enterprises
which have their own sources of water supply use an excessive amount
of water,[4] thereby pursuing illegal practices associated with the pollution of bodies of water. Instead of striving for a thorough treatment
of the sewage, the enterprises, taking advantage of their ability to
withdraw a surplus quantity of water, strongly dilute the industrial
wastes, artificially lower the concentration of harmful substances in
the sewage, and thus evade their responsibilities for treating it (since
weakly polluted effluent may be discharged into bodies of water without treatment). It is clear that such practice is not in accord with the
principle of rational utilization of water resources, and it must be
stopped.

In order to regulate the water use of industrial enterprises, the
legislation should provide for a standardization of the quantity of water withdrawn from source, on the basis of scientifically determined
standards of industrial water use for a unit of output of each kind of
product, and should establish also the obligation of the enterprise to
strive for a reduction in water use.

------

4. If the Novo-Lipetskii metallurgical factory uses 24 cubic meters
of water for one ton of metal produced, the Novo-Tul'skii factory uses
764 cubic meters—thirty times more. The ferro-alloy factories use
from 40 to 800 cubic meters of water for one ton of production. (From
the co-report of the Chairman of the Budget Commission of the Soviet
Union, Deputy I. S. Senin, at the third session of the sixth convocation
of the Supreme Soviet of the USSR, *Izvestiya*, 16 December 1963.)

Recirculating water supply systems, which are being used increasingly, are an effective means of reducing the amount of water used in industry and of decreasing the discharge of sewage.[5] It is the legal obligation of industrial enterprises to adopt recirculating water supply systems. The "Norms and Technical Conditions for Planning the External Water Supply of Industrial Enterprises and Associated Settlements" (NiTU 126—55) require that this obligation be honored at the planning stage, and establishes that the water supply plan for an industrial enterprise should provide, when there is the appropriate technical-economic justification, for water circulation and recirculation. In their turn, the Regulations for the Protection of Surface Waters from Pollution by Sewage forbid industrial enterprises to discharge into bodies of water sewage which may, with the observance of the technical-economic conditions, be dealt with by maximum utilization of a water reuse system.

The quality of water supplied for industrial needs must be established in accordance with the requirements of the technological processes of the units of the enterprise. As a rule, water destined for use by industrial enterprises (with the exception of the food industry and certain others) does not need to be of the same quality as drinking water.

The question of designating the special purpose for which water withdrawn for industrial needs is to be used is decided individually. If an industrial enterprise has its own water supply, that does not mean that it must use the water which is withdrawn only for its own needs. According to Article 3 of "Norms and Technical Conditions for Planning the External Water Supply of Industrial Enterprises and Associated Settlements" (NiTU 126—55), the planning of the external water

---

5. According to some calculations, the introduction of repeated use of water by means of a recirculating water supply system can lead to a significant reduction in water use per unit of production: 80 to 90 percent in the metallurgical and pulp and paper industries; 85 to 90 percent in the petroleum and ore-concentrating industries; 60 to 70 percent in the sugar industry; 90 percent in the coke-chemical industry, and so on.

At the suggestion of the State Water Inspector of the Dnestr basin and the Dunai River, recirculating water supply systems were introduced in seven Odessa enterprises; as a result the water consumption of these enterprises was reduced by 610,000 cubic meters a year. The introduction of recirculating water supply systems in an additional eighty-seven large industrial enterprises of the Ukraine will reduce water use by 5 billion cubic meters a year (see D. V. Leporskii, "The Conservation and Use of Water Resources in the Ukraine," in *The Treatment and Use of Sewage and Industrial Wastes* [Kiev, 1964], pp. 15—16.)

supply of enterprises is carried out with regard for the feasibility and
expediency of meeting a wide variety of water needs close to them.
It follows from here that in certain conditions the industrial enterprises have the right and are obliged to transfer part of the water
which is withdrawn to other enterprises or organizations. Enterprises
which have their own water supplies, and are therefore water users,
in this way become suppliers of a product—water.

Relations between enterprises which are the owners of industrial
water supply systems and their subscribers (the recipients of the water) are not directly regulated under the law. But since these relations
by their nature are similar to those of a centralized water supply system, in a supplementary way the Regulations on the Use of Communal
Water Supply and Sewerage Systems, together with the appropriate
norms of civil law, may in certain measure be applied to them.

The development of these relations governing water supply between
two industrial enterprises is determined primarily at the stage of planning the water supply, by the general agreement of the parties to connect the water supply systems of the subscribing enterprise to the
water supply of the water user enterprise. Subsequently the specific
conditions governing the water supply are regulated by agreements
concluded annually between the enterprises. The agreements indicate
the mutual rights and obligations of the parties—the obligation of one
enterprise regularly to supply the other with water for industrial needs
in a stipulated quantity and quality, and the obligation of the second
to pay the first the cost of the water received in accord with the account rendered (or in another way), to maintain this water supply system in technically good repair, and so on. Since the water relates to
output which has not been taken into account in a plan, the water supply agreements between the water user enterprises and their subscribers are concluded exclusively at the discretion of the parties
(Article 44 of the Principles of Civil Law of the USSR and Union Republics).

Industrial enterprises which withdraw water for productive needs
from natural sources are not obliged to set up zones of sanitary protection around the industrial water intakes, since this is not stipulated
by law and is not required in practice. However, they are obliged, in
our opinion, to take all necessary measures in the interests of the
safety of the public and also of domestic animals and other property,
which might happen to be where the industrial water intake is located.

In this way, industrial enterprises which use natural water resources
for productive purposes have, as water users, a complex of rights and
obligations relating to the conditions governing the construction of
technical water supply systems, the choice of sources, the withdrawal
of water and its subsequent use for their own needs and for the water
supply of nearby enterprises. Not all of these rights and obligations
are sufficiently defined. Therefore, one task for the further improve-

ment of water legislation will be the exact definition of the rights and obligations of water users under different forms of use, including the use of water for the needs of industry.

When the water requirements of industrial establishments are met through a centralized communal-domestic water supply system, the associated relationships are regulated basically in the same way as are the usual relations governing water supply that develop between the owners of communal water supply systems and their subscribers.

The question of the feasibility and expediency of using drinking water for industrial needs is settled at the stage of planning the water supply of enterprises under construction or reconstruction by the state agencies responsible for approving plans for capital construction.

These agencies and planning organizations are guided by the existing Norms and Technical Conditions for Planning the Water Supply of Industrial Enterprises and Associated Settlements (NiTU 126–55), which prescribe that when there is an industrial, municipal, or district water supply system close to the planned object, it must be considered as a possible source of water supply. The legislation does not contain any requirements concerning the justification and economic expediency of using drinking water for industrial needs.

The practice of using water supplied from city mains for industrial purposes is incompatible with the principle of rational use of water resources. Although it is quite evident that the use of water of a potable quality for industrial purposes is necessary only for enterprises of the food industry and certain others, in practice many enterprises of the metallurgical, mining, machine building, chemical, construction, and other branches of industry use potable water for industrial purposes when they could easily use water from natural sources. As a result, a great quantity of drinking water is used contrary to its purpose, and the regular provision of water for the population of towns and other centers of population is interrupted.

For example, in 1962 enterprises of the Donetskii Council of national economy in the Donetskaya Oblast used 106 million cubic meters of potable water for industrial purposes, which is 28 percent of the total quantity of water supplied for domestic purposes in the course of a year. There is a similar situation concerning the use of potable water by industrial undertakings in the Luganskaya Oblast.[6]

It is not possible to report favorably on Moscow enterprises in this regard. They also rely primarily upon potable water for technological purposes and do not use enough water from open bodies and artesian

---

6. See the decree of the Council of Ministers of the Ukraine SSR of 30 May 1963, "On Measures to Regulate the Use of Water Resources by Industrial Enterprises in the Ukraine" (*Collected Decrees of the Ukraine SSR*, 1963, No. 5, Article 38).

wells. The Likhachev Automobile Factory, the "Dinamo" Factory, the Telman Tannery, the "Borets" Factory, and others in 1963 alone paid more than 800,000 rubles for excess use of potable water. An irrational and inefficient use of drinking water is also permitted by big shops and public food enterprises which use purified drinking water for refrigerating plants.[7]

The Regulations on the Use of Communal Water Supply and Sewerage Systems, approved by the Ministry of Communal Management of the RSFSR on 9 August 1960, specifies the right of the executive committees of city councils to take the necessary measures to regulate the use of drinking water from municipal water supplies. Article 3 of the Regulations says that where it is possible and expedient to use local water sources for industrial needs, the executive committee of the city Council of Workers' Deputies may, according to "Vodokanal,"* order these enterprises to construct their own industrial—fire suppression water supply systems within a specified period of time and, when the time limit has expired, may limit the delivery of water for industrial needs from the municipal water supply to these enterprises or refuse it to them. Unfortunately, the executive committees of city Councils rarely use the rights given them and do not decide questions concerned with regulating the use of drinking water in cities and other centers of population.

For example, in Gork'ii more than one hundred industrial enterprises use drinking water from the municipal water supply system for industrial needs, consuming about 50 percent of the total quantity of water provided by the system. These enterprises include metallurgical, machine building, and construction material factories, which use water in the cooling of machine tools, the cleaning of machines and parts, and the preparation of astringent solutions, for which drinking water is not required. At the same time, because of the shortage of water in the municipal water supply system, interruptions frequently occur in the supply of water to the upper floors of multistoried apartment buildings. But the Gor'kii city executive committee has not once considered curtailing the use of drinking water for industrial needs by these or other enterprises.

A study of the practice of regulating the communal-domestic and industrial water supply in cities and other centers of population convinces one that Article 3 of the Regulations on the Use of Communal

---

*For an explanation of Vodokanal, see p. 153.

7. See the ordinance of the Executive Committee of the Moscow City Council of Workers' Deputies of 11 January 1964, "On Measures to Regulate the Use and Economy of Water of the Municipal Water Supply System" (*Bulletin of the Executive Committee of the Moscow Council of Workers' Deputies*, 1964, No. 2).

Water Supply and Sewerage Systems is insufficient for the establishment of a proper procedure governing the use of potable water for industrial purposes. It is necessary to establish a legal norm which
would clearly and categorically define when the use of drinking water
in industry is permitted and when it is not. It is necessary, in our
opinion, to allow drinking water to be used for industrial purposes
only by those enterprises which need to use it (the food industry and
others).

With regard to the regulation of the use of drinking water from municipal water supply systems for industrial purposes, firm rationing
of water to industrial enterprises might have a certain effect.

In this way the legal procedure governing the water supply for industrial purposes from communal municipal systems, which is basically
similar to the procedure for centralized, communal-domestic water supply systems, involves the resolution of a number of fundamental questions (that is, on the permissibility of using drinking water for industrial purposes and the necessity for its limitation). A discussion of
these questions brings out the imperfection of their legal settlement
and makes it desirable to see that consideration be given to the observations made above when the future water codes of Union Republics
are worked out.

2. *Use of Water Resources in Agriculture*

The availability of adequate natural reserves of suitable water is
as necessary in agriculture as it is in other branches of the national
economy.

In agriculture, primary reliance is placed upon the natural moisture
of the soil, that is to say, the reserves of water in the surface layers
of the ground which accumulate after the melting of snow, rainfall,
river flooding, the rise of subsoil water, and so on.

The utilization of soil moisture in agriculture does not by itself
have any legal significance, but is associated with land use, for natural moistness is a qualitative feature of cultivated land. Accordingly,
the right to use natural reserves of soil moisture in agriculture is in-
separable from the right to use land. Most of the legal norms which
regulate the use of soil moisture are, therefore, directed to land users.

The land user is obliged under our law not to be content with prevailing soil moisture conditions but to husband the soil moisture and
to conserve and use it rationally.

Since the amount of moisture in the soil depends to a large extent
on a favorable rate of surface flow over the land, the law directs land
users to carry out measures to control the seasonal flow of water from
the land surface into rivers and other bodies of water. These measures include snow retention on fields, the planting of trees, terracing

of hill slopes, gully control, correct agro-technical cultivation of the soil, and so on. Many of the most simple measures for artificially channeling and regulating water flow not only aid the farm which uses them, but improve the general conditions of the water resources. For example, snow retention on fields increases soil moisture and contributes to increased agricultural productivity. In addition, snow retention decreases the flow of water at the spring period of high water and replenishes the subsoil waters which feed the rivers more evenly than surface runoff does. As a result favorable hydrological conditions are created in the bodies of water, affecting a wide range of water users. However, in many regions of the country, even when the most simple measures to regulate surface runoff are practiced, the amount of soil moisture is insufficient for intensive agricultural production, which is a feature of a socialist national economy. When there is not enough natural soil moisture, the land must be irrigated.

The economic effectiveness and advantages of irrigation have long been evident. Highly productive irrigated agriculture is therefore becoming increasingly widespread in the USSR, and is practiced not only in arid areas—the deserts, dry steppes and so on—but in temperate zones as well—in both chernozem and nonchernozem regions.[8]

The Communist Party and the Soviet State attach great importance to the development of irrigated agriculture. As far back as the first years of the Soviet regime, V. I. Lenin time and again pointed to the great importance of irrigation to the national economy.

The problems and measures associated with the development of irrigated agriculture are defined both in important party documents and in legislative acts.

The Program of the Communist Party of the Soviet Union, which was adopted at the Twenty-second Party Congress, mentions that in order to secure stable, high, and steadily increasing yields and to protect agriculture from natural forces which might adversely affect it, especially drought, it is necessary to carry out, together with other very important measures, a broad program of irrigation development in order to supply water to millions of hectares of new lands in arid regions and to improve existing agriculture requiring irrigation.[9]

––––––––––

8. The amount of cultivated land in the USSR is 609 million hectares, including 222 million hectares of pasture. Irrigated lands occupy only a small area, about 10 million hectares, but give a high yield of valuable crops. For example, wheat crops on the irrigated lands of the Northern Caucasus, with proper irrigation management, yield from forty to sixty double centners per hectare regardless of weather conditions. Maize yield on irrigated lands reaches seventy to eighty double centners per hectare.

9. See *Materials of the Twenty-second Congress of the Communist Party of the Soviet Union* (Moscow: State Publishing House of Political Literature, 1961), pp. 379–380.

In execution of the Program of the Communist Party of the Soviet Union, the December 1963 and February 1964 plenums of the Central Committee of the CPSU defined specific measures for all possible development of irrigated agriculture which, together with the use of chemicals and the mechanization of agriculture and stock raising, is one of the principal trends in the intensification of agricultural production in the USSR. At the March 1965 Plenum of the Central Committee of the CPSU, serious attention was given to the need to utilize irrigated and drained lands correctly.

The Central Committee of the CPSU and the Council of Ministers of the USSR by their decree of 25 October 1963 formed the Union-Republic State Production Committee for Irrigated Agriculture and Water Management of the USSR[10] in order to improve the management of irrigation works, make more effective use of land requiring irrigation, and to facilitate the early cultivation of large irrigated tracts so as to achieve significant expansion of grain, technical, and other important crops. This agency and its local offices have full responsibility, not only for the supply of water to farms, but also for its correct use and for the whole organization of agricultural production on irrigated lands.

The artificial irrigation of the lands of collective farms (kolkhozy) and state farms (sovkhozy) and other state and public agricultural enterprises is carried out in two main forms—centralized and noncentralized. Flood irrigation and irrigation with sewage from cities and industrial enterprises are special situations.

When a centralized water supply is used, the lands are irrigated through large state irrigation systems which as a rule serve several adjoining farms, irrespective of whether they are collective, state, or other farms.

The state irrigation systems, which technically are a complex of canals and other hydro-technical structures and equipment that supply water to the water users, include both inter- and intrafarm facilities. Interfarm irrigation structures, being state property, are under the direction of specialized state enterprises—the irrigation system administrations. The intrafarm irrigation structures can be either the property of the State or of the collective farms. On the sovkhozy and other state farms, they are state property that is under the management of these farms. Irrigation structures which are erected on the lands of collective farms and with farm resources are collective farm property. Structures which are on collective farm land but which were erected with funds from the state budget are state property and appear

---

10. In accordance with Article 2 of the Law on Changing the System of Industrial Management Agencies and the Reform of Certain Other State Management Agencies, adopted by the Supreme Soviet of the USSR on 2 October 1965, this Committee has been reorganized as the Ministry of Land Improvement and Water Management of the USSR.

on the accounts of the state irrigation system administrations. In addition, they are used by the collective farms in accord with agreements for long-term use, free of charge, which are concluded with the state irrigation system administrations.

Under a decentralized method, the lands are irrigated with the aid of irrigation systems, water supply, pumping and sprinkling installations, and other water intake and water distributing structures which are set up separately by each farm to serve its own needs and which supply water directly from rivers, lakes, ponds, reservoirs, and other sources of supply. If these structures are built by sovkhozy or other state farms, they are state property operated by these farms and are under their management. Structures which are built by collective farms for their own needs are collective farm property.

In the irrigation of fields with sewage a special system of structures is built, which is connected to the sewage system of cities and industrial enterprises and which is, as it were, a continuation of the sewerage network. Such a method of irrigation is employed not only to increase soil moisture, but, principally and primarily, in order to purify communal and industrial sewage.

Flood irrigation, consisting of periodic, complete flooding of land in the floodplains of rivers, in dead river channels, dry valleys, and so on, is carried out by each farm individually or by several farms together, as a rule without using irrigation canals and other irrigation structures, but rather by building temporary dams and raising the level of water in small rivers and by retaining melted snow in natural depressions of the land surface.

Water-use relations which arise in connection with these methods of irrigation are in many respects similar, but they also have substantial differences. Accordingly, the legal regulation of these relations also has a number of its own special features.

It is noteworthy that quite inadequate attention has been given in juridical literature to studying the peculiarities of the legal regulation of relations of agricultural water use stemming from different organizational arrangements for irrigation. Although in works on water law the study of legal questions of irrigation in agriculture predominates, these questions mainly deal with water use from state irrigation systems. Noncentralized irrigation, irrigation with sewage, flood irrigation, as well as the water supply of livestock farms and similar enterprises of collective and state farms, have been outside the purview of the researcher. What is more, even the analyses of legal questions of water use from the state irrigation systems contain a number of inaccuracies.

All those concerned with legal questions of water use from the state irrigation systems identify as water-use relations only those relations that arise between the irrigation system administrations and the collective, state, and other farms which are served by the systems, and

relations arising between these farms and the collective farm households, workers, and employees, in connection with the irrigation of
private lots. The irrigation system administrations are regarded only
as special state agencies which are called upon to serve farms with
irrigated lands and to administer the use of the water resources within the irrigation systems.

For example, I. A. Koetkina, in defining the legal position of the
state irrigation system administrations, came to the conclusion that
"the state irrigation system administration is both an industrial enterprise and an administrative agency. Therefore the irrigation system
administrations should be classed with those juridical persons of dual
nature known to Soviet law, which are both agencies of state management and economic organizations (e.g., the State Bank of the USSR)."[11]

This is true. But it insufficiently defines the legal position of the
state irrigation system administrations and does not reflect fully the
special features of the legal relations of water use which stem from
the irrigation of land with the aid of the state irrigation systems.
I. A. Koetkina, like other authors, loses sight of the fact that the state
irrigation system administrations are not only industrial enterprises
and administrative agencies but water users as well.

One of the principal tasks of the state irrigation system administrations is to supply water at the right time to the irrigation network
of the water user, in a stipulated quantity necessary for the watering
of crops and to meet other needs. But in order to supply water to the
irrigation network of the water users, it must first of all be withdrawn
from the source. The withdrawal of water represents water use. The
water is withdrawn with the aid of head gate structures, which are
owned by the irrigation system administrations. Therefore, the administrations are water users in mutual relations with the State and
with enterprises, institutions, and organizations which use the same
water sources. Accordingly, the rights and obligations governing use
of water from the irrigation source apply to the irrigation system administrations and not to the farms which are served by the irrigation
systems.

As a water user, the irrigation system administration must observe
the rules governing the use of the irrigation source—river, lake, reservoir, and so on.

The fact that the irrigation system administration is a water user
provides the necessary legal prerequisite for it to be the subject of
the law of water use in relations with the farms which it serves.

As a water user, the irrigation system administration is responsible

11. I. A. Koetkina, *The Legal Relations of Collective Farm Water
Users with State Irrigation System Administrations in the RSFSR*
(Moscow: State Juridical Publishing House, 1959), p. 42.

for the rational use of the water resources within the whole irrigation system. It also has the right to manage the use of the water resources on the farms which it supplies.

Unfortunately, the legal position of the state irrigation system administrations as water users has not been adequately reflected in the legislation. Only in Article 13 of the Regulations on Water Use in the Georgian SSR are there instructions to the effect that industrial enterprises and institutions, which are under the jurisdiction of the Ministry of Water Management of the Georgian Republic and which are concerned with water management, are water users. The legislation of other Union Republics and of the USSR contains no such instructions.

In order to achieve the necessary clarity in the regulation of relations of agricultural water use, the regulations on the state irrigation system administrations should indicate that they are not only state-financed enterprises and administrative agencies, but water users with the right to use water from certain water sources and that they possess the corresponding responsibilities.

The activities of the irrigation system administrations, associated with ensuring correct use of irrigation water on the farms which they supply, are also subject to extensive legal regulation, as specified by the February 1964 Plenum of the Central Committee of the Communist Party of the Soviet Union.

The conditions of water use by the state irrigation systems, as generally is the case in the use of natural resources with the aid of capital structures, are to a considerable extent determined by the whole character of the entire complex of structures and installations which are employed. Therefore it is very important in the course of planning and building the irrigation system to create conditions which will permit the most effective and rational use of the water resources.

The basic requirements for ensuring an effective and rational use of water resources are legally reinforced and are directed not only to the water users (in this case, the irrigation system administrations), but also to the designing and building organizations. When planning and building irrigation systems, these organizations are obliged to abide by both the existing legislation and the special building standards and rules in which all of the requirements for the planning and building of irrigation systems are systematically set out.[12]

----

12. *Construction Standards and Regulations, Part II, Section VI, Chapter 3, "The Construction of Land Improvement Systems. Planning Standards"* (*SNiP II-VI, 3-62*), approved by the State Construction Committee of the Council of Ministers of the USSR on 14 December 1962 has been in force since 1 July 1963. This set of norms applies to the following types of land-improvement systems (irrigation

In accordance with the Construction Standards and Regulations, SNiP II—И, 3—62, irrigation systems must be planned and built in coordination with the organization of agricultural production, in order to secure high yields on irrigated areas, ensure reliability and the convenience of operating the system through automation and remote control, and to meet the water needs of all adjacent water users and the necessary sanitary requirements. The method of irrigation which is adopted in the plan must help increase the fertility of the irrigated land, prevent erosion, waterlogging, salination of the soil, or a rise in the level of subsoil water, and must ensure the most economical use of the sources of supply and the irrigation water. These requirements lie outside the bounds of water-use relations, since the designing and building organizations do not use water for irrigation and are therefore not water users. Nevertheless, observance of the established legislative requirements are mandatory when developing and approving plans and when building and authorizing the operation of irrigation systems which have just been created or which have received a major overhaul.

The rights and obligations of the state irrigation system administrations concerning water use arise the moment that the head gate structures are put into operation. They are essentially similar to the rights and obligations of water users who withdraw water from rivers, lakes, reservoirs, and other bodies of water, but they do have their own individual character.

The state irrigation system administration has the right and is obliged to withdraw water from the source in a quantity corresponding to the planned capacity of the irrigation system and the planned water requirements of the farms which it serves.

The systematic regulation of the volume of water consumption of the irrigation systems is carried out by setting up basic indices (annual limits) of water intake, which are worked out by the irrigation system administrations and approved by the agencies of water management for periods of three to five years. In addition, the rate of water intake is regulated on the basis of annual plans for water use by the system as a whole and of operating schedules for the supply of water to the farms. However, the maximum water intake from the irrigation source in a unit of time is a standard which is calculated in accordance with the plan for construction of the irrigation system. The

---

and drainage): Irrigation and drainage collection networks, flood irrigation, drainage networks, structures on irrigation and drainage networks, and agricultural sewage farms. The planning of structures affecting the water resources of rivers must be guided also by the construction standards and regulations for hydrotechnical river structures (SNiP II—И, 1—62).

planned standard of water intake, which is calculated in accord with
the scheme for the complex use of the whole body of water that serves
as the irrigation source, is taken into account in the regulation of the
use of the water resources of rivers, lakes, reservoirs, and so on. The
right of the irrigation system administrations to withdraw water from
the irrigation source in accordance with the plan, and within the
planned standard of water intake, is protected by law.

The responsibilities concerning the conditions and method of water
use must accord with the right to withdraw water from the irrigation
source (for example, a river, lake, or reservoir). The legislation defines these obligations in the form of a general requirement regarding
the rational use of the water resources of our rivers, lakes, and reservoirs. The obligations of the irrigation system administrations concerning water use are clarified in separate normative acts, but in a
measure that still falls far short of what is required.

The irrigation systems commonly use as a water source artificially
created reservoirs, which are intended for multiple use, though primarily for irrigation or hydroenergy. In these cases the rights and obligations of the irrigation system administrations acquire new characteristics, which should be reflected in the legislation.

If the state irrigation system uses water from a reservoir which has
been created especially or mainly for the storage of irrigation water,
the irrigation system administration should use its right of major or
chief water user and have preference over other water users.

In particular it is necessary to establish that in drought years, or
in drought periods of the year, or in other exceptional circumstances,
the use of water from these reservoirs for the needs of other water
users may be temporarily limited in the interests of the irrigation system, with the exception of water withdrawal for drinking needs, which
is not subject to restriction.

On the other hand, if the state irrigation system uses water from a
reservoir that is intended primarily for hydroelectric purposes, the
rights of the irrigation system administrations may in some circumstances be limited. The RSFSR, Azerbaidzhan SSR, and some of the
other Republics do have laws to this effect.

It is essential that similar laws be adopted in all the Union Republics.

Finally, the legislation should provide that, in the use of the same
river by several irrigation systems, the downstream systems should
have priority in the withdrawal of water over those upstream.

The rights and obligations of the state irrigation system administrations which have been considered above develop, or should develop,
out of what might be called extrasystem relations as opposed to intra-
system relations, the latter being water use relations between the irrigation system administrations and the farms which they serve.

In their relations with the collective, state, and other farms em-

ploying irrigation which they serve, the state irrigation system administrations are represented not as water users, but as enterprises obliged to supply water for crops and other needs, and as state agencies
which are obliged and competent to manage the use of water resources
within the irrigation systems.

Accordingly, in these relationships the rights and obligations of the
irrigation system administrations are of a different type.

Unlike a drinking water supply system, where relationships between
the owners of the water system and their subscribers are regulated
under civil law, the relations of irrigation system administrations and
the farms they serve are governed by water law, since use of water
from the main and other interfarm irrigation canals represents use of
a natural object. This is because the great majority of the main and
other interfarm canals that are operated by the irrigation system administrations are built in such a way that they are in effect a continuation of the river or other source from which water is withdrawn into
the irrigation network.

Under existing legislation, the irrigation of collective, state, and
other farms of the irrigation system administrations is carried out on
the basis of mutually coordinated plans of water use (water distribution).

The planning and implementation of plans for centralized irrigation
are analyzed in detail in juridical literature, particularly in the work
of I. A. Koetkina.[13] Although there is no need, therefore, to repeat this
analysis, it may be desirable, while going over the main characteristics of present methods of planning use of water from state irrigation systems, to examine the rights and obligations of the parties in
water use relationships.

Every farm which is served by the state irrigation system each year
draws up a plan of intrafarm water use, which takes into account all
the conditions relating to the use of the water (such as standards,
dates, sequence of watering crops, and so on) and conforms to the
plan of agricultural work. In this plan for intrafarm water use, all water needs are taken into account (such as needs for livestock, the water supply of subsidiary enterprises, the irrigation of household lots
and collective kitchen gardens, the leaching of salinated lands, and
so on), in addition to water requirements for irrigation; finally, the
total water requirements of the farm for the year are determined according to the main periods of water use.

After approval by the irrigation system administration, the plans for
intrafarm water use are ratified by the executive agencies of the local
Councils or by higher agencies of water management (depending on

---

13. See I. A. Koetkina, *Legal Relations of Collective Farm Water
Users with State Irrigation System Administrations*, pp. 42, 58—73.

the line of authority and the importance of the irrigation system) and
are subject to strict execution both by the water users and by the irrigation system administration.

In its turn, the irrigation system administration draws up its plan
of water use based on indices of productive capacity of the irrigation
system, on the capacity of the canals and other irrigation structures,
and so on, and also based on the plans for intrafarm water use which
it has approved. In addition the irrigation system administration draws
up operating schedules for the intake and distribution of water throughout the system and a number of other documents for planning the work
of the irrigation system. However, this plan of water use and the
other plans which are drawn up by the irrigation system administration
are mainly intended to regulate and organize the internal productive
activity of the agency itself as a state enterprise. The plans establish a procedure for the effective cooperation of different functioning
sections and links of the irrigation system; but they do not regulate
the relationships of the irrigation system administration with the farms
it serves, since they do not determine the mutual rights and obligations
of the parties involved in water use.

On the other hand, the intrafarm plans of water use for each of the
farms which are served do regulate the relations between the subjects
of water use within the framework of the irrigation system. These
plans define the mutual rights and obligations of the parties which
have water-use relations—the irrigation system administration on the
one hand and each of the farm water users on the other.

The intrafarm plan for water use, having been approved by the irrigation system administration and ratified, is legally similar to a contract.

The collective, state, or other farm submits the draft of its intrafarm
plan of water use to the irrigation system administration for approval,
essentially like a draft agreement on conditions of water use. If the
irrigation system administration has approved the draft intrafarm plan
of water use submitted to it (which is subsequently ratified), then it,
in effect, has given its consent to the proposed conditions of water
use and assumed the corresponding responsibilities regarding relations
with the collective, state, or other farm which it serves. In this way,
the intrafarm plan of water use becomes a legal fact, thereby enabling
the rights and obligations of the parties to water use, which are expressed in the abstract in the law, to become the specific rights and
obligations of these subjects.

However, by its nature the intrafarm plan of water use does not express the agreement of the parties directly, but only implies it. The
agreement, which exists in fact, remains, as it were, hidden from view.
This circumstance does not help to achieve the necessary clarity and
precision in the conduct of the parties involved. It would be better,
in the interests of organizing an all-around effective and rational utili-

zation of the water resources of irrigation systems, not to have merely
an accord on intrafarm plans of water use, but to draw up the agreement of the parties involved in the use of the water into an actual
contract. The contractual form would be helpful, not only because it
would permit a direct and smooth formulation of the mutual rights and
obligations of the parties, but because it would provide additional
legal means for each party to influence the other, by specifying the
responsibilities of the parties and by sanctions for failure to carry
them out. Therefore, the proposals in juridical literature on the de-
sirability of restoring the contractual form for relations of water use
from state irrigation systems, which used to be practiced but was
abolished in 1958,[14] merit approval and support.

From the moment that the intrafarm plan of water use of the collective, state, or other farm is ratified, the irrigation system administration becomes the obligated subject in respect to each of the farms
which it serves. It must supply water to the irrigation network of these
farms in the quantity and at the times specified in the plan of water
use and in accord with the conditions stipulated by this plan.

Under Union Republic law, the irrigation system administrations
are obliged to inform each water user in writing of the quantity, times,
and place of water supply. These notifications must be handed to the
water users not later than ten days before the start of irrigation. However, the legislation does not establish what the legal consequences
are of a nonfulfillment of this obligation and what influence the water
user could, in this event, bring to bear upon the administration. This
applies not only to this aspect of the irrigation system administration's
activities, but also to the fulfillment of its principal obligation—the
supply of irrigation water.

As soon as the intrafarm plan of water use is ratified, the collective, state, and other farm water users have the right to demand from
the irrigation system administration that it maintain a flow into the
interfarm irrigation network that will ensure, in accordance with the
plan, a supply of water to the intrafarm network sufficient for the irrigation of crops and plantations, the water supply of livestock farms,
and other farm and domestic needs. In addition, they are obliged to
take into their irrigation network all the water which is provided by
the irrigation system administration for fulfillment of the plan of water
use.

If it is necessary to interrupt or suspend the watering of crops and
plantations for agro-technical or management reasons, the water user
has the right, through his own unilateral decision, to refuse water due
to him under the plan.[15] He must give the authorized representative of

---

14. Ibid., pp. 103–105.
15. This question is decided somewhat differently in Georgian Re-

the irrigation system administration two to three days advance notification of this decision (except in the Tadzhik Republic where three
days is the minimum).

If the water user declines his entitlement of irrigation water, he
does not have the right later on to request compensation, that is, a
supplementary supply of water to the irrigation network at another
time of the year. However, compensation is possible in accord with
an application from the water user, but the final decision rests with
the state irrigation system administration or a higher agency of water
management, and there must be sufficient reserves of water in the irrigation system and in the water source which feeds it.

Normally, water is supplied to the water user from the state irrigation systems in strict accordance with the plan. But, in exceptional
circumstances, deviations from the plan are possible. The legislation
makes the following provisions for exceptional circumstances: (a) the
right of the irrigation system administration to supply water over and
above the plan into the irrigation network of the water user without
his consent, and the obligation of the water user to accept water supplied over and above the plan; (b) the right of the water user to apply
for a supply of water into his irrigation network over and above the
plan, and the obligation of the irrigation system administration to
meet such an application; (c) the right of the irrigation system administration to limit or suspend the supply of water to water users, and
the obligation of the water users to accept such restriction.

According to the regulations for the technical operation of the irrigation systems, if the irrigation system administration has to increase
the water supply because of an accident in the system or in other exceptional circumstances, the collective or state farm or other water
user is obliged to accept the surplus water into its irrigation network
and, as far as possible, to insure its rational use. The question of
what constitutes an exceptional circumstance is decided pragmatically
on the basis of the specific conditions in the irrigation system in
question. The legislation does not provide a list of exceptional circumstances.

---

public law. According to Article 56 of the Regulations on Water Use
in the Georgian SSR, if a water user, when receiving water from the
general state irrigation network, has a quantity of water above his
farm needs, he is obliged to notify the water management agencies.
The question arises, what should occur in consequence of this? Apparently the water management agency, in whose capacity the irrigation system administration usually acts, is obliged to reduce the
amount of water supplied to the water user. But whether this means
that the irrigation system administration should reduce the amount of
water to the limit of the plan, or below, is not defined in the legislation of the Georgian SSR.

The irrigation system administration is obliged also to meet requests from water users for water over and above the plan when exceptional circumstances occur on their farms, if of course it is physically possible, that is, if there is an adequate supply of water available to meet such requirements over and above the plan.

The mutual rights and obligations of the irrigation system administrations and the water users are not limited to the supply and acceptance of water in the irrigation network, but concern the operation of the irrigation systems in the broad sense. First and foremost is the obligation to achieve high and stable yields on irrigated land.

According to Article 1 of the Model Regulations for the Technical Operation of Irrigation Systems, the operation of the irrigation systems must be aimed at securing a major advance in agriculture, at achieving high and stable yields of agricultural crops, and at increasing gross yields of agricultural production. These gains would be realized through maximum use of water and land resources, full mechanization of agriculture, and highly efficient organization of labor in the collective and state farms served by the irrigation system. The responsibilities of the irrigation system administrations for organizing highly effective irrigated cultivation in the collective and state farms stem from these regulations.

Each collective, state, or other farm has the right within the plan, as it sees fit, to distribute the water it receives from the state irrigation system to the areas which are being irrigated. The water user is obliged to use the water strictly according to its specific purpose and to the greatest economic effect, by employing the latest techniques for irrigating crops and by reducing unproductive use of water to a minimum. The legislation particularly emphasizes that the willful diversion for use by others of irrigation water cannot be allowed. Such unwarranted transfer of water by the water user is regarded as a violation of the law of exclusive state ownership of the water resources.

The collective, state, or other farm has the right and is obliged to distribute the irrigation water it has received in accordance with the plan in such a way as to supply irrigated areas with water and to provide the necessary quantity of water for other needs—such as the water requirements of livestock farms and subsidiary enterprises and the irrigation of the personal plots of the collective farmers and the households of the workers and employees.

The state irrigation system administrations, while not interfering in the farm activities of the water users, are obliged to maintain permanent control over the use of the water provided to the farms and over the observance by them of the irrigation regulations. Since the irrigation system administrations, together with the land users, are responsible for the improvement of the land requiring irrigation, they are obliged to organize irrigation in such a way as to secure optimal conditions for an increase in the yield of agricultural crops on the

farms which they serve. They must avoid excessive wetting of the
soil, salination, and allowing irrigated lands to become waterlogged
and drop out of agricultural use. Officials of the state irrigation system administrations are obliged systematically to check both that the
irrigation system is being operated correctly and that the water is being utilized properly on the farms which they serve.

In this way, an intricate set of relationships develops in the irrigation of the lands of collective and state farms and other agricultural
enterprises when this occurs by means of the state irrigation systems.
A characteristic of these relations is the division of functions of water use between the irrigation system administrations, which extract
the water from the sources of irrigation but do not themselves use it,
and the farm water users who carry out irrigated cultivation by using
water supplied to them by the irrigation system administrations. Corresponding to this division of functions, differences in the rights and
obligations of the subjects of the right of water use are established,
with the proviso, however, that the irrigation system administrations
are responsible for the correct and economically effective use of the
water and land resources on the farms which they serve, although they
themselves are not involved in raising agricultural crops on irrigated
lands.

Water use relations are formed in another way when the collective,
state, and other farm lands use their own irrigation systems. Here
the functions of withdrawing and using the irrigation water are carried
out by the farm alone. Therefore, the rights and obligations of the
farm, as the subject of the right of water use, are unified. The collective, state, and other farms which use water for irrigation directly
from natural or artificial sources (such as rivers, lakes, reservoirs,
and so on) are obliged to observe both the rules relating to the regulation of water intake from these sources and the rules providing for
the fullest and most effective use of irrigation water so that high and
stable yields of agricultural crops might be achieved. In other words,
the rights and obligations of the farms which take irrigation water
directly from source correspond basically to the sum of the rights and
obligations of the state irrigation system administrations and the
farms served by them. However, all this still awaits legislative action.

In flood irrigation, water use relations have a completely different
character. Since here the land is irrigated primarily by the construction of permanent or temporary diversion structures on a small river
network, the main question of legally ensuring the rational use of
water resources is that of the right of the collective, state, and other
farms to build diversion structures.

Irrespective of the technical methods of flood irrigation, the water
users are obliged to observe a number of general requirements concerning the rational use of lands and water resources—waterlogging

and the accumulation of salt on irrigated areas must be avoided, soil erosion must be combated, and so on. For sanitary reasons, flood irrigation cannot be undertaken in the immediate vicinity of centers of population.

Unlike irrigation from natural water sources (that is, rivers and lakes) or artificially created water sources in natural surroundings (that is, reservoirs), irrigation with sewage from cities and industrial enterprises is carried out with the observance of many special conditions associated with such a method of irrigation—the biological treatment of sewage with its simultaneous use in agriculture.

For irrigation with sewage, so-called agricultural sewage farms are marked out from the lands of collective or state farms (without, however, being withdrawn from the use of the farms). The sewage farms are set aside in accordance with ordinances of the executive committees of local Councils and with the agreement of the land users.

In the USSR the area of such agricultural sewage farms is about 17,000 hectares, which includes about 3,000 hectares in the Moscow Oblast. New construction is under way on an area of 50,000 hectares, 23,300 hectares of which is the Bortnicheskie sewage farm near Kiev, 11,500 hectares in Stavropol' on the Volga, 6,000 hectares in the Moscow Oblast, and more than 3,000 hectares near the city of Zhdanov. The planning of similar sewage farms is being carried out for a number of cities on a total area of not less than 100,000 hectares.[16]

The legal regulation of the establishment and operation of these agricultural sewage farms is carried out in accord with appropriate construction standards and regulations[17] and also in accord with the sanitary regulations.[18]

---

16. See A. I. L'vovich, "The Role of Agricultural Sewage Farms in the Protection of Water Resources from Pollution by Sewage," in *The Treatment and Use of Sewage and Industrial Wastes* (Kiev, 1964), pp. 145—146.

17. See *Construction Standards and Regulations, Part II, Section Г, Chapter 6. Sewerage, Planning Standards (SNiP II—Г, 6—62)*, approved by the State Construction Committee of the Council of Ministers of the USSR on 24 August 1962 (State Publishing House of Literature on Building, 1962). See also *Construction Standards and Regulations, Part II, Section И, Chapter 3. The Construction of Land Improvement Systems (SNiP II—И, 3—62)*, approved by the State Construction Committee of the Council of Ministers of the USSR on 14 December 1962 (State Publishing House of Literature on Building, 1963).

18. See Temporary Sanitary Regulations for the Construction and Operation of Agricultural Sewage Farms for the Treatment and Use of Sewage, approved by the Chief State Sanitary Inspector of the USSR on 30 May 1957 in agreement with the Ministry of Agriculture of the USSR

In accordance with these normative acts, agricultural sewage farms are set up for round-the-clock and year-round reception of sewage, which is used for fertilizing and irrigating agricultural crops. Only sewage which does not contain harmful compounds or compounds that cause the quality of the crops to deteriorate may be supplied to the sewage farm. Untreated sewage which has come from isolated enterprises that process raw materials of organic origin, from hospitals and slaughterhouses that have their own sewage systems, is not permitted for use on agricultural sewage farms.

The development of agricultural sewage farms is permissible only on areas of collective or state farms where the soil is suitable for the treatment of sewage. The development of sewage farms is not permitted in areas within the zones of sanitary protection of sources of water supply, within the recharge areas of artesian and deep nonartesian waters, in areas of fissured rocks and karst not covered with impermeable strata, or where the level of underground water is less than 1.25 meters from the surface. These measures are designed to protect surface and underground waters from pollution.

The suitability of areas for irrigation, as well as plans for the development and operation of agricultural sewage farms, are considered by the agencies of sanitary supervision with the participation of representatives of the agricultural agencies, the agencies of communal management, and the water users (the collective, state, or other farm). The sanitary agencies also establish the conditions governing use of the sewage in each case. They set sanitary requirements for use of the sewage farms and see that these requirements are observed by the water users.

In concluding this treatment of questions concerning the legal regulation of irrigation of agricultural lands, it must be pointed out that all existing aspects of this form of water use are not yet reflected in the law.

Many questions concerning the use of water resources for irrigation are in practice decided, and not always wisely, on the basis of traditions which have been handed down. Because of the absence from the legislation of clear requirements for water users, the organization of the whole business of irrigated agriculture suffers.

The prospective codification of water legislation should result in the strengthening of the law and the development of a number of essential provisions based upon up-to-date experience in the organization of irrigated agriculture and an analysis of the existing legal regulation of agricultural water use relations.

---

and the Ministry of State Farms of the USSR, in *The Hygiene of Centers of Population* (a collection of official documents) (Moscow: State Publishing House of Medical Literature, 1962), p. 427.

The water codes of Union Republics should reflect the actual organizational arrangements for irrigation (the state irrigation systems, the irrigation systems of collective and state farms, flood irrigation, agricultural sewage farms) and should define and differentiate the rights and obligations of the water users accordingly. It is especially important to emphasize the obligation of all collective, state, and other farms which practice irrigation to use water rationally, with the greatest economic effect for the production of high and stable yields of agricultural crops without permitting a deterioration in the quality of the land under irrigation.

The use of water resources in agriculture is not limited to irrigation. Water is needed for livestock farms, processing agricultural products, and for other productive needs.

In accordance with the sanitary regulations for planning, building, and organizing the public services and amenities of rural populated areas, which were approved by the Chief State Sanitary Inspector of the USSR on 26 January 1956,[19] both centralized and local water supply is permitted in rural populated areas. Under a centralized system there should be as a rule a single water supply for drinking and industrial purposes.

The rights and obligations of the owners of water supply systems in rural districts are basically similar to the rights and obligations of the owners of water supply systems which are used for the drinking and industrial needs of cities and industrial enterprises.

For the local water supply of livestock farms and industrial agricultural enterprises, it is permissible to use both sources in general use and those which are in the use of individual farms.

The legislation does not forbid collective and state farms to use, either permanently or temporarily, for their water supply, sources located on the territory of neighboring farms. However, for such cases the legislation should also include certain supplementary provisions.

First, it should be established that the use of sources of water supply located on the territory of neighboring farms be permitted by written agreement between the farms concerned. The agreement may stipulate the obligation of the water users to share the cost of the upkeep and of the organization of public services and amenities of the water sources. If an artificially constructed body of water (such as a small reservoir or pond) is used for the water supply, then the farms concerned, by agreement among themselves, may also share the

---

19. *The Hygiene of Centers of Population*, p. 61. See also the Instructions for Planning the Layout and Development of Rural Centers of Population—*Construction Standards*, 107—60, approved by the State Construction Committee of the Council of Ministers on 16 April 1960 (Moscow: State Publishing House of Literature on Building, 1960).

cost of constructing the body of water in proportion to the amount they use it.

Second, in the event that the farms do not reach agreement on the use of a body of water which is located on the territory of one of them, the question of joint water use should be settled in accord with the findings of the agency of water management by the executive committee of the Council of Workers' Deputies, which is competent to determine the conditions of use of these farm lands.

However, in this case the legislation ought to stipulate the primary right to use of the water of the farm on whose territory is located the body of water serving as the source of supply. The primary right of water use should mean that the body of water which is on the territory of one farm can be used by other farms provided they do not obstruct permanent use of the water by the former. In other words, the satisfaction of the water requirements of this farm cannot be diminished in favor of the other farms.

The observance of these conditions, when there is joint use by several farms of bodies of water which are on the territory of one of the farms, will permit the introduction of clarity and precision into the mutual relations of these farms. This in turn will contribute to a more effective and correct use of small bodies of water for agricultural water supply.

Similar legal conditions should be extended as well to water-use relationships which arise in the use of the bodies of water of a neighboring farm for the watering of cattle when livestock are pastured. However, here it must be added that the use of the bodies of water of a neighboring farm for watering cattle may be permitted only in extreme cases, even if damage to crops, land, and so on, is avoided. As a rule cattle must be watered from surface bodies of water on the farm that owns the cattle. Questions of providing farms with water sources suitable for the watering of cattle must be settled when the land is allocated for use and developed.

3. Conditions and Procedure of Water Use for Drinking and Other Domestic Needs of the Population

Water is vital to human welfare. It has been calculated that over a twenty-four-hour period a man needs no less than two liters of fresh drinking water. A large quantity of water is also used for other domestic purposes. The higher the standard of living of the people, the higher the level of water consumption.[20]

20. At the present time in Moscow, the daily consumption of water is 500 liters per person. In twenty years it will double. In quantity

Water may be considered hygienic only if it meets certain requirements of purity and safety for human wealth, and does not possess microorganic characteristics (color, smell, taste) which limit its use.

In our country, particular importance is attached to public water supply. Sanitary and technical measures are carried out systematically in the water supply systems of cities and other populated areas, and continuous control is also maintained over the use of water resources for public domestic needs. The principal requirements which safeguard public water use are regulated by law.

The present legislation defines the general procedure for use of water for domestic purposes, specifies sanitary measures to protect sources of water supply which are mandatory for all, prohibits the operation of enterprises that pollute these sources with industrial sewage, provides special requirements for the use of underground water, and so on. The state standard "Drinking Water," which defines all the requirements concerning water quality, has been worked out and approved as a basis for determining the suitability of water used in a centralized public drinking water supply system. It contains hygienic standards which have been drawn up in accordance with data provided by special medical and biological studies. The suitability of a body of water for use as a source of water supply is also defined in accordance with a state standard (GOST[*]2761—57, "Sources of Centralized Drinking Water Supply. Regulations Governing Selection and Assessment of Quality").

The present legal regulation of water use for public domestic needs in the USSR is based upon two very important principles: first, the general availability of natural reserves of water for the maximum satisfaction of the personal needs of all citizens; and second, the provision of all necessary measures to protect human health.

In view of the paramount importance of providing the public with drinking water in sufficient quantity, the state agencies which regulate the use of water resources have established the principle of

---

of water used, Moscow already occupies a place among the leading cities of the world. It may be pointed out in comparison that water consumption in New York and San Francisco is about 800 liters a day per person, in Paris and Berlin, about 450, in Milan, 400, in Madrid, 300 liters. See N. N. Gorskii, *Water—Wonder of Nature* (Academy of Sciences Publishing House), p. 155. See also the ordinance of the Executive Committee of the Moscow City Council of Workers' Deputies of 11 January 1964, No. 2/33, "On Measures to Regulate the Use and Economy of Water of the Municipal Water Supply System" (*Bulletin of the Executive Committee of the Moscow City Council of Workers' Deputies*, 1964, No. 2).

[*]Gosudarstvennyĭ Standart.

special priority for the use of water for public drinking and domestic needs over other forms of water use. This means that when the same water source serves different purposes, water for drinking and other domestic needs of the public cannot be restricted in favor of industrial, agricultural, transport, and other forms of water use. On the other hand, the use of water for the needs of industry, agriculture, and transport may be limited accordingly if it interferes with the use of natural supplies of water for drinking and other domestic needs.

This principle is a general one for the regulation of water relations and for ensuring a rational use of water resources. It received indirect support in the decree of the Council of Ministers of the USSR of 22 April 1960, which states that "surveillance over the proper condition of bodies of water and the development of measures to protect water sources shall be carried out by the agencies of the Councils of Ministers of Union Republics concerned with the use and protection of water sources, in collaboration with the sanitary, navigation, and fishery inspectors, and communal and agricultural agencies (as appropriate) *with regard for the primary use of water for the drinking needs of the population*" [author's italics].

Since the requirements for the quality of drinking water are most fully met by underground water supplies (principally artesian), our water law should also establish the principle of first priority for use of underground waters of potable quality for drinking and other domestic needs of the people, permitting their use for other purposes only in exceptional cases and by special authorization of the agencies that manage the use of water resources.

The population of our country uses water for drinking and other domestic purposes either by individual withdrawal direct from natural sources, or through a centralized collective communal water supply system.

The use of water from natural sources for drinking and other domestic needs does not require any authorization from state agencies, if the water is taken from the sources by individual citizens without the construction of water intake facilities of a stationary type. Such water use is free and is regulated by legal norms in a very general way.

Under the present system, which unfortunately still does not have a sufficiently full and clear-cut legal structure, the organization of a noncentralized public water supply is mainly entrusted to local councils and their executive agencies.

The Statutes on the Rural Councils of Workers' Deputies, ratified by the Supreme Soviets of the Union Republics, define in different ways the functions of rural Councils concerning the regulation of domestic water use. In some cases, the statutes establish the responsibility of the rural Councils to organize the development of wells and other sources of water supply and to supervise their technical maintenance and proper sanitary condition,[21] while in others they only require the Councils to see that the sanitary condition of sources of supply is maintained.[22]

District Councils of Workers' Deputies and their executive agencies supervise the sanitary condition of open bodies of water, wells, and other sources of water supply. Depending on local conditions, they establish in their ordinances which bodies of water are available for public use and how they should be used—with or without restriction. For example, the washing of linen in sources which supply drinking water may be forbidden by ordinances of district Councils and their executive committees.

Under a system of individual noncentralized water use, all citizens have the right to use water for drinking and other domestic needs from any water sources, with the exception of those from which it is forbidden to use water in the interests of the users themselves in order to protect their lives and health, and with the exception, also, of certain bodies of water which are particularly suitable for other forms of use incompatible with the use of water for drinking.

The quality of water in sources which are used for a noncentralized drinking water supply must satisfy the established sanitary requirements.

Although the state standards "Drinking Water" (GOST 2874—54) and "Sources of Centralized Drinking Water Supply" (GOST 2761—57) do not apply to sources that are used for a noncentralized drinking water supply, such water sources must be suitable for drinking. The suitability of water for drinking in these cases is determined in accordance with "General Requirements Governing the Composition and Properties of Water at Points of Drinking and Other Domestic Water Use" and "Maximum Permissible Concentrations of Harmful Substances in Water Used for Domestic Purposes," which were approved by the Ministry of Health of the USSR,[23] and also in accordance with "Maximum

---

21. See paragraph 16 of the Statutes on the Rural Council of Workers' Deputies of the RSFSR, approved by the Edict of the Presidium of the Supreme Soviet of the RSFSR of 12 September 1957; Article 17 of the Statutes of the Rural Council of Workers' Deputies of the Azerbaidzhan SSR, approved by the Edict of the Presidium of the Supreme Soviet of Azerbaidzhan SSR of 23 April 1958, *Statutes on Rural Councils of Workers' Deputies* (Moscow: State Juridical Publishing House, 1959), pp. 9, 93.

22. See Article 11 of the Statutes on the Rural Council of Workers' Deputies of the Ukraine SSR of 31 May 1957, in *Statutes on Rural Councils of Workers' Deputies*, p. 20.

23. See Appendices 1 and 2 to the Regulations for the Protection

Permissible Concentrations of Radioactive Substances in Bodies of Water and Sources of Water Supply,"[24] which was approved on 25 June 1960 by the State Sanitary Inspection of the USSR and the State Committee of the Council of Ministers of the USSR on the Use of Atomic Energy.

The responsibilities of citizens who use water by noncentralized methods from sources in general use are mostly regulated in a general way along with the responsibilities of all other water users, or they may be specifically defined in regulations issued by local Councils to control water use in certain bodies of water. The most general and basic requirements which apply to individual water users stem from concern for the sanitary protection of sources of water supply and the fact that interference with the water use of other citizens, or of enterprises, institutions, and organizations, is impermissible. Consequently, each citizen who uses water from a source in general use is obliged to protect it from depletion, pollution, infection, and so on. He must not interfere with use of the water by others, and he must not permit any action which might lead to a change in the hydrological condition of the body of water.

In the legal regulation of domestic water use, the question of the right of citizens to develop individual wells on land which has been assigned for their use is particularly noteworthy.[25] This question is also discussed in juridical literature.

L. I. Dembo considered that the construction of wells "for domestic needs and for stock watering on areas which have been assigned to land users does not require the special authorization of state agencies. This is generally established in all republic water laws."[26] In support of his opinion he referred to Article 5 of the Law on Agricultural Water Use in the Uzbek SSR of 24 March 1941, and to Article 4 of the Regulations on Agricultural Water Use, Protection and Development of Irrigation Land Improvement Reserves in the Kirghiz SSR which was ap-

---

of Surface Waters from Pollution by Sewage, approved by the Ministry of Health of the USSR on behalf of the Council of Ministers of the USSR, and agreed upon with Gosplan of the USSR on 15 June 1961, in *Instructions on the Planning of the External Sewerage of Industrial Enterprises*, Chapter 1, "Construction Standards 173—61" (Moscow: State Publishing House of Literature on Building, 1961), pp. 206—210.

24. Ibid., pp. 212—217.

25. The construction by private citizens of wells on land which has not been allocated for their use is impermissible if it occurs after willful seizure of the land or other violation of land-use law.

26. L. I. Dembo, *Fundamental Problems of Soviet Water Law* (Leningrad, 1948), p. 94.

proved by the decree of the Council of National Commissars of the Kirghiz Republic of 24 January 1942.[27]

At the present time there is water legislation in all Union Republics. In six Republics, laws are in force on agricultural water use, and the Georgian Republic has its Regulations on Water Use (which cover not only agricultural water use, but other forms as well). However, only the laws of two Union Republics—the Uzbek and Georgian Republics— regulate the right of citizens to construct and use wells on land allotted to them. It is, therefore, hardly possible to contend that the right of citizens to install wells on their land without hindrance is established in all republic water laws.

How is the question of the right of citizens to install wells settled in the laws of the Uzbek and Georgian Republics?

Article 5 of the "Law on Agricultural Water Use in the Uzbek SSR" of 24 March 1941 states: "The construction of wells and the development of artesian sources[28] for domestic needs and watering may be undertaken without the authorization of the agencies of water management."

Article 22 of the Regulations of Water Use in the Georgian SSR of 19 February 1958 deals with questions relating principally to the method of using wells and springs on citizens' allotments. The article points out that if the well or spring is on an area of personal use, then water use is carried out by the owner of the area. The use of wells and springs for watering cattle is permitted if they are properly constructed and the sanitary regulations are observed.

In other Union Republics, including the RSFSR, whose legislation does not contain juridical norms similar to Article 5 of the Law of the

---

27. These regulations have been annulled in connection with the promulgation of the Edict of the Presidium of the Supreme Soviet of the Kirghiz SSR of 19 August 1946, which is now in force, "On Agricultural Water Use in the Kirghiz SSR." This Edict does not contain any instructions regarding the rights of citizens to construct and operate wells.

28. The construction of artesian wells is at present regulated by the decree on the Council of Ministers of the USSR of 4 September 1954, "On Strengthening State Control over the Use of Underground Waters and on Measures for their Conservation" (*Collected Laws of the USSR*, 1959, No. 17, Article 135), and, issued in fulfillment of this decree, the Regulations on the Use and Conservation of Underground Waters in the USSR, which stipulate that artesian wells may be built only with the authorization of the agencies of geology and the protection of minerals and in agreement with the agencies of state sanitary supervision and water management.

Uzbek Republic on Water Use or Article 22 of the Regulations of the
Georgian Republic, the question of the right of citizens to develop
and use wells for their own needs is settled in practice on the assumption that the development of wells on land allotted for individual
use is the inalienable right of the land user.

Such an assumption is based to a certain extent on Article 24 of
the Land Code of the RSFSR, where it is pointed out that the land user
has the right by law to erect and use structures and installations for
farm and livestock needs on his allotment.[29] Thus a well may be regarded as an installation necessary for farming purposes.

The Model Agreement on the Allocation for Permanent Use of Land
for the Construction of an Individual Dwelling with the Right of Personal Ownership, which was approved by Order No. 244 of the Ministry
of Communal Management of the RSFSR on 26 March 1949,[30] and which
specifies the right of the builder (land user) to use for domestic purposes building materials taken from his land allotment, is cited as
legal justification for the development of wells by land users on
municipal lands. This practice has been extended to recognition of
the right of the land user to extract not only building materials from
his allotment but also water by means of wells.

At the present time the right of citizens to use underground waters
by constructing wells is indirectly corroborated in union legislation.

According to Article 1 of the decree of the Council of Ministers of
the USSR of 15 December 1961, "On the Procedure for Compensating
Citizens for Buildings Belonging to Them Which Are Demolished in
Cities, Urban Settlements, and Other Populated Areas in Connection
with the Allocation of Land for State and Public Needs,"[31] when buildings belonging to citizens with the right of personal ownership are
demolished in connection with the allocation of land for state and
public needs in cities, urban settlements, and other populated areas,
the value of the demolished buildings and structures (such as houses,
barns, cellars, wells, and so on) is paid to the citizens or, if they
and their families so desire, instead of reimbursement they may be
allotted an apartment in accordance with existing norms. It is evident
that wells are included in the buildings and structures for which compensation must be paid in the circumstances outlined above. It follows that, if the State considers the installation of wells by citizens
on land which has been allocated for their use for individual housing
construction to be lawful, it must recognize, in consequence, the
right of citizens to use underground waters in connection with their
use of the land.

29. *Collected Edicts of the RSFSR*, 1922, No. 68, Article 901.
30. See *Collected Land Laws* (Moscow: State Juridical Publishing House, 1962), p. 135.
31. *Collected Laws of the USSR*, 1961, No. 20, Article 146.

Finally, it is necessary to refer to the footnote to Article 1 of the Regulations on the Use and Conservation of Underground Waters of the USSR, which were approved by the Deputy Minister of Geology and Protection of Minerals of the USSR and the Chief State Sanitary Inspector of the USSR, on 6—18 April 1960. The article establishes that the construction of dug wells for exploitation of subsoil waters, driven filter (Abyssinian) wells, individual boreholes up to twenty meters deep, and the catchment of sources without positively lowering the water level do not require the authorization of the agencies of geology and protection of minerals so long as they are not used for a centralized water supply. Private citizens who develop these installations must in all cases get the consent of the local agencies of state sanitary supervision and, in cities and workers' settlements, of the municipal or district agencies of communal management as well.

Thus, the right of citizens to install wells for personal drinking and domestic needs is also mentioned in Article 1 of the Regulations on the Use and Protection of Underground Waters of the USSR.

However, in our opinion, none of this can substitute for the direct and clear instructions which are needed in the law, that all citizens to whom land is allotted for use have the right to use underground waters on their lands and, in order to do so, may, either with or without authorization of the state agencies, develop wells (but not drilled wells). It is necessary to establish in the law (let us say, in the republic water code) that this rule applies not only to citizens who use land allotments to build individual dwellings, but also to collective farm households with personal plots, to citizens who have gardens, kitchen gardens, dachas, and similar pieces of land, as well as official allotments. At the same time, it is necessary to draw up a general procedure for use of wells developed on the lots of private citizens, and to establish the conditions under which such wells may be used both by citizens who are not the owners and for fire protection measures.

As the organization of public services and amenities of urban and rural centers of population improves, the importance of a centralized, communal-domestic water supply grows, the legal regulation and nature of which conflicts with the legal procedure governing direct water use by citizens.

In those cases where the water requirements of the population are met by centralized means through a communal domestic water supply system, the owners of the systems—the state and public communal or other enterprises and organizations—are the subjects of the law of water use.

In cities and urban settlements, the owners of the communal water supply systems and, therefore, the subjects of the law of water use, are usually the managements or trusts of the water supply and sewerage system of the executive committees of the municipal (or settlement) Councils of Workers' Deputies which, in mutual relationships

with the State—the owner of the water resources—are responsible for
water use and possess corresponding rights.

The owners of the drinking water supply systems and, consequently,
water users, are frequently industrial enterprises, and, in rural areas,
state and collective farms.

The procedure for developing and operating the water mains under
a centralized drinking and domestic water supply system is regulated
by legislative acts of the USSR and Union Republics, by regulations
and instructions issued by the agencies of communal management and
health, and also by ordinances of local Councils and their executive
committees. All important questions concerned with establishing the
quantity of water to be taken from a source and the selection of the
source, place of diversion, and so on, are normally decided in the
course of planning and building the water supply system, and these
decisions are sanctioned when the project is approved by the state
agencies. After the water supply system has been built and put into
operation, the rights and obligations of the owner of the system take
effect. These relate to the rational use of the water resources and
the maintenance of the necessary conditions for sanitary protection
of the source of water supply in the area of the head gate structure,
which includes the maintenance of the required conditions in the pro-
jected zones of sanitary protection.

In prerevolutionary Russia there was no special legislation to protect the sources of a centralized drinking water supply. However, in
the early 1900s attempts were made to provide for the sanitary supervision of the Moscow River Basin in connection with the operation of
the Rublevskii water supply system. In 1914—15 the zone of sanitary
protection of the Moskvorets water supply system was officially established by the Moscow city and zemstvo self-government.

With the birth of the Soviet state, great importance was attached
to the question of public water supply and the effective sanitary protection of water sources. In 1924 the Peoples' Commissariat of Health
and the Peoples' Commissariat of Internal Affairs recommended that
zones of sanitary protection for all sources of centralized water supply be established. Owners of water supply systems have been
obliged by law to establish zones of sanitary protection since the enactment on 6 July 1928 of the decree of the Council of Peoples' Commissars of the RSFSR, "On the Establishment of Zones of Sanitary Protection of Water Sources Which Are Used for the Central Water Supply
System of Cities, Workers' Settlements, and Other Populated Areas"[32]
and the corresponding decrees of the Councils of Peoples Commissars
of the Ukraine, Belorussia, and other Union Republics.

---

32. *Collected Edicts of the RSFSR*, 1928, No. 79, Article 546 (at
present this decree has lost force); *Collected Decrees of the RSFSR*,
1962, No. 24, Article 121.

The sanitary protection of sources of water supply was first directly connected with obligations to undertake precautionary measures to protect bodies of water from pollution by domestic and industrial sewage in the decree of the Central Executive Committee and the Council of Peoples' Commissars of the USSR of 17 May 1937 "On the sanitary protection of water mains and sources of water supply,"[33] which provides for the establishment of zones of sanitary protection for both surface and underground sources of water supply.

In accordance with Article 1 of this decree, zones of sanitary protection of water systems and sources of supply were established in all cities and other populated areas for each drinking water supply system in operation or under construction, regardless of its departmental affiliation.

The zone of sanitary protection of sources of water supply is divided into three belts, in each of which special conditions apply.

The first belt (zone of strict regulation) embraces the source of water supply in the area of water intake and water diversion facilities. Within the boundaries of this belt, persons and buildings not directly connected with the maintenance of the water supply installations are not permitted.

The second belt (restricted zone) covers the area surrounding the source from which water is withdrawn, and the basin which feeds it, the surface and underground drainage of which can affect the composition and properties of the water in the area of water intake. Within this belt restrictions are imposed on water users and land users in order to preclude any deterioration in the quality of the water.

For example, in connection with the use of the Moscow Canal as a source of water supply for the city of Moscow, the Council of Peoples' Commissars of the RSFSR, by their decree of 4 September 1940,[34] established boundaries for the zones of sanitary protection of the canal and specific requirements for all water and land users. In particular, they established that in the second belt of the zone of sanitary protection of the Moscow Canal large-scale industrial construction should be completely prohibited, and small-scale industrial construction, which would not produce industrial wastes requiring sewers which empty into open bodies of water, and housing construction regardless of size, would be permitted only with the authorization of the agencies of state sanitary supervision.[35]

---

33. *Collected Laws of the USSR*, 1937, No. 35, Article 143.

34. *Collected Decrees and Instructions of the RSFSR*, 1940, No. 16, Article 65.

35. At the present time, the state sanitary supervision in the USSR is carried out by agencies and institutions of the sanitary-epidemiological service of the Ministry of Health of the USSR and Ministries of Health of the Union Republics. See the Regulations on State Sani-

All industrial enterprises located in the second belt must be
equipped with appropriate facilities for the removal of wastes and
sewage. The emptying of sewage, including treated sewage, into
canals and reservoirs (the Yakhromskoe, Ikshinskoe and Klyaz'minskoe
reservoirs) is completely prohibited, except for the Ivan'kovskoe reservoir in a section of the canal below the Klyaz'minskoe reservoir where
sewage may be discharged after treatment. The pollution of rivers,
streams, and other bodies of water and their banks with refuse, sewage, manure, and so on is prohibited. The development of cemeteries
and cattle burial grounds may be permitted, on the authorization of the
state sanitary inspection, no closer than one kilometer from the canal
reservoirs and drains. All building and tilling of the land with the application of manure within a 150 meter strip from the water's edge is
prohibited. Cattle are permitted only if impermeable dung depositories
and water receptacles are provided. The use of the reservoirs and
canal for the laundering of linen, watering and bathing of cattle is
prohibited.

The third belt (control zone) is usually set up around the second
zone in populated areas where an epidemic condition would, if it occurred, affect the sanitary condition of the second belt.

Such a legal organization of sanitary protection of sources of drinking water supply has recommended itself well over the many years of
its existence, and at the present time it is an essential part of the
complex of conditions by which the legislation integrates the use of
water resources for domestic needs into a centralized communal water supply system.

Zones of sanitary protection of water mains and sources of water
supply are established in accordance with plans worked out by the
planning organizations for the client (the owner of the water system).
The plan must satisfy the requirements specified in the Regulations
on Planning Zones of Sanitary Protection of a Central Water Supply
System and Water Sources, which was approved by the All-Union State
Sanitary Inspection of 7 April 1938.[36]

In accordance with Article 6 of the decree of the Central Executive
Committee and the Council of Peoples' Commissars of the USSR of 17
May 1937, "On the sanitary protection of water mains and sources of
water supply," zones of sanitary protection of water mains and sources
of water supply, and their corresponding subdivision into belts, are
set up in each settlement by ordinances of the local Councils. These
ordinances are subject to subsequent approval by the Councils of

tary Supervision in the USSR, approved by the decree of the Council
of Ministers of the USSR of 29 October 1963 (*Collected Decrees
of the USSR*, 1963, No. 20, Article 199).

36. See *The Hygiene of Centers of Population*, pp. 335–343.

Ministers of the Union Republics—for the capitals of Union Republics and settlements in the important health resort regions (such as the south coast of Crimea, the Caucasian spas, the Sochi-Matsesta region, and others), and for territorial and oblast centers and all cities with a population of more than 200,000. For other settlements the ordinances of local Councils on the establishment of zones of sanitary protection must be approved by the Councils of Ministers of the Autonomous Republics and the territorial and oblast executive committees of Councils of Workers' Deputies.

The local Councils must notify the public of the boundaries of the zones of sanitary protection of sources of water supply and their belts and of the conditions in force within these zones.

The agencies of state sanitary supervision of the USSR maintain constant surveillance over the observance by all water users of the sanitary requirements governing a centralized drinking water supply system.

The quality of the water in the sources of a centralized drinking water supply must conform to the requirements of the state standard "Sources of Centralized Drinking Water Supply" (GOST 2761—57) and also to "General Requirements Governing the Composition and Properties of Water at Points of Drinking and Other Domestic Water Use." The quantity of pollutants in these water sources must not exceed "The Maximum Permissible Concentrations of Harmful Substances in Water Used for Domestic Purposes," which was approved by the Ministry of Health of the USSR. The concentration of radioactive substances in sources of drinking water supply must not exceed "The Maximum Permissible Concentrations of Radioactive Substances in Bodies of Water and Sources of Water Supply," which was approved by the Chief State Sanitary Inspection of the USSR and by the State Committee of the Council of Ministers of the USSR on the Use of Atomic Energy on 25 June 1960.

For a centralized drinking water supply any water sources which are suitable for this purpose may be used; but the legislation recommends that reserves of underground water should be used primarily.

According to Article 2 of the Regulations for the Selection and Assessment of the Quality of Sources of Centralized Drinking Water Supply (GOST 2761—57), artesian waters which are safely protected from external pollution should be selected first as sources of water supply. If such sources are not available or use of them is not possible, either because of insufficient discharge or the unsatisfactory quality of the water or for technical-economic reasons, other sources must therefore be selected, in the following order: (1) interstratum nonartesian waters (including springs), (2) subsoil waters, (3) open bodies of water (such as reservoirs, rivers, lakes, canals).

The principal juridical norms governing the use of underground water resources for a centralized drinking water supply are contained in the

decree of the Council of Ministers of the USSR of 4 September 1959,
"On Strengthening State Control over the Use of Underground Waters
and on Measures for Their Conservation,"[37] and in the Regulations on
the Use and Conservation of Underground Waters in the USSR of 6—18
April 1960, which were issued in elaboration of this decree.

In accordance with these legislative acts, the drilling of operational wells, the reequipment of exploratory wells already in operation, the equipping of exploratory wells for operation, and the building and reequipment of other water intake facilities for the utilization
of underground waters, are carried out only with the authorization of
the republic agencies of geology and protection of minerals or the
territorial geological administrations (trusts). Such authorization is
not required in those cases to which the footnote to Article I of the
Regulations on the Use and Conservation of Underground Waters of
the USSR refers, of which we spoke above (see page 147).

Underground waters are used for a centralized drinking water supply in accordance with plans for drilled wells and the water supply
systems associated with them. These plans are agreed upon with
oblast (or territorial) municipal or district agencies of the state sanitary supervision, with the agencies of communal, rural, or water management, with the state mining technical supervision [Gosgortekhnad-
zor], or with the territorial (republic) health resort administrations,
depending on the site of water intake. Finally, the geological agencies must approve these plans before they can authorize the drilling
of the wells. Such multilateral agreement on plans for developing a
public drinking water supply system from underground water sources
is necessary in order to ensure both the effective use and protection
of underground water resources and a safe supply of drinking water
for the consumers.

The owners of drilled wells and other water intake facilities, being
users of underground water resources, are obliged to keep a detailed
account of the quantity and quality of water which is withdrawn, to
see to the condition of the underground waters in the territory adjoining the water intake, and not to permit wasteful use of underground
waters or their pollution. The water users are obliged to keep a register of water intake, including all data on the condition of the water
resources and how they are used. If there is a sudden change in the
quantity and quality of the water which is withdrawn from the underground source, the water users are obliged immediately to notify the
controlling agencies of geology and protection of minerals and of sanitary supervision.

Each well or other source of underground water which is used for a
drinking water supply must have the zone of sanitary protection referred to above.

---

37. *Collected Decrees of the USSR*, 1959, No. 17, Article 135.

The provisions governing the supply of drinking water to consumers are of a general nature and do not depend on the kind of source—surface or underground. They apply to all owners of water systems that are intended for a centralized drinking water supply, irrespective of whether they are communal enterprises of cities and other populated areas, industrial enterprises, state, or collective farms. However, the legal regulation of relations which arise in connection with a centralized drinking water supply is most developed in the communal water supply system of cities and other populated areas.

The owners of communal drinking water supplies, the municipal (or settlement) management, or trust, of water supply and sewerage "Vodokanal"), enter into legal relationships concerning the supply of water with the consumers—the individual enterprises, institutions, organizations, and citizens, who are the subscribers to "Vodokanal." Private citizens may be subscribers to "Vodokanal" if they have, with the right of personal ownership, dwelling houses equipped with a water supply, or if they use water from street hydrants of the municipal water system. Citizens who live in state-owned housing which is equipped with running water are not in legal relations with "Vodokanal." They are using water from the municipal water supply system as part of the housing services they receive, and therefore they are in legal relations with the house-maintenance offices, the house-management offices, or enterprises (in departmental housing), which are the subscribers to "Vodokanal."

In the Russian Federation relations between "Vodokanal" and its subscribers are governed principally by the Regulations on the Use of Communal Water Supply and Sewerage Systems, which were approved by an Order of the Ministry of Communal Management of the RSFSR of 9 August 1960[38] and by ordinances of the local Councils and their executive committees.[39] These relationships are regulated differently in the other Union Republics: in some there are republic regulations for the use of water supply and sewerage systems; while in others the regulations are issued after approval by the town executive committees only.

The Regulations on the Use of Communal Water Supply and Sewerage Systems, which were approved by the Ministry of Communal Management of the RSFSR, are mandatory for all subscribers who are connected to the municipal water supply system, irrespective of their departmental affiliation.

---

38. See *The Regulations for the Use of Communal Water Supply and Sewerage Systems* (Moscow: Publishing House of the Ministry of Communal Management of the RSFSR, 1960).

39. For example, tariffs for water released from city communal water supply systems are established by ordinances of the Councils of Ministers of Autonomous Republics and of the Executive Committees of Territorial, Oblast, and City Councils.

The Regulations define the mutual rights and obligations of "Vodo-kanal" and its subscribers in such matters as the installation of an internal water supply system in dwelling houses, industrial buildings, and structures, the linking of an internal water supply system to the municipal water mains, the operation of water meters and auxilliary facilities (local pumping installations, pressure tanks, fire hydrants, and so on), and the repair and preparation for winter of the different units of the water supply system. They also specify all conditions for use of drinking water from the water supply system.

Water supply relationships between "Vodokanal" and each of its subscribers develop the moment that the internal water supply of the subscriber is connected to the municipal water supply system, and they are formalized as contracts which are concluded each year for a period of up to one year. Contracts are not made with small home owners or with small organizations—that is, with small water con-sumers. The supply of water to them is provided on the basis of agreed annual claims for water which they submit to "Vodokanal," and sub-scribers' cards which are drawn up for an unlimited period. The con-tractual form of relationships governing communal-domestic water supply is, however, the prevailing and typical one.

Under the contract, "Vodokanal" is obliged to supply the subscriber regularly with drinking water from the municipal water system in a stipulated quantity; and the subscriber is obliged to pay "Vodokanal" at the right time a money payment for the water he has received in accordance with the local water tariffs, and to fulfill all obligations imposed by the Regulations on the Use of Communal Water Supply and Sewerage Systems.

The quantity of water to be supplied from the city water mains is determined in the contract for a period of a year, with a monthly break-down on the basis of demand estimates presented by the subscriber to "Vodokanal." The water actually consumed by the subscriber is ac-counted for as a rule by the readings of the water meter, which is checked and sealed by an inspector of the Committee on Measures and Measuring Devices and installed on the lead-in between the mu-nicipal water main and the internal water supply system of the sub-scriber.

Responsibility for the safekeeping and accuracy of the water meter is entrusted under the contract to the subscriber, who must also pro-vide free access to the water meter junction to "Vodokanal" personnel.

The accounts of "Vodokanal" with the subscribers are settled by systematic payments (in the case of large consumers of water, in ac-cordance with a record approved by the town executive committee), or (in the case of the remaining consumers of water, excluding the public) by presenting statements not more than twice a month on the basis of the cost of water for the corresponding period the previous month, with a definitive account submitted at the end of the month on the basis of the reading of the water meter. In the case of house-maintenance offices and house-management offices, settlements are made by statements once a month on the basis of the readings of the water meter.

The consumption of water by subscribers who do not have water meters and of water from hydrants is calculated in accordance with existing standards of water consumption. For enterprises, institutions, and organizations, the consumption of water is calculated on the basis of the number of working days; for the public, according to the number of calendar days in the month.

In places where water use from hydrants occurs, the entire public that uses the hydrants is involved in paying for it.

The Regulations on the Use of Communal Water Supply and Sewerage Systems stipulate the obligation of subscribers to pay fines for delays in payments for drinking water they have received. It also stipulates the right of "Vodokanal," in cases of prolonged delays over payments for water or of fines which have been imposed, to discontinue the supply of water to the subscriber, having given him five days warning in advance.

After issuing a warning five days in advance, "Vodokanal" has the right to discontinue the supply of water to the subscriber by shutting off his internal water supply from the mains, if the subscriber has refused to allow the inspector of "Vodokanal" to examine the water meter and the water supply installations, if he has refused to supply information necessary for calculating the amount of water which has been used, has not removed causes that prevent the water meter to be read, or has not repaired by a set date a leakage which has been discovered by the "Vodokanal" inspector. If the subscriber willfully connects his internal water supply system to the municipal system, if he changes his internal system in deviation from the approved plan, if he refuses to admit the "Vodokanal" representative to his internal system to regulate the valves and plumbing installations when the limit established in the water supply contract has been exceeded, then "Vodokanal" has the right to cut off the subscriber's water supply without warning. Consumption of water by the subscriber over and above the quantity stipulated in the contract does not by itself warrant a discontinuation of water supply, but it gives "Vodokanal" the right to reduce the supply of water to the amount corresponding to the provisions of the contract.

In addition, in the event of natural calamities, or if it is necessary to increase the supply of water to the locality of a fire, if the supply of electricity to the pumping stations has been cut off, or if there is an accident to the water supply system, "Vodokanal" is entitled to discontinue temporarily the supply of water to individual subscribers or to whole districts without warning.

The Regulations on the Use of Communal Water Supply and Sewerage

Systems do say that in these cases "Vodokanal" is not responsible
to the subscriber for failing to supply water. But on the whole they
give no indication of when "Vodokanal" is responsible to the subscriber for not meeting his obligations to supply water. While sanctions are provided for the nonfulfillment of the numerous obligations
of the subscribers, no sanctions are provided with regard to "Vodokanal." Besides, a sudden discontinuation of water through the fault
of "Vodokanal" may cause property damage to the subscriber, compensation for which, in our opinion, should be charged to "Vodokanal."
Such a measure would guarantee a normal, uninterrupted water supply
to the subscribers.

Obviously legal relations which develop in a centralized communal
water supply system differ from the relations associated with the use
of natural reserves of water.

When the recipients of water are the house-maintenance offices or
house-management offices, they are obliged to make available the
water they receive for the use of the tenants.

Relations between the house-maintenance offices (or house-management offices) and the tenants regarding the supply of drinking water
to apartments are of a special variety similar to, but not identical with,
the relations between "Vodokanal" and its subscribers. In these relations the provision of drinking water is associated with the use of the
dwelling space. The water supply in the apartment is considered a
necessary domestic convenience, use of which is covered by the lease
and is normally paid for in the rent.

Thus, in a centralized communal water supply system there arise
as a rule three main, consecutively connected, series of legal relations: (1) between the exclusive owner of the water resources and
the owners of communal water supply systems, that is, the producers
of drinking water; (2) between the owners of the water supply systems
and their subscribers (or subsubscribers); (3) between the house-
maintenance offices (or house-management offices), being the subscribers to the owners of the water systems, and the individual tenants.

Of these, only the first series of relations are legal relations of
water use. The second and third represent a variety of relations under
civil law.

The emergence of different legal relations in the course of water
use for drinking and other public domestic needs is brought about by
the change in the economic characteristics of water as an object of
use. When the object of use is the water resources in the form of
natural reserves of water, the resulting relations of water use are regulated under water law, which itself is a constituent part of Soviet land
law in the broad sense. However, when the object of use is water
that has been separated from its natural medium by human labor and
turned into a marketable commodity, the water use relations become
relations of civil law and are regulated under civil and not land law.

4. *Use of Waters for Medicinal Purposes*

Some of the water resources of the USSR contain special qualities and are consequently of particular public value. These are underground mineral waters which have an excess of physiologically active chemical constituents, gases, radioactivity, or other properties which cause them to have a beneficial effect on the human system and to be used for therapeutic purposes.

In the USSR more than 500 sources of medicinal mineral waters have been discovered with more than 4,000 active springs.

The use of sources of mineral waters for medicinal purposes is governed primarily by general norms of water law regulating the withdrawal of underground waters, and by norms for the sanitary protection of health resorts and areas of medicinal importance. In addition, the legislation provides special norms which relate solely to the use of natural reserves of medicinal mineral waters.

According to Article 1 of the decree of the Council of Ministers of the USSR of 4 September 1959 "On Strengthening State Control over the Use of Underground Waters and on Measures for Their Conservation,"[40] the drilling of wells for the withdrawal of underground water, including mineral waters, is permitted only with the authorization of the agencies of geology and protection of minerals, and with the agreement of the agencies of the Councils of Ministers of the Union Republics concerned with the use and protection of water resources, and of the local agencies of state sanitary supervision. The use of naturally flowing mineral sources without a forced lowering of the water level (including the construction of catchment and other water intake facilities) is possible without the authorization of the agencies of geology and protection of minerals, but the agreement of the local agencies of sanitary supervision[41] is necessary.

The Regulations for the Sanitary Protection of Health Resorts and Areas of Medicinal Importance, which were approved by the decree of the Council of People's Commissars of the USSR of 10 April 1940,[42] stipulate that areas of sanitary protection, comprising three zones, be established around the sources of medicinal waters.

The first zone covers the outlet of the mineral waters, and mud and salt lakes, estuaries, and sea beaches which have medicinal significance. In this zone no one who is not directly connected with the work of the health resort is permitted to reside, and similarly all build-

40. *Collected Decrees of the USSR*, 1959, No. 17, Article 135.

41. See the Footnote to Article 1 of the Regulations on the Use and Conservation of Underground Waters in the USSR, approved on 6–18 April 1960 (*The Hygiene of Centers of Population*, p. 348).

42. *Collected Decrees of the USSR*, 1940, No. 12, Article 289.

ing and landworks not connected with the operation of the spa, or
with repair work and construction of means of communication passing
through the zone, are forbidden. When the water of the mineral source
is used for drinking, zones of sanitary protection are set up in accordance with the provisions of the decree of the Central Executive Committee and the Council of People's Commissars of the USSR of 17 May
1937 "On the Sanitary Protection of Water Mains and Sources of Water
Supply."[43]

The second zone includes an area in which measures are taken to
preserve the therapeutic qualities of the resort.

The third zone extends over the whole drainage area of the mineral
waters. Mining, drilling of wells, widespread felling of timber, creation of dumps, cattle burial grounds, cemeteries and sewage farms,
the emptying of untreated sewage into rivers and other bodies of water
may be permitted in this zone only if authorization is received from
the local Councils of Workers' Deputies.

In addition to general provisions governing use of underground mineral waters, there are special requirements which stem from the nature of the object and methods of water use. These requirements are
contained mainly in Union Republic legislation and in departmental
normative documents.

Thus, under the Regulations on Water Use in the Georgian SSR,
authorization for use of medicinal mineral waters is made only on the
basis of investigations that are carried out by the Ministry of Health
of the Georgian Republic, after which the suitability of the waters for
special use is confirmed by the Scientific Council of the Ministry of
Health.

The Ministry of Water Management of the Georgian SSR is obliged,
in accordance with instructions of the Council of Ministers of the Republic, to grant to the Georgian Ministry of Health at the latter's request a monopoloy to use for special purposes the medicinal mineral
waters, permanently and free of charge. Mineral waters which are not
utilized by the Ministry of Health may be turned over for industrial
use (exclusively or partially) to special medical institutions, to the
Georgian drug trade [Gruzmedtorg] or to the district industrial combines.

The Georgian Ministry of Health is obliged to notify district and
municipal executive committees of the suitability of the mineral waters
in their areas, with an indication of the appropriate dosage that might
be adopted for medicinal use. If the mineral water is unsuitable for
people, cattle, and crops, the district and municipal executive committees must put up notices on the spot prohibiting use of the water.

In this way, the Regulations on Water Use in the Georgian SSR establish a number of important requirements of principle concerning the
use of mineral waters, namely:

---

43. *Collected Laws of the USSR*, 1937, No. 35, Article 143.

First, priority for the use of mineral waters for medicinal purposes and the corresponding prior right of health institutions and organizations to use them. These waters may be used for purposes unconnected with health only if a medicinal use is not found for them;

Second, the necessity for scientific substantiation of the suitability of a mineral water source for medicinal use;

Third, if the water can be used medicinally, the obligation to turn over mineral sources for the exclusive (monopoly) use of health agencies and institutions, free and for an unlimited period.

The legislation of the other Union Republics on the use of mineral waters for medicinal purposes is neither so complete nor so precise as that of Georgia. In the future, therefore, when the water codes of the Union Republics are worked out, it would be advisable to use the experience of the Georgian Republic, since the norms governing the use of mineral waters, which are contained in the Regulations on Water Use in the Georgian SSR, are essential for the regulation of the use of mineral waters in any Union Republic.

In past use of underground water resources, irregular practices were permitted which led to an unjustified loss of water from underground sources. Wells were frequently left open, through which water poured out needlessly, or underground aquifers were polluted. In this connection the Council of Ministers of the USSR, by their decree of 4 September 1959, obligated the Councils of Ministers of Union Republics and Ministries and Departments of the USSR in the years 1959 to 1961 to undertake measures to put all existing water intake facilities into proper order, to equip with valves drilled wells which tapped naturally flowing underground water, to eliminate uneconomical use of underground waters, and to prevent their pollution by sewage from industrial and communal enterprises. Although these measures had to be implemented by a certain date, they retain their importance today, since they are, in essence, permanent conditions for ensuring the rational use of underground water. In other words, if it was necessary in 1961 to prevent the uneconomical use of underground waters, it is equally necessary to prevent it today.

In order to regulate the use of mineral waters for needs unconnected with health, the legislation ought to stipulate that authorization to drill wells and extract mineral waters for such use may be issued if there are sufficiently good reasons for it. For example, in certain cases it is possible to authorize the use of mineral waters as an industrial raw material for the extraction of valuable chemical elements (such as iodine, boron, bromide, and so on) and for irrigation, not so much for purposes of wetting the soil as for fertilization, in order to increase the yield of agricultural crops. Mineral waters may not be used in the preparation of building materials, washing of equipment, flushing of streets, and so on.

Mineral waters are used for medicinal purposes not only in health resorts. In the USSR mineral water is bottled on a large scale, and

as a result it has become possible to use it for health needs far from
its place of extraction. It is bottled in special factories.[44]

Sources of mineral waters may be used for bottling purposes only
if they are especially equipped to insure the stability of the chemical
content of water, its immaculate sanitary condition, the efficient withdrawal of mineral water from the aquifer, and the possibility of systematically controlling its regime in the zones of sanitary protection.
All the requirements applying to the organization of the production of
bottled mineral water are set out in special instructions on the sanitary requirements for bottling mineral water, which were approved by
the Chief State Sanitary Inspector of the USSR on 18 March 1959.

In certain cases (Article 1 of the Regulations on the Use and Conservation of Underground Waters in the USSR), the authorization of
the agencies of geology and protection of minerals and other competent state agencies must be secured in order to use sources of mineral
waters for bottling. But in all cases authorization must be received
from the agencies of state sanitary supervision and from the Chief
Administration of Health Resorts and Sanitoria of the Ministry of
Health of the Union Republic.

_____

44. In prerevolutionary Russia there were four primitively equipped
factories for bottling mineral water—the Kislovodskii, Essentukskii,
Borzhomskii, and Izhevskii factories, where the bottling was carried
out by hand. Today in the USSR about 100 factories and shops in thirteen Union Republics are involved in bottling mineral water. In 1963
they produced 656.4 million bottles of mineral water of 114 different
varieties, and the planned output for 1965 is 869.6 million bottles.
See P. L. Yakovskii, *Mineral Waters of the USSR* (Moscow, 1964),
p. 25.

Chapter 3

Legal Regulation of Water Use Not Associated with Water Consumption

1. *Basic Legal Requirements for Use of Water Resources of Hydroelectric Station Reservoirs*

The water resources of our country are widely used for hydroelectric purposes.

In the USSR, more than sixty large- and medium-sized reservoirs associated with hydroelectric stations are in existence or under construction. Nineteen of them have a water surface area of more than 1,000 sq. meters* and they rank with the largest lakes in the world.[1] The hydroelectric resources of the USSR are not yet exhausted. Construction of large hydroelectric stations will continue, particularly in mountainous regions and in the East.[2] In addition, a large number of hydroelectric stations of medium and small capacity are being operated, built, and planned in the USSR.

---

*This is the figure quoted in the original, but it would appear to be an error.

1. A. B. Avakyan and V. A. Sharapov, *The Reservoirs of Hydroelectric Stations of the USSR* (State Publishing House of Energy Literature, 1962), p. 3.

2. For example, it is intended to create a cascade of three hydroelectric stations on the Lena River: the Yakutskaya, the Mukhtuiskaya, and Nizhne-Lenskaya. The capacity of the latter will be 20 million kilowatts and the surface area of the reservoir will be 61,000 square kilometers. It is intended to construct hydroelectric stations on the rivers Vitim, Aldan, Kolyma, and others. (*Pravda,* 17 June 1964).

The reservoirs of hydroelectric stations have a considerable and varied influence on the condition of water resources.

Reservoir development changes the river flow, creating favorable conditions for the production of low-cost electrical power and opening up new potentialities for improving navigation and timber-floating routes, increasing the area of irrigated lands, expanding fisheries, and so on. At the same time, however, reservoirs can have unfavorable effects, such as flooding and inundating large areas of fertile lands, preventing anadromous and other fish from reaching their spawning grounds, preventing high water from reaching the floodplains of rivers below the dams and thus causing insufficient wetting of fertile flood-lands, or increasing the level of subsoil waters and causing excessive wetting of lands in areas affected by the reservoirs, and so on.

In view of the effect that the creation and operation of reservoirs of hydroelectric stations has on the national economy and the public, it is obvious that decisions made concerning the construction and operation of reservoirs of hydroelectric stations must be sound and responsible in every way. Similarly, the legal regulation of relations which arise in the construction and operation of reservoirs becomes more important.

As a result of many years of practice in the development of hydroelectricity in our country, general principles have evolved that reflect a scientifically based approach to the use of such a valuable natural resource as hydroenergy.

First, a general maxim has been established, by which reservoirs of hydroelectric stations must be built as economically as possible, but in such a way that all favorable natural conditions and economic opportunities remain available for use, and the national economy suffers the least harm, not only at the time but in the distant future.

Second, in the construction and operation of reservoirs of hydroelectric stations, conditions for the complex use of the water resources of reservoirs must be safeguarded so that they may be utilized to the fullest extent in order to meet the needs of all the water users concerned.

These principles are reflected in the legislation. As a result, certain requirements for the development and operation of reservoirs have been strengthened and the rights and obligations of the water users have been established.

The legislation governing hydroelectric power development and the use of water resources of reservoirs has not yet been analyzed in a study of Soviet law, in spite of its great importance and complexity. The following discussion of questions concerning the legal regulation of the development and operation of the reservoirs of hydroelectric stations, therefore, which is the first attempt at a scientific analysis of the legislation, does not claim to be an exhaustive interpretation

of the material. It tries, however, to clarify points of principle and
to explain the basic features of the existing legal regulation of the
use of water resources in the development and operation of the reservoirs of hydroelectric stations.

In the USSR there is no general law which regulates in a comprehensive fashion the development and operation of the reservoirs of
hydroelectric stations.

In accordance with the general procedure for capital construction
in the USSR, the construction of hydroelectric stations and their reservoirs is carried out on the basis of plans for the national economy.

The planning of new hydroelectric stations is carried out in accordance with the Basic Planning Regulations,[3] which are a set of norms
mandatory for all planning organizations and which stipulate the basic
requirements for the planning of hydro-technical structures on rivers.

The plans for dams, for reservoirs which are created by the dams,
and also for hydro-technical installations for the development of the
water resources of the reservoirs, must ensure the fullest and most effective use of reservoirs and bodies of water for different national
economic purposes. They must provide for economic utilization of
shallows, including use for timber sorting, and ensure a normal rate
of flow in the tailrace to meet the requirements of all interested water
users. The plans must include measures to ensure that the amount of
damage that might be caused with the development of the hydroelectric
system through flooding, the washing away and eroding of channels,
the transformation of banks, the changing of ice conditions, fishery
conditions, and so on, be reduced to a minimum.

In compliance with the Law on the Protection of Nature in the
RSFSR, it is necessary in the planning and construction of reservoirs
to avoid the creation of unproductive shallows and to make provision
for the protection and reproduction of fish.

The laws for the protection of nature in some other Union Republics
contain similar provisions.

Long practice in the development of hydroelectric power in the
USSR has shown that in plans for the construction of reservoirs a
whole complex of national economic benefits associated with hydroelectric power development are in general achieved. However, it does
happen that, owing to bad planning, undesirable conditions for use of
water from the reservoirs are created, causing damage to the natural
wealth and to the whole national economy.

---

3. See *Construction Standards and Regulations*, Part II, Section
И, Chapter 1, "Hydrotechnical River Constructions. Basic Planning
Regulations" (SNiP II—И, 1—62), approved by the State Construction
Committee of the Council of Ministers of the USSR on 28 June 1962
(Moscow: State Publishing House of Literature on Building, 1962).

In order that the planning and construction of reservoirs of hydroelectric stations may be completely sound, the legislation establishes
a procedure for coordinating technical plans for hydroelectric schemes
(including reservoirs) with state agencies and interested water users
or their departments.

For example, in order to ensure that issues relating to the development of the national economy in areas adjacent to reservoirs are dealt
with in a comprehensive fashion, plans for the reservoirs must be approved by the Councils of Ministers of Union Republics and, if the
cost of the reservoir is more than 50 million rubles, they must also
be approved by the State Planning Committee of the USSR.

According to Article 18 of the Regulations on the Use and Conservation of Underground Waters in the USSR, building organizations
which undertake hydro-technical construction that causes the level
of groundwater to rise (and the construction of reservoirs of hydroelectric stations does as a rule influence the level of groundwater)
are obliged to coordinate construction plans with the agencies of geology and protection of minerals and the local agencies of state sanitary
supervision.

In accord with the decree of the Council of Ministers of the USSR
of 22 April 1960 "On Measures to Regulate Use and Increase Conservation of Water Resources of the USSR,"[4] plans for the construction of
new enterprises and for the reconstruction of existing enterprises associated with the use of water resources, with their conservation and
with the struggle to combat the harmful action of water, must be referred to the republic agencies for the use and conservation of water
resources, which take action on them that has mandatory force for
planning and other organizations.

In spite of the importance of legal regulation of the planning and
building of reservoirs of hydroelectric stations (since it is at this
stage that the conditions of future water use are determined to a large
extent), such regulation does not cover all the legal requirements for
the use of the water resources of reservoirs. The use for which the
reservoir is intended begins after the construction work is completed
and the hydroelectric scheme is put into operation.

From this moment the hydroelectric station, being the owner of the
dam and other hydro facilities that regulate the water regime of the
reservoir, becomes in effect the principal water user and the subject
of water use.[5] The legal requirements for rational use of the water
resources are addressed primarily to it.

---

4. *Collected Decrees of the USSR*, 1960, No. 9, Article 67.
5. The position of the hydroelectric station as principal water user
is not reflected in the legislation and is not juridically formulated.

All responsibility for the use of the power capacity of the reservoir belongs to the hydroelectric station, as a specialized enterprise for generating electricity. But since the reservoir is used by a large number of water users for a variety of purposes, the hydroelectric station also has the responsibility of managing (in the technical sense) the reservoir as a whole, in accordance with the requirements of the legislation and special normative acts (Dispatching Rules for Flow Regulation).

In order to achieve the optimal economic effect, with the observance of the legal requirements, management of the reservoir is carried out on the basis of a system of rules and instructions which are developed for each reservoir or cascade (series) of reservoirs and which have both juridical and technical significance.

For example, in the RSFSR the leading documents governing the use of the water resources of reservoirs (under normal operating conditions) are:

(1) Regulations on the Use of the Water Resources of Reservoirs of the RSFSR, which were approved by the State Committee of the Council of Ministers of the RSFSR for Water Management and which apply to all reservoirs, with the exception of natural and artificial ponds under the jurisdiction of state and collective farms;

(2) Basic Provisions of the Regulations on Use of the Water Resources of a Reservoir or Cascade of Reservoirs. These "Basic Provisions" are worked out by the organization which draws up the plans for the reservoir; they are coordinated with the organizations concerned and the state sanitary supervision of the Republic, and are approved by the Ministry of Land Improvement and Water Management of the RSFSR;

(3) Rules, instructions, and other technical documents for regulating the level and discharge of water, which are worked out by the organization which operates the facilities. This organization is usually the hydroelectric station. It works out and issues, in particular, rules for managing the water regime which are drawn up for specific years and seasons, and instructions for the operation of individual installations, for the passage of high water, operational control, estimates of water resources, notification, information, and so on. The rules and instructions issued by the hydroelectric station are mandatory both for the station personnel who manage the activities of the hydroelectric system and, to a certain extent, for enterprises, institutions, organizations, and citizens who use the water resources of the reservoirs.

The regulations in force in the Union Republics, governing use of the water resources of reservoirs, specify that the water stored in reservoirs must be used to the greatest benefit of the national economy, while at the same time taking into account the interests of all water consumers and water users, including those associated with the protection of nature and the use of bodies of water for cultural-domestic purposes.

The regulation of the storage level of reservoirs and the release of water into the tailrace, that is to say, the operating regime of the reservoirs, are most important for a proper use of the water resources of the reservoirs in order to meet the requirements of all interested water users.

The legislation provides that standard storage levels, that is to say, maximum and minimum water levels in the reservoirs which are permissible during normal operation of the hydroelectrical system, be established for each reservoir or cascade (series) of reservoirs.

Standard storage levels of reservoirs are set up not only for extremes (maximum and minimum) but also for intermediate levels. For example, in reservoirs which are used for navigation, minimum navigation levels are established (which are different for different periods of navigation), and also minimum levels which are guaranteed for the period when the vessels are laid up for the winter if they are above the planned level of greatest drawdown of storage. Intermediate standard storage levels are also established in order to guarantee water for irrigation systems during the period when crops are watered.

In the use of reservoirs for flood control, the level of obligatory drawdown of storage prior to high water is established, in addition to the standard storage levels.

In order to ensure the most effective hydrologic conditions in the water below the dam, maximum and minimum levels of the tailrace for different periods of the year are established. In particular, minimum levels for certain sections of the tailrace are established conforming to the interests of navigation, timber-floating, communal and industrial water supply, irrigation, and so on. The maximum water levels which are permitted in the tailrace are usually set up for periods of high-water flow. When necessary the standardized limits of the levels of the tailrace may be supplemented or changed in accordance with the rate that has been set for discharge of water into the tailrace from the reservoir (to preserve the quality of the water and so on).

Depending on local conditions, a more detailed regulation of the water regime of reservoirs may be possible by establishing the maximum permissible range of daily fluctuations and rate of change of the levels of the headrace and the tailrace.

Finally, a system of indices of standard water levels is established for a reservoir, in which the fixed normal head level of storage, which must be strictly observed, and the volume of discharge of water into the tailrace are known at any given moment of time.

The standard water levels of reservoirs are specified in the "Basic Provisions of the Regulations on Use of the Water Resources of a Reservoir or Cascade of Reservoirs," which are approved by the agencies of water management of Union Republics.

The regime for the release of the water stored in reservoirs (in particular the volume of water discharged into the tailrace) is set out in the Dispatching Rules for Flow Regulation, which are a constituent part of the "Basic Provisions of the Regulations on the Use of the Water Resources of Reservoirs."

For a practical application of the principle of the complex use of the water resources of reservoirs of hydroelectric stations, the water regime established in the "Basic Provisions of the Regulations on Use of the Water Resources of Reservoirs" (the Dispatching Rules for Flow Regulation) should above all be consistent with the requirements of all interested water users.

Not all the needs of the water users are taken into consideration when the standard water levels and operating regime of the reservoirs are set. Only the following are taken into account:

(a) Needs that exist when the Basic Provisions are approved and substantial prospective needs which will arise during the periods for which long-term planning is being undertaken;

(b) Needs of a permanent character. Ephemeral needs do not have to be considered;

(c) Needs which are within the technical means of the reservoir. Needs which a reservoir is not capable of meeting cannot of course be considered.

When there are conflicting interests of water users, the agency that approves the Basic Provisions has the right to meet the requirements of individual water users either fully or in part, and to refuse demands which are incompatible with the complex use of the water resources.

The standard water levels and the regime for use of the stored water resources, which are laid down in the Basic Provisions of the Regulations on Use of the Water Resources of Reservoirs, are binding on all water users who participate in the operation of the reservoir. But they are binding in the first place on the enterprise or organization which is the owner of the dam and water regulating structures, in other words, the hydroelectric station.

The hydroelectric station is the owner of the dam forming the reservoir and of the water discharge (water passage) structures by means of which the level of the water in the reservoir is regulated. As a rule the hydroelectric station has a monopoly of use of the hydromechanical power of the reservoir by the release of water through the apertures of the dam and the turbines. It also has the right to discharge water directly into the tailrace. Other water users do not enjoy this right.

However, these rights of the hydroelectric station are not exercised arbitrarily but in strict accordance with the regime prescribed by the Dispatching Rules for Flow Regulation.

The Dispatching Rules for Flow Regulation define the conditions for the use of the water resources for the current and immediately forthcoming period, depending on the time of year (the date, phase of the

water year, and so on), the amount of water in the reservoir or in several interrelated reservoirs, the rate of flow (for the current period or,
if it is possible to make a reliable hydrological forecast, for the forthcoming period), and the needs of the national economy. In particular,
the Rules indicate the size of the releases into the tailrace (daily
average and base, that is, daily minimum) for navigation and other
obligatory purposes, the volume of output of energy at the hydroelectric stations, the permissible range of daily and weekly adjustment
of water discharge, and so on.

The daily and weekly regulation of discharge of water for the output of electricity is carried out on the basis of dispatching graphs.
These are drawn up in accordance with the requirements of the power
system, observing at the same time the restrictions on the operation
of the hydroelectric system or of separate installations which are imposed for reasons of safety and to prevent silting up of the reservoir
and other restrictions which are agreed upon with the other water
users concerned. These include, for example, restrictions on the
range of daily and weekly discharge of water by hydroelectric stations,
or restrictions on the extent of drawdown of the reservoir for sanitary,
fishery, navigation, irrigation, and other considerations. In each case
the amount of water discharged into the tailrace must not be below the
amount specified in the plan for sanitary reasons, ensuring the uninterrupted work of communal and industrial water intake facilities which
are located on the river downstream. And during the period of navigation the release into the tailrace on rivers where shipping is carried
out must not be less than the amount guaranteed by the plan.

The hydroelectric station may deviate from the Dispatching Rules
for Flow Regulation only in exceptional circumstances.

Under the law the hydroelectric station has the right to deviate
from the regime prescribed by the Dispatching Rules for Flow Regulation and to increase the discharge of water into the tailrace in unfore-
seen, exceptional circumstances which threaten the security and
preservation of the main installations and which require the adoption
of urgent measures. In these circumstances the operating regime of
the hydroelectric system is changed by order of the official responsible for its operation, and simultaneously all interested organizations
and enterprises, and agencies responsible for the safety of the public
and the economy in the area of the reservoirs and on the river downstream, are informed.

With these exceptions, the hydroelectric station does not have the
right to violate the set standard storage levels of the reservoir and
the regime for the release of the stored water resources.

However, in fact, the hydroelectric stations frequently violate this
requirement by maintaining the water level in the reservoir above or
below the normal head established for that period. When this happens,
if the level of the water in the reservoir rises above the normal head,

flooding of the adjacent land occurs which causes damage to collective and state farms and other enterprises. On the other hand, if the water supply in the reservoir falls below the normal head, this impedes the operation of water transport and can damage the fishing industry, hinder the withdrawal of water for irrigation, industrial, and communal water supply, and create other difficulties for water use. In addition, a premature drawdown of the reservoir may complicate the operation of the hydroelectric station itself.

Let me quote some examples in support of what I have said. In the period from 1952 to 1963, the level of water in the Tsimlyanskoe reservoir six times rose above the normal head level, and as a result flooding of large areas of land occurred over quite a long period. The damage which was caused to agriculture alone came to about 648,000 rubles.[6]

In the same Tsimlyanskoe reservoir, as a result of an excessive drop in water reserves in the winter of 1954, the storage level at the end of March was three meters below the normal head level. All the depressions and pits along the banks, where the sazan carp spend the winter, were cut off from the main body of water and were covered by accumulations of ice. An enormous loss of fish resulted. In individual depressions and pits the layer of dead fish reached 40 to 50 cm. It was estimated that about 25,000 centners [2,500,000 kilograms] of sazan perished, which in terms of cash was between 1.6 and 1.7 million rubles. In addition, at the beginning of the spring spawning the water in the reservoir did not reach the spawning grounds.

In the summer of 1963, as a result of a lowering of the level of the water in the Tsimlyanskoe reservoir below the standard level, difficulties arose at the timber-loading base at Tsimlyansk and there was danger that it might not be possible to take out by water the timber which had arrived there.

Similar occurrences are caused to a certain extent by shortcomings in the existing procedure for managing the productive activity of hydroelectric stations and by features of their legal position that contain inherent contradictions.

The fact is that the hydroelectric stations, being under the jurisdiction of the agencies of power and electrification, as a rule work not in isolation but in coordination with several electric stations which make up the power system. These are administered centrally, but outside the management of the hydroelectric stations as water

---

6. The extent of damage is determined on the basis of an average damage of twenty rubles resulting from flooding on one hectare of crops. Only cases where crops are flooded for more than fifteen days are considered, since it is assumed that only where such prolonged flooding occurs are agricultural crops completely destroyed.

users. The agencies managing the power systems, having their own dispatching service, determine the productive load and operating conditions of each electric station, depending on seasonal and daily fluctuations of power consumption, as well as on other circumstances (which are interconnected to a certain extent). Accordingly, the capacities of the hydroelectric stations are frequently used for meeting the deficit of electricity in periods of so-called peak loads. In this way, the agencies which manage the power systems establish the regime of the hydroelectric stations under them and, consequently, determine the conditions for using the water resources of the reservoirs. But these agencies, in striving to provide more low-cost (from their point of view) electricity and following, consequently, narrow bureaucratic interests, do not take account of the principle of complex use of water resources. The hydroelectric stations then find themselves in the situation of, on the one hand, being obliged to observe the Dispatching Rules for Flow Regulation which are based on the principle of complex use of water resources, and on the other hand of having to follow the instructions of the agencies managing the power systems, which ignore these rules.

In some cases the power management agencies assume the function, which is not theirs, of establishing the water regimes of the reservoirs.

For example, in September 1962 the "Chief Power Administration," although not competent to establish standard storage levels of reservoirs, informed the organizations concerned (in particular, the Volga Basin Waterways Management of the Ministry of Inland Water Transport of the RSFSR) that the level of prespring drawdown of the Kuibyshevskoe reservoir in 1963 would be below the forty-eight meter mark. In fact what happened was that the hydroelectric station named after V. I. Lenin on the Volga used an excessively large quantity of water before the spring high water, as a result of which the level of the reservoir at the end of March 1963 was already below this mark. The Ministry of Inland Water Transport of the RSFSR was forced to request that further drawdown be halted, since it might damage the fleet which was at its winter moorings in the backwaters. The "Chief Power Administration" of the Integrated Power System of the European part of the Soviet Union declined the request of the Ministry of Inland Water Transport of the RSFSR, on the grounds that a halt in the work of the hydroelectric station would involve limiting the electricity supply to industry and, consequently, would harm the national economy.

Moreover, the hydroelectric station did not observe the standard storage levels established for the reservoir for the following period of 1963 either. In June the water level in the Kuibyshevskoe reservoir was above the standard head level (which resulted in flooding that was not envisaged in the plan of the hydroelectric system), while in September there was an increase in the discharge of water through the turbines of the hydroelectric station which threatened an excessive drop in the level of the reservoir.

It is quite clear that violations by hydroelectric stations of the Basic Provisions of the Regulations on Use of the Water Resources of Reservoirs provoke very serious and justified claims against the hydroelectric stations from other water users. A large portion of the claims contain all the elements of legal controversy, namely, the restoration of the legitimate interests of one water user which have been violated by the illegal activities of another. However they are not resolved through juridical proceedings. They are not even given the importance of legal disputes, and consideration of them is generally carried out through current official correspondence between the organizations (in the form of requests, wishes, and so on), as if there were no reciprocal obligations binding upon them.

Even the intervention of the republic agencies of water management, which try to assure the complex use of the water resources of reservoirs and to prevent illegal activity by the hydroelectric stations, appears to have little effect.

For example, when in the summer of 1963 the Lenin Hydroelectric Station on the Volga maintained the storage level of the reservoir above the standard head level, the former State Committee of the Council of Ministers of the RSFSR for Water Management wrote to the "Kuibyshev Power Administration" and ordered them to decrease storage to the standard head level at the earliest possible date. However, on 5 July the State Water Management of the RSFSR ascertained that the "Kuibyshev Power Administration" had not carried out its instructions to reduce storage to the standard head level, and in this connection ordered the manager of the Central Volga Basin Inspection of the State Water Management to take all the necessary measures on the spot, right up to the application of sanctions, against the officials responsible, in accordance with the Edict of the Presidium of the Supreme Soviet of the RSFSR of 3 March 1962.

Obviously, this case also involved a contradiction, since the State Committee on Water Management was empowered to regulate the use of the water resources, but did not have the right to determine the power load of the hydroelectric station, on which depends the conditions for the use of the water resources. The right to determine the power load of the hydroelectric station belongs to the agencies of power management. These agencies do not consider themselves obligated to observe the standard levels and conditions for use of the water reserves, which ensure the complex use of the water resources of the reservoirs. But the hydroelectric stations, being under the jurisdiction of the agencies of power and electrification, are obliged to carry out both the Dispatching Rules for Flow Regulation and the orders of higher agencies that contradict these Rules.

Such a situation makes it necessary to clarify the relationships of water users, and to seek ways of preventing and suppressing infringements of the law and to seek forms and methods of settling conflicts which arise in the use of the water resources of reservoirs.

First of all, it must be recognized that the Dispatching Rules for Flow Regulation are mandatory, not only for hydroelectric stations, but also for the Integrated Power System. It is necessary to establish in legislation categorically and unconditionally that the Integrated Power System does not have the right to determine a load for a hydroelectric station that does not comply with the Dispatching Rules for Flow Regulation, and the hydroelectric station is not obliged to carry out this part of the orders of the Integrated Power System. If the hydroelectric station submits, it must bear full responsibility for possible undesirable consequences.

In this connection it is appropriate to raise the question of property (civil law) responsibility of the hydroelectric station for damage caused to other water users (and non-users)—enterprises, institutions, organizations, and citizens.

When property damage is caused to enterprises, institutions, organizations, and citizens, as a result of unlawful activities of hydroelectric stations in violation of the "Basic Provisions of the Regulations on Use of the Water Resources of Reservoirs" (Dispatching Rules for Flow Regulation), all the conditions are present for the development of obligations arising out of the causing of damage. Compensation for damage in these cases should be made according to the rules of Article 90 of the Principles of Civil Law of the USSR and Union Republics, since the activity of the hydroelectric station involves increased danger for the surrounding area.

In practice, however, the responsibility under civil law of the hydroelectric stations for damage caused by their activity in the use of the water resources of reservoirs is not applied. It is difficult to say how such practice has become established. Apparently it is explained by the singularity of the conditions under which the property damage occurs. However, there is in fact no reason to place hydroelectric stations in a privileged position and to absolve them from their responsibility to compensate for damage caused by them. It is therefore necessary to supplement the legislation regulating the activities of hydroelectric stations by special rules, which would clearly indicate the obligation of the hydroelectric station to compensate for damage caused through the use of the water resources of the reservoirs to enterprises, institutions, organizations, and citizens.

As regards the possibility of imposing administrative fines on hydroelectric station officials guilty of violating the "Basic Provisions of the Regulations on Use of the Water Resources of Reservoirs" (Dispatching Rules for Flow Regulation), this is provided for in the legislation.[7]

---

7. See Article 13 of the Edict of the Presidium of the Supreme Soviet of the USSR of 12 June 1961, "On Further Limiting the Application

2. *Use of Inland Transport Waterways*

The development of rivers, lakes, reservoirs, canals, and other waterways for transport is one of the main elements of the complex use of water resources.

At the present time in the USSR there are 138,000 kilometers of shipping routes in use on which, for example, more than 400 million tons of freight were carried in 1961—almost thirteen times as much as the maximum tonnage carried by river transport in prerevolutionary Russia. During the navigation period (May to October), more than 15 percent of the general freightage in tons and about 12 percent of all freight turnover are carried by river transport. River transport is most economical for the carriage of bulk freight such as timber, oil, coal, mineral building materials, salt, mineral fertilizers, and raw materials for heavy industry.

In the USSR, 142,000 kilometers of rivers and lakes are operated for the floating of timber, which includes 126,000 kilometers in the RSFSR. There will be little extension of the timber-floating routes in the future, since the increase in the transportation of timber by water will be handled by vessels and towed rafts.

Since the transportation of freight and passengers by inland waterways is of great importance for the national economy of the USSR, the Soviet State is constantly developing water transport and improving the inland waterways and the method of their operation. The program of the Communist Party of the Soviet Union envisages the interconnection of the separate river basins and the formation in the European part of the USSR of a single deepwater transport system.[8]

The achievement of a high economic efficiency of water transport, the maintenance of regular and uninterrupted movement of vessels along the waterways, with the observance, at the same time, of the principle of complex use of the water resources of the rivers, lakes, and other bodies of water through which the waterways pass, is closely associated in Soviet law with the regulation of the use of the inland waterways.

---

of Fines, Imposed Administratively" (*Records of the Supreme Soviet of the USSR*, 1961, No. 35, Article 368), and the legislation of Union Republics in the field of water management, for example, the decree of the Council of Ministers of the RSFSR of 18 February 1963, "On the Establishment of Fines for Violation of the Regulations for the Conservation and Use of Water Resources" (*Collected Decrees of the RSFSR*, 1963, No. 5, Article 28).

8. See *Materials of the Twenty-second Congress of the CPSU* (Moscow: State Publishing House for Political Literature, 1961), p. 373.

The main legislation defining the procedure for utilizing inland
waterways for transport purposes is the Statutes of Inland Water Transport of the USSR, which were approved by the decree of the Council
of Ministers of the USSR of 15 October 1955.[9] The Statutes apply to
the Aral Sea, and to all shipping and timber-floating rivers, lakes
used for navigation, and artificial waterways in the USSR. They apply
to boundary waterways, with exceptions which are set out in special
laws, decrees, and orders of the Government of the USSR, and in
treaties and agreements concluded by the USSR with foreign States.

The use of rivers, lakes, reservoirs, and other bodies of water as
transport routes is also regulated by other legislative acts of the
USSR and the Union Republics, by ordinances of the executive committees of local Councils of Workers' Deputies and by departmental
normative documents, the most important of which are the Regulations
for Navigation on Inland Waterways issued by the river transport
agencies of the Union Republics.[10]

In accordance with the Regulations for Navigation on the Inland
Waterways of the RSFSR, for separate basins and sections of them
where specific navigation conditions prevail, local navigation rules
may be issued which are approved by the manager of the corresponding

---

9. *The Statutes of Inland Water Transport of the USSR* (Moscow:
"River Transport" Publishing House, 1956). The Statutes of Inland
Water Transport are a complex legislative act in the sense that they
contain norms of different branches of Soviet law. However, norms of
civil law, regulating relationships of the transportation of freight and
passengers, predominate. Comparatively little space is given to the
regulation of the use of shipping and timber-floating routes in the
Statutes. A number of matters relating to use of the waterways are
decided from the narrow bureaucratic standpoint of the agencies of
river transport. For example, Article 16 of the Statutes of Inland Water
Transport stipulate the clearing only of shipping rivers from sunken
timber, and Article 18 speaks of standard storage levels of reservoirs
during the navigation period only.

10. In the RSFSR the Regulations for Navigation on Inland Water-
ways were put into force on 15 March 1963 by Order No. 33 of the
Ministry of Inland Water Transport of the RSFSR of 28 February 1963.
In other Union Republics such regulations are issued by the river
transport management agencies of the Councils of Ministers of the
Union Republics.

The Republic Regulations for Navigation apply to waterways in
each Union Republic. However, there are numbers of waterways in
the USSR which pass through two or more neighboring Union Republics,
and the application of the Regulations for Navigation to such waterways is not defined in the legislation.

basin navigation inspection. For example, temporary local regulations for navigation on the inland shipping routes of the North-West Basin were approved by an order of the manager of navigation inspection of the North-West Basin of 24 February 1964.

The procedure for using timber-floating routes is regulated by comparable legislative and departmental acts, rules, and instructions which are issued by the state agencies that manage timber-floating.

Not all bodies of water and water courses are included in the inland waterways of the USSR, but only those rivers, lakes, reservoirs, and canals, located within the state boundaries of the USSR, which are suitable for navigation and the floating of timber. The suitability of bodies of water for navigation and the floating of timber is based on technical-economic conditions, and lists of those which are considered to be suitable are drawn up and published by the timber-floating agencies in agreement with the agencies of river transport.[11]

In compliance with Article 11 of the Statutes of Inland Water Transport, lists of inland waterways open for navigation are drawn up and published accordingly by the Ministry of Inland Water Transport of the RSFSR[12] and the river transport management agencies of the Council of Ministers of other Union Republics. Lists of timber-floating routes are drawn up and published by the agencies which manage timber-floating in agreement with the river transport agencies of the Union Republics.

Although the movement of vessels and other floating devices along the rivers, lakes, reservoirs, and canals does not occur on the whole body of water, but along the fairway (ship's passage) which is limited by fixed dimensions (depth, width, turning radius on bends), the concept of the waterway embraces the body of water as a whole, both the navigable and nonnavigable parts, including the shallows. In other words, the waterway is the whole area of the body of water, even if only a part of it is used for navigation and timber-floating. An understanding of this point is important for the establishment of limits on the rights exercised by the water users. One cannot, for example, erect a structure on a river which is a waterway without the approval of the agencies of river transport on the grounds that the structure will be on a part of the river which is not used for navigation, for

---

11. There are no instructions in the law on objective criteria for relating bodies of water to inland waterways. The concept of what bodies of water are suitable for navigation and timber floating needs clarification.

12. See *Lists of Inland Waterways Operated by the Ministry of Inland Water Transport of the RSFSR*, approved by the Ministry of Inland Water Transport of the RSFSR on 14 April 1962 (Moscow: "River Transport" Publishing House, 1962).

under the law, construction on the inland waterways is permitted only
by agreement with the agencies of river transport.

The concept of the waterway also includes areas of rivers, lakes,
and reservoirs where regular navigation or timber-floating does not
occur (such as inlets, harbors, roads, and so on), but which are used
for subsidiary river transport operations. However there are no grounds
for including in the waterways riparian strips of land and land sections
alloted for the use of river transport to meet certain of its needs.

All the inland waterways of the USSR are under the jurisdiction of
special state agencies of water transport and timber-floating—in the
RSFSR, the Ministry of Inland Water Transport, the river transport management agencies of the Councils of Ministers of Union Republics,
and the timber-floating inspections.

In compliance with the law, these agencies carry out the general
management of shipping and timber-floating routes, regulate their use,
issue the appropriate regulations, undertake the development of waterways, and supervise their condition and the observance of the rules
governing their use.

Thus the Regulations on the Ministry of Inland Water Transport of
the RSFSR, which were approved by the decree of the Council of Ministers of the RSFSR of 7 January 1957,[13] specify that the Ministry of
Inland Water Transport of the RSFSR should carry out the following
functions in the administration of the inland waterways:

Supervise navigation and construction on the inland waterways and
adjacent riparian strips;

Work out and approve regulations for navigation on the inland waterways, and issue instructions, rules, and regulations on the use of
the inland waterways of the RSFSR and of the riparian strips and lands
which have been allocated to the inland water transport. These instructions, rules, and regulations are mandatory for all ministries,
departments, organizations, and citizens;

Undertake research and planning for the development of new inland
waterways for navigation, and also work out and undertake measures
for the reconstruction and improvement of inland waterways already in
use.

The chief Administration of Waterways and Hydrotechnical Constructions and its territorial agencies—the basin managements of the waterways, the technical centers, and areas of hydroconstructions (such
as canals, sluices, and so on)—which come under the Ministry of Inland Water Transport of the RSFSR, are directly in charge of the inland
shipping routes of the RSFSR.

---

13. See *Chronological Collection of Laws and Edicts of the Presidium of the Supreme Soviet and Decrees of the Government of the
RSFSR* (Moscow: State Juridical Publishing House [n.d.]), Vol. 6, p. 3.

Control over the observance of the navigation regulations and other rules regulating the use of waterways is maintained by navigation inspections, which are also under the ministry of Inland Water Transport of the RSFSR.

The management of the use of timber-floating routes is carried out by specialized agencies of the Union Republics. In particular, in the Russian Federation there is a state inspection for the floating of timber, which has the following functions in the field of waterways management:

Control over the observance by the timber-floating organizations of the Statutes of Inland Water Transport and of the regulations, technical conditions, and instructions governing the floating of timber;

Settlement, in conjunction with the Ministry of Inland Water Transport of the RSFSR and the Ministry of the Marine Fleet, of questions associated with the operation of shipping rivers for timber-floating and the transportation of timber by them;

Supervision over the conditions and development of nonshipping timber-floating routes and the regulation of their use for the floating of timber.

All the inland waterways of the USSR (shipping and timber-floating) are routes of general use.

The essence of the legislation which conceives of the inland shipping and timber-floating waterways as routes of general use may be examined in three parts:

(a) According to subject of use;

(b) According to the transportation features of the waterways in use;

(c) According to methods of use.

With regard to subjects, a legal policy of general use means that vessels and other floating devices belonging not only to specialized transport organizations, but to other enterprises, institutions, organizations, and citizens, may move freely (that is, without special authorization on each occasion) along the inland waterways of the USSR. In this sense, the legislation governing the inland waterways is similar to the legislation governing motor roads, movement along which is permitted by law to all owners of means of transport.

It must be emphasized that the transport water users on the inland waterways are the owners of the vessels and not the owners of the freight, nor the passengers on the riverboats. The legal requirements concerning the use of rivers, lakes, reservoirs, and canals for transport purposes apply only to the owners of craft. The relations associated with the transportation of freight and passengers which develop between the owners of vessels and the owners of the freight and the passengers are not regulated by the law of water use but by civil law.

The water users—the owners of the craft—are the state enterprises, institutions, and organizations which have under their management motorized and nonmotorized vessels and other floatage which they operate on the inland waterways. The majority of vessels in the USSR, belonging to the State, are operated by specialized water transport enterprises—such as the steamship lines of the agencies of river transport of the Union Republics.

Public organizations and private citizens who use their own fleet and other floatage on the inland waterways are also water users.

In the floating of timber, the water users are not the owners of the timber that is being floated, who, in their position under the law, resemble the owners of the freight that is carried by the inland water transport, but the specialized timber-floating organizations. The subjects of use of the floatable routes are defined in accordance with Article 16 of the Statutes of Inland Water Transport, which specifies that the floating of timber be carried out by only one timber-floating organization in any one area.

Enterprises and organizations that operate craft, which they have leased for a period of not less than one year, on the inland waterways must also be recognized as water users.

In order to achieve the best organization of the work of river transport and to control the safety of navigation on the inland waterways, all motorized vessels, and all nonmotorized vessels of a freight-carrying capacity of more than five tons, must be registered by the basin navigation inspections. All vessels subject to registration are given a special name or number, and their owners are given certificates of registration (for each vessel). The certificate of registration must without fail be on the vessel while it is in operation. Vessels and other floatage which are to be operated for less than a year do not have to be registered.

The legal significance of registering vessels is the proof it provides of the ownership of the vessel or of the right to use it, and also the evidence it provides of the right to use the inland waterways, thus indicating who the principal users are. Motorized vessels, and also nonmotorized vessels of a freight-carrying capacity of more than five tons, that have not been registered are not allowed to use the inland waterways. According to Article 40 of the Statutes of Inland Water Transport, navigation inspections are obliged to halt the movement of vessels that do not have certificates of registration.

In this way the legal policy of general use which has been established for the inland waterways creates for each Soviet enterprise, institution, organization, and citizen the right to use these routes. On the other hand, it eliminates spontaneous and uncontrolled use of our rivers, lakes, reservoirs, and canals for transport purposes, since for enterprises, institutions, organizations, and citizens to exercise the right which is theirs to use the inland waterways, preliminary technical examination and registration of the craft which serve as the instruments of transport water use[14] must in a number of cases be carried out, and other conditions must be observed.

The legal policy of general use means that all inland waterways are available for the movement and the stationing of vessels and other floatage (with the observance of the navigation rules) in a manner consistent with the transport features of the waterways.

Two exceptions from this general rule are specified in the Statutes of Inland Water Transport. First, where military objects (forts, naval bases, and so on) are located, use of the inland waterways is carried out by agreement with the military command, which may restrict the access, movement, and stationing of transport, fishing, and other nonmilitary vessels on certain sections of rivers, lakes, reservoirs, and canals. Second, by decision of the agencies that regulate navigation and timber-floating, sections of the inland waterways which are taken

---

14. The question of state registration of small craft (principally, sporting and rowing boats) belonging to organizations and citizens is not settled uniformly in the legislation. In some Autonomous Republics, territories, and oblasts, the registration of small craft is carried out by ordinances of local Councils of Workers' Deputies and their executive committees. For example, the Regulations on Security Measures on the Waterways and Water Bodies of Leningrad and its Environs, approved by ordinance of the executive committee of the Leningrad City Council, stipulates that the owners of boats are obliged to register them in the district Department of Communal Management, and to acquire a number and certificate (*Bulletin of the Leningrad City Council*, 1954, No. 11).

The ordinance of the Khabarovsk Territorial Council of Workers' Deputies of 28 June 1963, "On Measures to Regulate the Use of Motorboats in Private Ownership," introduced the obligatory registration of all motorboats and defined the procedure for issuing certificates and licenses to operate the boats. Administrative responsibility in the form of warning or fine was envisaged for violation of this ordinance. (*Tikhookeanskaya Pravda*, 4 September 1963).

The registration of small vessels is provided for in individual Union Republics, too. For example, in accord with the Regulations for Fishing in State Waters of the Moldavian SSR, approved by decree of the Council of Ministers of the Republic of 30 June 1959 (*Collected Laws of the Moldavian SSR*, 1959, No. 7, Article 134), all boats, both for fishing and for other economic and sporting purposes, must obligatorily be registered in the executive committees of urban or rural Councils of Workers' Deputies. The registration number is affixed to both sides of the boat, on the bow.

up by inlets and roads may be transferred to the exclusive use of individual departments and organizations (which are water users), or
they may be permitted to develop new inlets and roads for their own
needs.

Inlets and roads are transferred for exclusive use by agreement between the basin managements of the waterways and the enterprises
and organizations concerned. The conditions governing the use of
those parts of the waterways which are taken up by inlets and roads,
when these are transferred for exclusive use, are defined in these
agreements. In each case, the access, movement, and stationing of
vessels of all transport water users on these sections of the inland
waterways are restricted in the interests of the exclusive users (or
are permitted with their authorization).

The legal policy of general use established for the inland waterways means, finally, that all water users may utilize the waterways
for transport needs by any methods permitted under the law (for example, navigation, timber-floating, different types of ferries, the erection of structures on the water, and so on).

The rights and obligations of the users of the inland waterways are
determined in accordance with the requirements of the law, providing
for the safe and regular movement of craft on the waterways, the protection of the waterways and means of transport from damage and
deterioration, and the observance of the principle of complex use of
the water resources of the rivers, lakes, reservoirs, and canals along
which the waterways pass.

Since the inland waterways are used not only for transport but for
other needs of the national economy and the public, the legislation
specifies a number of mutual obligations of the transport and other
water users for the purpose of protecting their economic and other interests.

Thus, the erection of structures on the inland waterways (such as
bridges, dams, overhead lines, submerged cables, pipelines, wells,
booms for storing and sorting timber, moorings, and so on) is permitted
only with the authorization of the agencies which regulate navigation
and timber-floating. Owners of bridges, dams, aerial and underwater
lines across the waterways are obliged to meet the requirements of
the shipping and timber-floating management agencies for the safety
of shipping and for the proper maintenance of the shipping and timber-
floating routes. In particular, the owners of these structures are
obliged to carry out the following: to keep their structures in good
repair so as to avoid accidents to shipping; at their own expense to
make, install in accord with the instructions of the navigation inspection, and maintain all the signs indicating navigation conditions which
are specified by the Regulations for Navigation on the Inland Waterways; periodically, during the navigation season and also at the conclusion of activities, to clear the channels of the shipping routes and

the areas of roads, moorings, and timber harbors and booms of building debris, sunken wood, rigging, and other objects which might hinder the movement of vessels; and constantly to maintain the proper
heights of suspended lines and the proper depth of submerged lines.
The owners of bridges are, in addition, obliged: to make and maintain,
at their own expense, the devices which are necessary for the safe
and unhindered passage under the bridges of vessels and rafts, and,
on timber-floating rivers, of loose logs; to undertake dredging and
clearing the river bottom after the construction and repair of bridges;
and to swing and raise the spans of pontoon and drawbridges in accordance with the regulations for navigation on the inland waterways.

In their turn, the owners of vessels and other floatage (the transport water users) are obliged to observe the conditions governing
navigation which are aimed at precluding breakage and damage to
hydrostructures, bridges, and overhead and underwater crossings on
the inland waterways.

Thus, in the interests of preventing damage to underwater crossings
(such as electric cables, lines of communication, oil pipelines, gas
pipelines, and so on), and to ensure permanent access to them for their
owners, Paragraph 16 of the Regulations for Navigation on the Inland
Waterways of the RSFSR prohibits all transport water users to drop
anchor, cast lead, and station vessels and rafts in places, guarded
by warning signs, where there are underwater crossings.

However, the Regulations for Navigation on the Inland Waterways
of the RSFSR do make an exception to this general prohibition, by permitting anchor to be dropped and vessels to be halted in the locality
of underwater crossings when there is the threat of an accident to the
vessels or rafts. This exception does to a certain extent reduce the
guarantee of safety to underwater crossings, but an accident to a vessel or raft may threaten not only valuable freight but the lives of people (such as the passengers or crew of the vessels). In order to protect human lives, therefore, it is right to run the risk of damaging
underwater cables, lines of communication, oil pipelines, or gas pipelines.

In the legal regulation of the use of inland waterways, the question
of coordinating the interests of the transport water users and the organizations which use the power potential of rivers is a very live one.
It is a question, in essence, of the observance by the owners of dams
of the standard storage levels of the reservoirs and of the levels of
water in the tailrace below the dams. It was considered above in a
general way. It remains to be considered here as it applies to the observance of requirements for the use of the inland waterways.

According to Article 18 of the Statutes of Inland Water Transport,
all organizations which have under their jurisdiction hydroelectric
stations, dams, and other water-raising structures, are obliged to
maintain the water below and above the structures at a level neces-

sary for unhindered and safe navigation and timber-floating, which
has been agreed upon with the Ministry of Inland Water Transport and
the Ministry of Timber Industry of the USSR and with the river transport management agencies of the Councils of Ministers of the Union
Republics. They are also obliged to release water from the reservoirs
at times set by the agencies regulating navigation or timber-floating
without the levy of any fee or collection.

The owners of dams do not always carry out the instructions of the
law. This applies, in particular, to the maintenance of the necessary
water levels on rivers below the dams. But the agencies which maintain the inland waterways do not have sufficient legal means to force
them to fulfill their obligations.

For example, in the spring of 1963 the trust "Kuibyshev Power" and
the Board of the Lenin Hydroelectric Station on the Volga disregarded
the request of the Ministry of Inland Water Transport of the RSFSR for
concentrated releases of water into the tailrace, that were necessary
for the creation of a sufficiently high head of water at the mouth of
the inlet to allow the fleet to leave its winter quarters for the river at
the proper time. However, while arguing went on between the power
agencies and the agencies of river transport, the level of water at the
mouth of the inlet remained low and the vessels wintering there began
operating late.

In this case, the Ministry of Inland Water Transport of the RSFSR
based its request for concentrated releases of water into the tailrace
of the Kuibyshevskoe reservoir on paragraph в of Article 18 of the
Statutes of Inland Water Transport, which specifies the obligation of
the owners of hydroelectric stations to release water from the reservoirs at times established by the agencies regulating navigation or
timber-floating. "Kuibyshev Power" and the Volga Hydroelectric Station refused to meet the request of the Ministry of Inland Water Transport of the RSFSR, referring to the Dispatching Rules for Flow Regulation, which do not provide for concentrated releases of water during
the period of spring high water; and a hydroelectric station does not
have the right to deviate from the Dispatching Rules for Flow Regulation. Each of the disputing parties was right in its own way. And it
would have been useless to try and settle the dispute on the basis of
the law, for the law itself is inconsistent in its regulation of the activities of river transport and the hydroelectric enterprises. Moreover,
the river transport agencies did not make any property claims on the
Volga Hydroelectric Station, although losses, due to the idle fleet,
were evident.

One of the most important responsibilities of the organizations in
charge of hydroelectric stations, dams, and other water-raising structures, is to ensure the unhindered and safe passage through the dams
of vessels and rafts, and, on timber-floating rivers, of loose logs
(paragraph 6 of Article 18 of the Statutes of Inland Water Transport).

However, the owners of dams frequently do not fulfill this responsibility either, imposing long delays on water transport vessels. At the large dams, where there are navigation locks and timber sluices which are under the jurisdiction of the agencies of navigation and timber-floating, the owners of the dams must maintain reservoir levels to guarantee the normal work of the facilities for shipping and passage of the timber. Meanwhile, it not infrequently occurs that, because of the low level of the reservoirs, the access of vessels into the locks and of timber into the timber passage facilities is impeded.

Associated with the responsibilities of the owners of the dams for the maintenance of the necessary levels for navigation and timber-floating are the responsibilities of the transport water users (the owners of vessels and rafts). These concern the observance of requirements for the safety of shipping and for the protection of hydrotechnical structures and the prevention of any hindrance to their operation. Transport water users in particular are obliged to observe the rules governing the operation of reservoirs and associated structures, and the instructions for the operation of individual hydroconstructions, which have been approved by the owners of the dams, and so on.

Since the inland shipping and timber-floating routes are frequently fisheries as well, the legislation includes a number of requirements to be observed by transport water users, in order to protect fish reserves and to ensure the necessary conditions for fishing and fish breeding.

Thus, the Regulations for the Protection of Fish and Control of Fishing in Waters of the USSR stipulate that those organizations responsible for the technical condition of the routes and transport water users, that wish to do blasting on inland waterways which are fisheries, must get advance authorization from the agencies of fish protection. If there is an urgent need to dredge in order to maintain navigation and timber-floating on parts of rivers which have become shallow, or to open up timber-floating rivers by force, or to carry out other operations in order to prevent accidents, blasting is permitted as an exception without the prior authorization of fish protection agencies, but these must be informed immediately.

In the case of inland waterways that are also fisheries, it is forbidden to deposit soil collected in the course of dredging and bottom-cleaning operations in the locality of spawning grounds and holes where the fish winter.

In accordance with the Regulations for Navigation on the Inland Waterways of the RSFSR, vessels and other floating structures must not go where fishing equipment has been established if these places are equipped with appropriate warning signs.

A number of the requirements applicable to transport water users in the interests of the fishing industry are specified in fishing regulations, which are approved by the Councils of Ministers of the Union

Republics and by other competent agencies, for the basins of individual rivers or of lake-river systems. These regulations prohibit
fishery and transport vessels to halt in areas closed to fishing. As
an exception, the stationing of vessels in such areas is permitted at
villages, in order to service signal devices and navigation installations, and also in cases of extreme need (such as storm, fog, accidents, and so on).

In their turn, the fishery organizations and enterprises, in using
fishery waters through which the inland waterways pass, must observe
the legal requirements that protect the interests of navigation and
timber-floating. In particular, they do not have the right to occupy
with their fishing equipment more than two-thirds of the width of a
river or arm of a river.

The legislation does not contain instructions on the permissibility
of setting up fishing equipment on shipping rivers in the shipping
channel, that is, in the area between the red and white buoys where
the regular movement of vessels occurs. It is quite clear, however,
that to set up fishing equipment in the shipping channels would
threaten the safety of navigation. The legislation should, therefore,
take a very definite stand on this question by introducing an uncon-
ditional prohibition of fishing equipment in the shipping channel during navigation.

The legislation does not contain direct instructions either on the
rights of the fishery organizations and enterprises to erect auxiliary
structures (for fishing and fish breeding) on the inland waterways.
However, this question may be settled in some cases under Article 17
of the Statutes of Inland Water Transport, which specifies that the
erection of structures on the inland waterways is permitted only with
the authorization of the agencies which regulate navigation and timber-
floating.[15]

---

15. In order to apply Article 17 of the Statutes of Inland Water
Transport in this case, it is essential that the concepts "fishing
equipment" and "fishing structures" be brought into proper correlation, since fishing equipment may be placed on the inland waterways
without the authorization of the agencies of navigation and timber-
floating, while structures may be erected only with the authorization
of these agencies. It is hardly possible to make a sharp distinction
between these concepts. It is well known that some structures (such
as certain trapping devices) are no more than fishing equipment.
Nevertheless, only structures which are set up for a short time and
are not permanently connected with the bottom of the water body or
the adjacent land can be regarded as fishing equipment permitted on
inland waterways without authorization from the agencies of navigation and timber-floating. Facilities, the foundations of which rest in
the soil and which are intended for continuous prolonged use, must
be considered as structures.

Conditions governing timber-floating are regulated in fair detail in the legislation, both in the interest of associating it correctly with the use of waterways for navigation, and in the interest of using the bodies of water for other purposes and for the protection of the water resources.

In order to avoid interference with shipping on the waterways, the legislation prohibits the floating of timber on shipping routes.

The Statutes of Inland Water Transport of the USSR (Article 15) mention that "the floating of timber, loose or in rafts, without a tow" is forbidden on shipping routes. This means, in fact, a complete prohibition of floating, for it is accepted that floating is the movement of timber, loose or in rafts, along the rivers by force of the current without the use of mechanical power.[16] If the timber moves with the assistance of a vessel, then this is not floating, but towing, which is not prohibited on shipping rivers.

Thus the floating of timber is permitted, in the main, only on timber-floating routes. "In the main," because in Articles 15 and 16 of the Statutes of Inland Water Transport there are legal norms which give grounds for supposing that the floating of timber is possible not only on floating routes, but on certain shipping routes, too.

The possibility of using a river for timber-floating sometimes depends on special conditions unconnected with navigation. Thus on some rivers, although they are not used for shipping, timber-floating is completely forbidden in order to protect the sources of water supply of large cities or industrial centers, or to protect the fish, or for other reasons. On certain timber-floating rivers where valuable species of fish (salmon and sturgeon) come to spawn, timber may be floated only in rafts, and the driving of loose logs is forbidden in order to preserve the conditions which are necessary for the fish to breed. In any case, rivers which provide spawning grounds for salmon and sturgeon may be used for the floating of timber only with the agreement of the agencies of fish protection.

Use of inland waterways for timber-floating is accompanied by pollution of the water with debris from the timber. In order to combat this our legislation specifies certain requirements, including the obligation of the timber-floating organizations to clear the river channels.

It is noteworthy that the Statutes of Inland Water Transport (Article 16) define the obligation of the timber-floating organizations to clear the river channels of debris from the timber only with regard to shipping routes, but they say nothing about whether these organizations are obliged to clear nonshipping, timber-floating rivers from sunken wood, bark, branches, and so on.

Long experience in the use of nonshipping rivers for timber-floating

---

16. M. E. Khodunov, *A Practical Commentary on the Statutes of Inland Water Transport* (Moscow: "River Transport" Publishing House, 1955), p. 37.

on a large scale has fully convinced the lawmakers that the pollution
of rivers with debris from timber-floating causes great damage not
only to the inland water transport but to the fishing industry as well,
impedes the operation of hydro structures, and pollutes sources of
water supply and waterside resorts. Therefore, it is necessary to
clear not only shipping rivers of sunken wood, bark, branches, and
so on, but all rivers on which timber is floated.

In this connection, in addition to the Statutes of Inland Water Transport of the USSR, the responsibilities of the timber-floating organizations for clearing river channels from debris are provided for on a
broader plane in the legislation.

Thus, the Regulations on the Protection of Fish and Control of Fishing in Waters of the USSR (Article 11), in the interest of preserving
conditions necessary for the spawning of valuable species of fish and
protecting the fish, forbids that chips, bark, sawdust, and other debris
created in logging, the making of rafts in winter, and the building of
structures for the floating of timber, be thrown into fishery waters or
left on the ice and submerged banks of these waters. When timber is
floated in unpeeled form, the timber-floating organizations are obliged,
by order of the agencies of fish protection, to clear the bottoms of
water bodies from bark and sunken logs in places where the salmon
and sturgeon spawn and along the approaches to them. If the timber-
floating organizations build booms on the rivers with barriers, and
other temporary devices necessary for the floating of timber, they
must not take up more than two-thirds of the active section of the
river with these devices and, at the end of the timber-floating operations, remove them.

Obligations to clear rivers from the debris of timber-floating are
frequently stipulated in separate legislative acts of the USSR and
Union Republics concerning the regulation of the use of the natural
resources of different geographic regions.

The decree of the Council of Ministers of the RSFSR of 9 May 1960,
"On the Protection and Use of the Natural Wealth in the Lake Baikal
Basin,"[17] contains norms which obligate the economic agencies of the
Buryat Autonomous Republic and the Irkutskaya Oblast each year to
clear the river channels from sunken wood.

Nevertheless, our legislation has no universal norm on the obligations of the timber-floating organizations to clear completely all
timber-floating rivers from sunken wood and other debris from the
floating of timber. As a result the legal norms in this field are not
uniform and not sufficiently effective in practice. Frequently the
timber-floating organizations avoid with impunity clearing the channels of shipping rivers from sunken wood and other debris. Since this

---

17. *Collected Decrees of the RSFSR*, 1960, No. 22, Article 92.

goes on from year to year, timber-floating rivers are filling up with
wood and the debris of timber-floating and are gradually becoming unsuitable for use, not only for navigation and other purposes, but for
the floating of timber as well.[18]

A very serious shortcoming of the legislation regulating the use of
rivers and other bodies of water for timber-floating has been the absence of a system of requirements aimed at preventing the pollution
of rivers with the debris of timber and, above all, preventing the loss
of wood during floating. As a result, the timber-floating organizations
have not bothered either to protect the timber or preserve the rivers
from pollution.[19]

The Regulations for the Preparation and Authorization of Timber for
Floating,[20] put into force on 1 July 1964, provide measures aimed at
preserving the timber and reducing losses during floating. Norms for
losses of floated timber, aside from deterioration, were reviewed and
reaffirmed by the Council of Ministers of the RSFSR. In particular,
the driving of loose logs of leaf-bearing tree species and of larch
(which are most subject to losses in floating) was strictly standardized. The driving of logs of leaf-bearing tree species is permitted as
a rule after biological drying (that is, timber laid in during the summer), or after air-drying with the obligatory sealing of the butt ends
of the logs with water-insulating materials.

However, with the authorization of the economic agencies, the
driving of logs of commercial leaf-bearing trees may be permitted as
an exception when the timber is assembled in the autumn/winter season and has been felled before the sap has begun to flow. In addition,
the decision whether or not to permit driving of loose logs in specific
cases is determined only by the economic expediency of this or other
forms of timber-floating, without consideration for the interests of
other branches of the economy and other water users. There are

---

18. For example, the newspaper *Pravda Severa* of 21 December
1962 reported: "If twenty years ago the rivers Mezen', Vaga, Pinega,
and Emtsa were navigable, today they are so shallow that they are
suitable for navigation only in spring and fall, since the bottom of
these rivers is covered with logs."

19. In 1960 timber-floating organizations lost about three million
cubic meters of wood in floating operations and recovered not more
than 20 percent of this loss from the river bottoms. In 1963 the situation improved. More wood was recovered from the river bottoms than
was lost in floating during the year. However, it is still necessary to
do much work in order to clear the channels of timber-floating rivers
from many years' accumulation of sunken timber.

20. See the *Regulations for the Preparation and Authorization
of Timber for Floating* (Moscow, 1964).

grounds for fear that, under such a procedure for deciding whether to
permit driving of logs, the necessary guarantees will not be provided
for the observance of the principle of complex use of water resources,
and certain branches of the economy will be damaged, particularly the
fishing industry.

Considering the extraordinary lack of coordination in the legislation on the use of waterways for the floating of timber, the narrow
bureaucratic character of the different legislative norms, and also,
associated with this, the unfavorable situation regarding the protection of timber-floating rivers from pollution by sunken wood and other
debris, the adoption of urgent measures to put this legislation in order
must be recognized to be necessary, without waiting for the Principles
of the Law on Water Use of the USSR and Union Republics and of republic water codes to be issued. As one such urgent measure a specialized legislative act might be passed—Regulations on Timber-
floating on the Inland Waterways of the USSR—which would need to
specify all the requirements for ensuring the fullest and most rational
use of bodies of water for timber-floating in conjunction with their
use for other needs in the national economy.

3. Use of Water for Fish-breeding and Fishing

Along with the use of rivers, lakes, inland seas, reservoirs, and
other bodies of water in the USSR for agricultural, industrial, hydroelectric, and other needs of the national economy and of the people,
there is the use of the vast majority of these waters by enterprises,
organizations, and private citizens for fish-breeding and fishing.

All bodies of water (the territorial waters of the USSR, inland seas,
rivers, lakes, ponds, reservoirs, and their adjoining waters) which are
used, or can be used, for the commercial harvesting of fish and other
aquatic animals and plants, or which are important for the propagation
of commercial fish, are considered to be fishery* waters.

The Soviet Union has an abundance of fishery waters. Besides the
territorial waters and inland seas it has forty-six river systems (the
total length of which exceeds 3 million kilometers), about a hundred
reservoirs of hydroelectric stations (with a total area of approximately
4 million hectares), numerous lakes (with an area of more than 25 mil-

---

*The term *fishery* as used here is the translation of the adjective
rybokhozyaistvennyi, from *rybnoe khozyaistvo*, which is a branch of
the national economy devoted to the harvesting, developing, reproduction, and increase of stocks of fish, and sometimes of other water
organisms, and includes commercial fishing, amateur and sport fishing, and fish-breeding.

lion hectares), and ponds (with a total area, according to tentative
data, of more than 350 to 400 thousand hectares).[21] About 18 percent
of the total annual catch of fish on an average is taken from the inland seas and lakes and rivers.[22] Tens of millions of Soviet citizens
spend their leisure time fishing. Consequently, the use of bodies of
water for fishing plays an important role both in the national economy
and directly in the life of the people.

In fishing and activities associated with the fish industry, there
are at least two natural objects in use at the same time by enterprises
or citizens—the water resources of the bodies of water and the fish
in them. However, juridically the use of these natural objects does
not coincide. In relations of fishing and fish-breeding, the principal
object of use is the fish. Use of the water resources occurs by way
of necessity, since water is the environment in which the fish live
and from which they are taken. Water use is hence conditioned by
the right to the use of the fish resources. Enterprises, institutions,
organizations, and citizens who do not have the right to use of the
fish resources do not have the right either to use of the water for fishing and fish-breeding.

In accord with the fact that in relations of fishing and fish-breeding
the fish and the water resources appear as juridically different objects
of use, there exist different groups of legal norms—those which regulate the method and conditions of using the fish resources and those
which regulate the use of the water for fishing and fish-breeding. The
first group of norms lies outside the sphere of the law of water use
and is studied in this work only insofar as it is associated with water
use. The second group of norms is a component part of the institution
of the law of water use and therefore comes within the scope of the
present work.

The principal legislative act, regulating use of the fishery waters
of the USSR and containing norms on the use of waters for fishing and
fish-breeding, is the Regulations for the Protection of Fish and Control
of Fishing in Waters of the USSR, which were approved by the decree
of the Council of Ministers of the USSR of 15 September 1958.[23] Together, and in accord with these regulations, the use of fishery waters
is regulated by separate decrees of the Council of Ministers of the
USSR, by laws and sublegislative acts of the Union Republics, by
fishing regulations approved by the former Ministry of Fisheries of

---

21. See *The Natural Resources of the Soviet Union, Their Use
and Renewal* (Moscow: Publishing House of the Academy of Sciences
of the USSR, 1963), pp. 230—231.

22. Ibid., p. 219. About 82 percent of the total average annual
catch of fish in the USSR comes from the oceans and open seas.

23. *Collected Decrees of the USSR*, 1958, No. 16, Article 127.

the USSR, by the State Planning Committee of the USSR and the
Councils of Ministers of Union Republics, and also by rules and instructions issued by the state management agencies of the fish industry and by ordinances of the local Councils of Workers' Deputies
and their executive committees. The use of water for fishing and fish-
breeding is regulated to a certain extent by rules and instructions
issued by public organizations to which fishery waters are assigned
for permanent use.

There are two types of fishing, commercial and amateur (including
sport), depending on their purpose and economic significance.

Commercial fishing is carried out in order to create state or public
supplies of fish products, as a rule in fulfillment of plans for the national economy. Commercial fishing is characterized by the use of
quantity harvesting equipment (nets, seines, trawls, and so on), and
the catch is usually distributed to state storage centers—fish-
processing plants.

The right to commercial fishing in bodies of water in the USSR belongs to enterprises of the fish industry and to collective fisheries,
which are the main fish purveyors, and also to consumer cooperatives
and other organizations.

Amateur fishing serves mainly to provide recreation for citizens,
and therefore implies fishing in small quantities for personal consumption. Amateur fishermen are permitted to use only the kind of equipment that develops sporting practices and skills in fishing. The sale
of fish caught by amateur fishermen is not permitted in any republic,
with the exception of the RSFSR.[24]

The right to amateur fishing belongs to all workers (Article 6 of the
Regulations for the Protection of Fish and Control of Fishing in Waters
of the USSR).

The use of fishery waters for commercial fishing is in most cases
carried out in commercial fishery sections, which are granted in free
and permanent use to the fishery enterprises.

In accordance with Article 4 of the Regulations for the Protection of
Fish and Control of Fishing in Waters of the USSR, commercial fishery
sections are allocated for use through contracts which are concluded
between the territorial agencies of fish protection and the fishery enterprises.[25] Fisheries are in the first instance granted for use to state

---

24. By the decree of the Council of Ministers of the RSFSR of 24
November 1964 (*Collected Decrees of the RSFSR*, 1964, No. 21, Article 149), citizens are permitted to sell fish that have been caught
in compliance with the established fishing regulations.

25. The model form of agreement was approved by the Chief State
Fishery Waters Administration [*Glavgosrybvod*] of the RSFSR on 31
March 1961.

fishery enterprises and to collective fisheries which supply fish to state enterprises, and, secondly, to other fish purveying organizations.

The contract for the use of fisheries contains the mutual obligations of the fish protection agency and the fish purveying enterprise regarding the conditions and procedure for rational use of the body of water (or part of it) and the fish, aquatic animals, and plants in it.

Under the contract, the territorial agency of fish protection allocates, and the fish purveying enterprise, which in the contract is referred to briefly as the fish purveyor, receives, in free and indefinite use, a fishery section which is designated by name and number. The exact restrictions and boundaries of the fishery are indicated in a certificate which accompanies the contract. Its actual boundaries are marked by the fish purveyor in the presence of, and according to the instructions of, a representative of the agency of fish protection.

The fish purveyor accepts the responsibility to make full use of the fishery allotted to it, and only with the fishing equipment intended for that particular fishery. It does not have the right to transfer the fishery to other organizations without the agreement of the agency of fish protection, and, obviously, does not have the right to invite other organizations to use the fishery on a sharing basis or on other conditions. If the fish purveyor is not able to manage the fishery on its own, it should relinquish its use and return it to the agency of fish protection. At the same time, it does not have the right to prevent private citizens from fishing in the area for personal consumption with equipment and methods permitted by the fishing regulations.

The fish purveyor does not have the right without the authorization of the agency of fish protection to undertake any work on the fishery, or to erect structures or facilities, which would change the natural conditions of the body of water.

The agency of fish protection has the right to control use of the fishery by the fish purveyor-user. If the fish purveyor persistently violates the Regulations for the Protection of Fish and Control of Fishing in Waters of the USSR, or the Fishing Regulations, or does not abide by the contract for the use of the fishery, including not using the area fully, then the contract may be cancelled by order of the agency of fish protection.[26]

---

26. The model form of agreement on the allocation of a fishery, which was approved by the People's Commissariat of the Fishing Industry of the USSR on 2 December 1939, envisaged a judicial procedure for dissolving the contract. In the existing model form of agreement, it says that the contract may be dissolved in the prescribed way, but prior to dissolution its implementation may be suspended by the fish protection inspection. However, the procedure for dissolution of the contract is not actually established.

Although the contract for the use of the fishery sets out the mutual obligations of the agency of fish protection and the fishery enterprise, it is not a contract under civil law but is a type of land law (in the broad sense of the word) contract. It is possible to put forward at least two arguments in support of such an interpretation of the legal nature of the contract.

First, the heart of the contract is the agreement on the transfer for use of a fishery, which is a water area and a natural object. Relations concerning natural objects do not come under civil law (Article 2 of the Principles of Civil Law of the USSR and Union Republics).

The commercial fisheries come under the law of exclusive ownership of the Soviet State and are under the general direction of the agencies of fish protection, but not in their ownership and not under their operative management. Therefore, in allocating a fishery for use, the agency of fish protection is not exercising civil authority, which in respect to the fishery it does not have, but authority of general administration.

Second, the rights and obligations of the parties to the contract for the use of the fishery represent only the mutual rights and obligations of the agencies of fish protection and the fishery water users, established directly by the law with regard to a specific object and based on the administrative subordination of one party to the other. Thus, a fishery enterprise which has the use of a commercial fishery is obliged, with its own means and at its own expense, to maintain the area, not only because of the terms of the contract but, independently of it, because of a direct order of the law—Article 10 of the Regulations for the Protection of Fish and Control of Fishing in Waters of the USSR. Irrespective of the agreement of the parties, the law establishes the obligation of the fishery enterprise to obey the orders of the agency of fish protection regarding clearing the hauls, drifts, and other localities where fishing operations are carried out, undertaking fish-breeding and land improvement measures, and so on. Also, irrespective of the contract, the agency of fish protection has the authority under the law to direct and inspect arrangements for proper use of the fisheries.

In this way, the contract for use of a commercial fishery is in fact not a transaction under civil law but a form of organization for the interaction of the state agencies, which administer the use of fishery waters, with the fishery enterprises, which use these waters. The contract here is a way of defining specifically the obligations of the fishery water users before the state and at the same time an additional means for the agency of fish protection to exercise its administrative authority.

In accordance with Article 4 of the Regulations for the Protection of Fish and Control of Fishing in Waters of the USSR, for each fishery a set form of certificate is drawn up, which accompanies the contract for use of the fishery. The certificate contains a diagram of the section, a description of it and of its location and fishery characteristics, and information on the yearly catch of fish.

The description of the fishery gives its location, the boundaries and dimensions of the water area, the type of body of water, the quality of the bottom and banks, and times of freezing and spring high water. If the area includes several bodies of water, these are listed (with the names of the rivers, lakes and streams, and so on). In addition, information is given on any water intake or other hydrotechnical structures in the area, as well as information concerning pollution from the sewage of industrial enterprises, centers of population, timber-floating debris, and so on.

The description of the fishery gives the condition of the fishery resources—a list of the food fish and other harvestable products, information on spawning, hatching of young, fish-kills, and so on. It also indicates what fish-breeding and land improvement work should be undertaken in the fishery, what fishing equipment is permitted and in what quantity, and how many permanent fishing localities (hauls, drifts, and so on) there are. The fish processing plant, to which the fish and other products which are harvested in the area should be sent, is also indicated here.

The purpose of this certificate, as an appendix to the contract, is to help organize the rational use of the water wealth and fish resources in the fishery. A single copy of the certificate is drawn up, and it is signed by an inspector of fish protection and a representative of the fishery organization. Subsequently, the fishery organization notes in the certificate the yearly catch (according to species) and the average number of fishermen operating in the area.

The contract for use of the fishery is concluded only between the agencies of fish protection and the enterprises (organizations) which do the fishing. If fishery locations are assigned which lie within zones allotted for transport and hydrotechnical constructions, railway bridges, commercial and military docks, ports, ship building and ship repair yards, fortified areas, military camps and reserves, the contract must have the concurrence of the organizations that have the use of these zones.

The fisheries may be used without contracts for amateur fishing or for scientific collecting of aquatic animals and plants. Amateur fishermen must observe the fishing regulations but do not need special authorization from the agencies of fish protection or the fishery organizations which have the use of the areas; and scientific research institutions may take fish and other aquatic animals and plants for research purposes in all fishery waters and with any equipment, in agreement with the agencies of fish protection. The agreement of the agencies of fish protection is expressed in a document authorizing fishing for research purposes, which is issued to each scientific research vessel.

The contractual form of relations governing the use of waters for commercial fishing applies only to the use of the fisheries. The fish and other aquatic animals and plants in fishery waters outside the boundaries of offshore commercial fisheries are harvested by enterprises, collective farms, and organizations with permits which are issued by the agencies of fish protection for each vessel or commercial fishing device.

A feature of the use of fishery waters outside the commercial fisheries is that the body of water is not assigned to any one subject but is in general use. But here the right to fish commercially is conditional upon the acquisition of a fishing permit from the agency of fish protection. This is necessary in order to maintain control over the amount of use of the body of water for fishing. By issuing permits the agency of fish protection is able to secure a relatively balanced (in proportion to the supply of fish) use of bodies of water for fishing: overfishing, which upsets normal conditions for conservation and propagation of the fish, is avoided and yet the body of water is not left unexploited.

Unlike commercial fishing, amateur fishing is permitted for all workers in all bodies of water, both in the designated fisheries and outside of them, with the exception of areas which are set aside as reserves, fish hatcheries, pond, and other cultivated fish farms. Other limitations on amateur fishing are specified in the legislation of the Union Republics.

For example, in accordance with Article 8 of the Regulations on Fishing in the Belorussian SSR, which were approved by the decree of the Council of Ministers of the Belorussian Republic of 6 April 1962,[27] amateur fishing is forbidden in bodies of water (ponds, canals, rivers) which are on the territory of pond fish farms, fish hatcheries and reserves, and in bodies of water where work is being carried out on the adaptation of new kinds of fish, and where seine nets are being used and in places where stationary fishing equipment has been set up.

The Regulations on Fishing in the White Sea Basin, which were approved by the decree of the Council of Ministers of the RSFSR of 3 January 1960,[28] prohibits amateur fishing not only in reserves and bodies of water of cultivated fish farms but also in rivers where salmon spawn.

The Regulations on Fishing in Fishery Waters of the Central Oblasts of the RSFSR, which were approved by the decree of the Council of Ministers of the RSFSR of 14 May 1960,[29] preclude amateur fishing on lakes which are suitable for the breeding of marketable carp.

---

27. *Protection of Nature—A National Matter* (Minsk, 1962), p. 108.

28. *Collected Decrees of the RSFSR*, 1960, No. 1, Article 1.

29. Ibid., 1960, No. 19, Article 86.

The legislative acts of the Union Republics concerned with the regulation of fishing do not permit amateur fishing closer than 500 meters from dams, locks, bridges, and other structures on the water or between the abutments and cribs of bridges.

In connection with the increasing interest of the public in amateur fishing, and in order to encourage various forms of organized amateur (sport) fishing, the legislation specifies that the agencies of fish protection may allot bodies of water or individual sections for these purposes.

Bodies of water for organized amateur fishing are selected and granted for use (assigned, registered) to public workers' organizations— to associations of voluntary societies of hunters and fishermen, "Dinamo," branches of the All-Army Military Hunting Society, and others. As a rule a body of water is assigned for amateur fishing as a result of an application from the interested organization. A decision on the application is taken by the agency of fish protection, both in accordance with its own judgment in exercise of its right and on the basis of an action of the executive committee of the local Council of Workers' Deputies. But in all cases a contract is drawn up between the agency of fish protection and the public organization, for use of the body of water which is assigned for sport fishing.

This contract is basically similar to the contract for use of a commercial fishery in that it sets out the rights and obligations of the parties. But since the purposes for which a commercial fishery and a body of water for amateur fishing are used are different, the contract for the use of a body of water for amateur fishing has its own features which are expressed chiefly in an expansion of the range of rights and obligations of the user.

Thus, the contract for the allotment to the Moscow voluntary society "Fisher-Sportsman" of areas in the Klyaz'minskoe, Pyalovskoe, and Pestovskoe reservoirs specifies, besides the general conditions governing the use of fishery waters, the right of the user to open four sport-fishing bases with a total of 550 boats on the allotted areas. The society does not have the right to open new bases or to increase the number of boats in the areas beyond what has been stipulated by the contract. In addition, the society does not have the right to prevent citizens who are not members of the society "Fisher-Sportsman" from fishing in the areas of the reservoirs allocated to the society, if these citizens are not breaking the fishing regulations.

Under the contract the society is obliged to share with other water users in the financing of work connected with the fishing which is carried out on the reservoirs, to provide the necessary number of inspectors of fish protection from the society and to organize their work, to undertake to provide information to the amateur fishermen, including issuing posters and slogans on themes agreed upon with the fish protection inspection.

In another case, the contract for the use of an area for amateur fishing stipulated the responsibility of the user to see that sport fishing is correctly carried out by society members who have access to the area by means of a society pass. The contract also specified the obligation of the user to keep an account of the fish caught by the amateur fishermen.

In this way, the contract for the assignment of a water area for amateur fishing defines both the general conditions governing the use of a fishery water and special requirements which are made in order to ensure organized (rather than disorganized) fishing and to prevent poaching.

While the Regulations for the Protection of Fish and Control of Fishing in Waters of the USSR give the agencies of fish protection the right to allocate bodies of water or sections of them for amateur fishing, they do not indicate for what period water areas may be granted for this purpose. In practice bodies of water are allocated both for permanent use and for a more or less extended period (usually not less than five years). It is possible to concur with this. However, to improve the law and the use of fishery waters, it should be established that an organization which has a contract for the use of an area for amateur fishing for a certain period and which fully carries out the conditions of the contract should, when the contract expires, have preference in acquiring the area for the next period. It is necessary to define the conditions under which the contract may be canceled before expiration of the contract (by withdrawal of the area from use), and also the procedure for premature cancellation of the contract and transfer of the area.

The use of waters for the propagation of marketable fish in collective, state, and subsidiary farms, fish farms, and other fish-breeding enterprises, as distinct from water use for commercial and amateur fishing, has a number of important characteristics.

For marketable fish production, small lakes and ponds are primarily employed which are in the exclusive use of individual farms. Collective and state farms, fish farms, and fish production enterprises, by their own efforts and means, breed fish in these bodies of water, obtaining either fertilizer or a marketable fish product. Fish artificially produced in these bodies of water cannot be considered as a natural object and have nothing to do with the fish reserves of the USSR, but are the property of these farms (or state property under the operative management of the farms) and are considered to be a product in the course of production. For this reason commercial and amateur fishing are not permitted in such bodies of water. The right to harvest and appropriate fish artificially produced here belongs only to the farms— the users of these bodies of water.

The artificial propagation of fish in the bodies of water of collective and state farms, subsidiary farms, fish farms, and other fish-breeding enterprises is a highly profitable branch of the economy and is encouraged in every possible way in our country. The decrees of the Central Committee of the Communist Party of the Soviet Union and of the Soviet Government repeatedly emphasize the great importance of pond fish culture for the national economy. They recommend that local bodies of water be used for fish-breeding and that ponds and small reservoirs be constructed on small rivers, ravines, and gullies; and they provide measures to assist collective and state farms and state fishery enterprises to develop pond fish culture. However, insufficient attention has been given to the development of legislation to regulate the method of creating and using bodies of water for artificial fish culture. Water use relations associated with fish-breeding are not sufficiently regulated either in union or republic legislation and there are, therefore, serious shortcomings in the use of water resources for marketable pond fish farming.

Thus, the decree of the Council of Ministers of the RSFSR of 8 May 1956, "On the Development of State and Collective Farm Pond Fish Culture in the RSFSR," specifies the assistance and work necessary to develop artificial fish culture but does not regulate the relationships of water use which arise in connection with it.[30] Paragraph 5 of this decree establishes the obligation of republic fishery agencies to undertake planning research work for the construction of fish hatcheries and fish-breeding ponds. In establishing this obligation, the Council of Ministers of the RSFSR evidently assumed that the construction of fish-breeding ponds can only be carried out in accordance with plans. However, in fact such a requirement is not specifically stipulated by the law and is therefore not always observed. Many farms, especially collective farms, considering planning research work to be costly and not obligatory, construct fish-breeding ponds without plans and without preliminary research.

The question of the rights of collective and state farms, fish farms, and other concerns to construct ponds and use small bodies of water on their land is not settled in the existing legislation (in most Union Republics there are no legal instructions on these questions). The opinion is widely held that collective and state farms, fish farms, and other concerns, as land users, have the right, at their own discretion and without any permission of the state agencies, to construct ponds and use them and other small bodies of water on their land. Such a

---

30. See *Chronological Collection of Laws and Edicts of the Presidium of the Supreme Soviet and Decrees of the Government of the RSFSR* (Moscow: State Juridical Publishing House, 1959), Vol. 5, p. 444. See also the decree of the Council of Ministers of the Kazakh SSR of 6 April 1959, "On the Development of the Fish Industry on Collective and State Farms of the Kazakh SSR," in *Reference Book of the Soviet Worker* (Alma Ata, 1962), p. 329.

view is not in accord with the general legal requirements of principle (in any case with regard to the Russian Federation).

In the RSFSR there are Provisional Regulations on the Construction, Reconstruction, and Maintenance of Dams on a Small River Network, which were approved by decree of the All-Russian Central Executive Committee and Council of Peoples' Commissars of the RSFSF of 12 July 1926.[31] They specify that such structures on a small river network (that is, dams which form ponds and small reservoirs) be constructed and reconstructed by the farms concerned, with the permission of the executive committees of oblast and territorial Councils of Workers' Deputies and the Councils of Ministers of Autonomous Republics. Although the Provisional Regulations are out of date to a certain extent, they have not been abolished. Therefore, it cannot be considered that authorization of the competent state agencies (currently, the oblast, territorial, and republic Departments of Water Management) is not required for the construction of small dams and ponds on the lands of collective, state, and other farms.

The unsystematic, unplanned construction of fish-breeding ponds on collective state, and other farms not only runs counter to the law but frequently does damage to the farms themselves and to the whole development of pond fish culture.

The state farm "Novolikeev" in the Gor'kovskaya Oblast in 1947 constructed a system of fish-breeding ponds on a small river, where it developed a highly profitable cultivated fish industry.

In 1960 the neighboring state farm "Komintern," which lay upstream on the same river, constructed a pond on it for breeding water fowl and watering cabbages. After this pond had been built, the supply of fresh water to the fish-breeding ponds of the "Novolikeev" state farm ceased, as a consequence of which it was forced to give up fish farming and suffered losses. No one was able to settle properly the dispute which arose between the two farms, since the legislation does not contain the necessary instructions on this question, and modern practice permits the construction of ponds by every farm at its own discretion.

In some Union Republics, in particular in the Moldavian and Kirghiz Republics, there are special legislative acts governing the use of local bodies of water by collective, state, and other farms. The experience of these Republics in this regard is of great interest.

The Regulations on the Use of Bodies of Water of Collective, State, and Subsidiary Farms of the Moldavian Republic, which were approved by the decree of the Council of Ministers of the Moldavian Republic of 30 July 1959,[32] apply to ponds on the lands of these farms which

---

31. *Collected Edicts of the RSFSR*, 1926, No. 47, Article 356.
32. *Collected Laws of the Moldavian SSR*, 1959, No. 7, Article 134.

are used for fishery purposes and also to natural bodies of water of local significance (lakes, rivers, and streams) which are not important for commercial fishing and the reproduction of stocks of food fish.

Collective, state, and subsidiary farms, in whose use are ponds and natural fishery waters and also bodies of water of hydroelectric stations and mills, are obliged by their own efforts and with their own means to carry out very simple measures concerned with fish-breeding and land improvement. The plans for these measures are approved by the executive committees of district Councils of Workers' Deputies and are checked by the local agricultural agencies. Pond and other cultivated fish enterprises of collective, state, and subsidiary farms are operated in agreement with and under the supervision of agricultural agencies. This includes the establishment of fishing seasons, the release of water and filling of bodies of water, stocking with fish, periodical draining of the ponds, and the implementation of other sanitation measures. Amateur fishing is forbidden with any equipment, including rods, on cultivated fish farms.

It is forbidden to release into bodies of water and to remove from them for breeding purposes the young and eggs of fish without the permission of the agencies of veterinary inspection. It is also forbidden to pollute fishery waters. This includes a prohibition on the retting of flax, hemp, bast, or leather, the soaking and washing of wine barrels and containers for solutions used in spraying and pollinating woods, gardens, vineyards, and market gardens.

The withdrawal of water from the fishery waters of collective, state, and subsidiary farms, for the needs of industry and communal enterprises and for irrigation, may take place only if special devices are installed to prevent the fish from falling into the water intake structures.

Collective, state, and subsidiary farms may construct new and reconstruct old ponds and other bodies of water only in accordance with design specifications. These must cover the development of the body of water for fishery purposes, and in particular the layout of its bed, the construction of groundwater outlets, the reinforcement of dams, planting the banks with protective forest and orchard belts ten to twenty meters wide, and, in addition, for undrained bodies of water, clearing the hauling areas.

In the Kirghiz Republic, the Regulations on the Use of Bodies of Water of State and Subsidiary Farms, Fish Farms, and Hatcheries are in force, which were approved by the decree of the Council of Ministers of the Republic of 4 November 1959[33] and which apply both to

----

33. See *Records of the Supreme Soviet and Government of the Kirghiz Soviet Socialist Republic*, 1959, No. 28(95), Article 234.

artificially created bodies of water and to lakes, rivers, and other natural water bodies which are on the lands of these farms. These regulations apparently do not apply to bodies of water on collective farms.
The use of bodies of water on collective farms in the Kirghiz Republic,
as in other Union Republics, is not sufficiently regulated.

In accordance with the regulations, the bodies of water of state
and subsidiary farms, fish farms, and fish hatcheries are used for fish-
breeding only by these farms. The farms may forbid outsiders to be in
the area adjoining the fish-breeding waters and to have buildings in
this area. It is forbidden to discharge sewage, irrigation water, wastes
of industrial enterprises, refuse and rubbish, sewage from stock fat-
tening grounds and livestock farms into the water-supply systems and
directly into the fishery waters. It is also forbidden to swim or boat,
to launder linen, wash machinery, to keep privately owned waterfowl,
to pasture or drive cattle and fowl along the dams and banks of the
fishery waters, and similarly to do anything which might damage the
hydrotechnical structures and the dams of the ponds, or to cause the
water level to drop or the fish to die.

In this way there is a legal system governing fishery waters in the
Moldavian and Kirghiz Republics which provides favorable conditions
for the development of marketable pond fish culture and protects the
interests of the farms which engage in this activity. It is necessary
to use the experience of these Republics in order to improve further
the legislation on the use for fishery purposes of small bodies of water, especially when working out the water codes of the Union Republics.

4. Water Use for Sport and Health Improvement Needs of the People

Water sports and recreation on the water are very popular in our
country. The many opportunities for using natural bodies of water for
sport and health improvement needs of the public are protected by law.

Citizens of the USSR, at any time and as they wish, without special
permission from state agencies, have the right to swim and use boats
and other simple craft on all natural bodies of water, except in certain
areas where swimming and boating are completely forbidden or restricted.

Places where swimming and boating are forbidden are determined by
the competent state agencies and publicized accordingly in the interests of public safety, protection of the lives and health of the citizens
themselves, as well as for industrial and other reasons—such as to
ensure the uninterrupted work of transport in navigation channels, at
moorings and roads, and to guarantee the normal functioning of dams
and fords and water intake and other structures. In some cases, areas

which are closed to swimming and boating are specifically stipulated in legislative acts of the Union Republics. Thus, the Regulations on the Use of Bodies of Water of State and Subsidiary Farms, Fish Farms, and Hatcheries, which were approved by the decree of the Council of Ministers of the Kirghiz SSR of 4 November 1959,[34] prohibit swimming and boating in fish-breeding ponds, reservoirs, lakes, and rivers which have been stocked with fish and are on the lands of state and subsidiary farms, fish farms, and hatcheries.

According to the decree of the Central Executive Committee and Council of People's Commissars of the USSR of 17 May 1937, "On the Sanitary Protection of Water Mains and Sources of Water Supply,"[35] it is completely forbidden to swim within the first belt of zones of sanitary protection of sources of water supply.

In those areas where it is not forbidden to swim and boat, citizens must observe certain rules which are designed to protect their lives and health and to prevent interference in the activities of other water users. Thus, according to Section 12, paragraph к of the Regulations for Navigation on the Inland Waterways of the RSFSR, rowing and motorboats, launches, and sporting yachts are categorically forbidden to approach transport vessels and cut across their path.

The use of bodies of water for sport and health improvement needs frequently occurs in organized forms through sporting and cultural-health improvement organizations, holiday homes, and sanitoria. In places which are most suitable for mass recreation and are frequently visited by the public, and in areas of health and summer resorts, bodies of water or sections of them are set aside and appropriately equipped and adapted for large-scale bathing, relaxation, and sport.

Bodies of water or water areas are set aside for the construction of bathhouses, boat stations, and water stadiums by ordinances of the executive committees of local Councils, in compliance with applications from the interested organizations and with the agreement of the agencies of state sanitary supervision, water transport, and others.

The procedure for building and operating bathhouses and water sports facilities, and for use of water bodies, is regulated by Union Republic legislation, by ordinances of the local Councils of Workers' Deputies, and by departmental normative acts.

In compliance with the Sanitary Regulations for the Development and Maintenance of Beaches and Bathing Areas, which were approved by the All-Union State Sanitary Inspection on 26 June 1944,[36] the cre-

---

34. Ibid.

35. *Collected Laws of the USSR*, 1937, No. 35, Article 143.

36. See *The Hygiene of Centers of Population* (a collection of official materials) (Moscow: State Publishing House of Medical Literature, 1962), p. 189.

ation of beaches and bathing areas is permitted after a preliminary
survey of the water bodies has been made, and if a favorable decision
is reached by the local agency of state sanitary supervision. The
size of the water area set aside for bathing is determined in accordance with local conditions and the sanitary standard of one and one-
half to three cubic meters of water per bather.

Bathing places must be located outside areas where sewage is discharged and away from port facilities, coal piers, oil loading facilities,
and so on, but at the same time they must not serve as sources of pollution of water which is used for a drinking water supply.

In order to protect the favorable properties and natural therapeutic
qualities of health resorts and therapeutic areas of beaches, the shore-
lines of seas and other bodies of water in resort areas are included
in the districts of sanitary protection which are formed in accordance
with the Regulations on the Sanitary Protection of Health Resorts and
Areas of Medicinal Importance, approved by the decree of the Council
of People's Commissars of the USSR of 10 April 1940.[37]

The procedure for the use by the public of bathhouses, boat stations,
and water stadiums is defined by regulations issued by the executive
committees of local Councils. The water users, that is, the organizations to whom the bodies of water (or water areas) are assigned for
the recreation of workers, are obliged to ensure the observance of
these regulations and of the legislation governing water use for sport
and health improvement purposes.

The Council of Ministers of the RSFSR, by its decree of 20 February
1957, "On Measures to Safeguard Human Lives on Rivers, Lakes, and
Seacoasts,"[38] obligated physical culture, economic, and other organizations which use water sport facilities and waterways in their activities, to organize at their own expense lifeguard stations in the areas
under their authority.

In compliance with an ordinance of the executive committee of the
Moscow Oblast Council of Workers' Deputies of 25 April 1962, and
with similar ordinances of the executive committees of Councils of
Workers' Deputies of other oblasts and territories, economic, sporting,
and public organizations, including pioneer camps, sanitoria, and holiday homes, which undertake large-scale physical culture activities on
the water (contests, festivities, regattas, boating, and so on), are
themselves obliged to organize lifeguard stations for the duration of
these activities.

_____

37. *Collected Decrees of the USSR*, 1940, No. 12, Article 289.
38. See *Chronological Collection of Laws and Edicts of the Presidium of the Supreme Soviet and Decrees of the Government of the
RSFSR*, Vol. 6, p. 63.

Chapter 4

The Legal Regulation of the Discharge into Bodies of Water of Sewage, Industrial, and Domestic Wastes

1. *General Conditions and Requirements*

Seas, lakes, and other bodies of water have for a long time been used for the disposal of industrial and domestic wastes.

In the past, when there was a low level of industrial development, such use of water bodies did not threaten society with dangerous consequences and did not require general regulation. But with industrialization, the discharge of industrial and domestic wastes into bodies of water has increased and a large quantity of substances enters the water, which cannot assimilate them. The pollution of water has begun to threaten public health, and the supply of high quality water to the population has deteriorated. One of the most difficult problems of modern water resource management has arisen—the problem of protecting bodies of water from pollution by domestic and industrial wastes.

Of particular importance is the protection of bodies of water from pollution by sewage from industrial enterprises and cities.

In our country, considerable attention has been given since the early years of Soviet power to the sanitary protection of water resources and to the regulation of the discharge into bodies of water of sewage and industrial and domestic wastes. Even during the Civil War the Supreme Council of National Economy on 20 February 1919 adopted the decree "On the Central Committee on Water Conservation,"[1]

---

1. *Collected Statutes of the RSFSR*, 1919, No. 4, Article 45.

which specified the establishment of a special state agency for the protection of water resources—the Central Committee on Water Conservation—which was designed to protect bodies of water from pollution and to work out measures to combat the harm which is caused by the sewage of factories, mills, and other enterprises. Its tasks included inspecting bodies of water which were receiving sewage from every kind of enterprise, seeking means of combating pollution from sewage, and examining and consulting on all questions associated with the treatment of sewage. The Central Committee on Water Conservation was granted the right to assemble all material concerning the protection of bodies of water from pollution, to inspect bodies of water and enterprises, to work out standards for combating the pollution of bodies of water and to implement them through the appropriate institutes of Soviet authority, to consider and approve plans for water treatment installations, to resolve disputes arising between enterprises and inspection agencies on the treatment of sewage, and to prepare presentations concerning the permanent or temporary suspension of the activities of enterprises that pollute bodies of water.

Such treatment of issues concerned with organizing the conservation of water resources fully accorded with V. I. Lenin's concept of a rational, scientifically based use of natural wealth and the protection of nature under socialism.

However, for the next forty years, that is, until the harmful impact of discharging untreated industrial effluent became evident, the conservation of the water resources of the USSR was not sufficiently elaborated in the legislation. Not until 31 May 1947 did the Council of Ministers of the USSR pass a decree "On Measures to Eliminate Pollution and to Provide the Sanitary Protection of Water Sources,"[2] which established the general conditions governing the discharge of sewage into bodies of water and the requirements for water users and designing and building organizations to protect water resources from pollution. In subsequent years, legislative acts of the USSR and Union Republics were issued concerning the conservation of water resources, which were largely of a limited nature. These acts contained requirements on the need to carry out measures concerned with the treatment of the sewage of separate groups of enterprises, and the elimination and prevention of pollution of the basins of the principal rivers and lakes. At the same time work was conducted to find new ways and means of eliminating pollution of water resources, which was also reflected in the legislation.

Whereas the decree of the Council of Ministers of the USSR of 31

---

2. See *The Protection of Nature and Conservation in the USSR*, Bull. No. 1 (Moscow: Publishing House of the Academy of Sciences, 1956), p. 42.

May 1947 provided only one measure for protecting bodies of water
from pollution—the mandatory provision of all sewerage systems of
cities and enterprises with treatment facilities—the decree of the
Council of Ministers of the USSR of 22 April 1960 "On Measures to
Regulate Use and Increase Conservation of Water Resources of the
USSR"[3] now aims to remove the causes which give rise to the discharge
of sewage.

The existing legislation lays down the principles for protecting water from pollution by measures which reduce or eliminate the production
of sewage and remove the need to discharge it into rivers and other
water sources. These measures include the introduction of waterless
methods of production, of efficient technological processes, of recirculating water supply systems and repeated use of water, and also the
utilization and treatment of sewage on sewage farms.

In recent years important work has been done in our country to eliminate pollution of bodies of water by industrial and domestic sewage.
Several thousand sewage-treatment facilities have been built and are
in operation. Some enterprises have achieved high standards of efficiency in the operation of treatment facilities, and sewage is released into bodies of water with the minimum amount of harmful substances. Examples of such enterprises are the Novogor'kii Oil Refinery, the Izhevsk Metallurgical Works, the Ryazan Oil Refinery, the
Gor'kii Automobile Factory, and there are others. As a result, the sanitary condition of some rivers, lakes, and reservoirs has improved. In
particular, there has been a noticeable reduction of pollution of the
Volga by oil products in the region of Gor'kii (in comparison with 1956,
when the oil content of the water of the Volga in this region was seventy
times higher than the maximum permissible standards).

However, it would not be right to overestimate the successes which
have been achieved in the protection of water resources from pollution,
for on the whole they have been very local. The development of the
national economy, the population growth in cities and industrial centers, and the organization of public services and amenities in villages
and rural populated areas lead not only to increased consumption of
water for domestic and industrial needs, but to increased discharge
into bodies of water of sewage and other wastes.[4] Many enterprises

----

3. *Collected Decrees of the USSR*, 1960, No. 9, Article 67.

4. In 1952 the discharge of industrial effluents in the USSR did not
exceed 27 billion cubic meters; in 1958 it increased to 50 billion m^3;
it is estimated that by 1965 the discharge of industrial effluents will
have reached 100 billion m^3 a year, and the discharge of domestic
wastes removed by sewerage systems will also double in comparison
with 1958. See N. N. Gorskii, *Water—Wonder of Nature* (Moscow:
Publishing House of the Academy of Science, 1962), pp. 206–207.

still continue to discharge untreated sewage into bodies of water.
Some enterprises are put into operation without the necessary treatment facilities. Only 50 percent of the total quantity of domestic
sewage discharged into bodies of water undergoes treatment. Hundreds of rivers and other bodies of water in the USSR are still therefore being polluted, and many of them are polluted to such an extent
that they are no longer of importance to the fish industry and cannot
be used for drinking, bathing, or even irrigation.

Measures for the increased use of chemicals in the national economy and for the intensification of agriculture, which are carried out
in accordance with the Program of the Communist Party of the Soviet
Union and with the resolutions of the December 1963 and February
1964 Plenums of the Central Committee of the Communist Party of the
Soviet Union, require that an even greater quantity of new water resources be drawn into the economic sphere. The discharge of sewage
will increase too. Under these circumstances, there is an even greater
need to improve the legal regulation of the discharge of industrial and
domestic sewage and other wastes into water bodies.

The ideal would be legislatively to prohibit completely the discharge of sewage and industrial and domestic wastes into bodies of
water everywhere. But in practice it would be technically impossible
to bring this about in the foreseeable future. Under these circumstances, Soviet law does not try to prohibit but to regulate the discharge of sewage and other wastes into bodies of water by defining
conditions of such water use.

However varied and complex from the juridical point of view the
conditions of discharge of sewage, industrial, and domestic wastes
into water bodies may be, they are all grouped together in a certain
way, and this permits the assertion that the use of water resources
for these purposes is regulated by Soviet law as one form of water use.
The distinctiveness of this form of water use is occasioned by the
special method of water resource use that is involved—not as a
source from which water is withdrawn, nor as a spatial operational
base, but as a means for removing the by-products of human activities.

Although in some cases sewage is discharged into bodies of water
by enterprises which themselves withdraw water, this does not provide
a basis to consider juridically the discharge of sewage and the withdrawal of water to be a single process of water use and to deny its
distinctiveness as a form of water use, for in many cases the enterprises which discharge the sewage get their water from the water mains
of cities or neighboring enterprises and are not the subjects of the
rights and obligations involved in the withdrawal of water. In addition, it is frequently not sewage, but other domestic and industrial
wastes, not associated with water consumption, which are discharged
into the water.

All this calls for a legal regulation of the discharge of sewage and industrial and domestic wastes into bodies of water, apart from other forms of water use. In addition, the legal conditions of this form of water use are not the same for both surface bodies of water and underground aquifers, and they need to be considered separately.

2. *Discharge of Sewage into Surface Waters*

Every enterprise, institution, organization, and citizen that needs to, and observes the requirements and procedure established by law, has the right to empty sewage into surface bodies of water.

The subjects of the law of water use in these cases are the owners of the outfalls from which the sewage enters directly into the body of water. If the same outfall is used jointly by several enterprises, then each of them may be recognized as a water user. In those cases where communal sewage is emptied, every owner of an outfall is a subject of water use, and under a centralized sewerage system the subject is the owner of the sewerage outfall. In cities and other populated areas, the subject is more often a specialized enterprise (trust), which is under the jurisdiction of the water supply and sewerage management of the appropriate executive committee of the local Council. When sewage (human wastes, washings, and so on) is discharged by inland water transport vessels, the subjects of the law of water use are the owners of the vessels—steamship lines, timber-floating organizations, commercial fishery enterprises, and so on. It is specifically to these subjects that the legal requirements governing the conditions and procedure for using surface bodies of water for the removal of sewage apply.

If enterprises, institutions, and organizations empty sewage into the municipal sewerage network, they are not water users, but are in contractual relations under civil law with the municipal communal enterprises as their subscribers, since the sewage of these enterprises, institutions, and organizations does not enter directly into the bodies of water.

Private citizens may be water users if they empty sewage produced in the course of housework or small-scale manufacture of handicrafts directly into bodies of water. But this occurs comparatively rarely, and does not have any substantial effect on the condition of the water resources. The discharge of sewage into bodies of water by the households of private citizens is therefore not taken into account, either in practice or in the law.

Conditions of water use and the requirements for water users who discharge sewage into surface bodies of water vary greatly.

First of all, it must be pointed out that in a number of cases the legislation prohibits completely the discharge of sewage into surface bodies of water, regardless of the extent of treatment.

For example, paragraph 3 of the decree of the Central Executive
Committee and Council of Peoples' Commissars of the USSR of 17 May
1937, "On the Sanitary Protection of Water Mains and Sources of Water
Supply,"[5] forbids any construction, except in connection with the technical servicing of the water mains, in the first belt of zones of sanitary protection of sources of centralized water supply. The construction and operation of sewage outfalls in the first belt of zones of sanitary protection of sources of water supply are therefore also forbidden.
Consequently, the emptying of sewage cannot be permitted either.

No sewage discharge whatsoever is permitted in the first zone of
districts of sanitary protection of health resorts[6] and in areas set
aside for bathing in seas and fresh-water bodies.[7]

In addition, the legislation specifies certain conditions where sewage discharge into surface bodies of water is prohibited absolutely.
It is forbidden, for example, to discharge into nonflowing lakes, ponds,
and reservoirs sewage containing radioactive substances or stable
substances which do not submit to biochemical, chemical, or physical
processes of self-purification.

Surface runoff (from a sewerage network) may not be discharged
into nonflowing ponds, areas of water bodies specially set aside for
beaches, closed hollows and depressions subject to bogging, fish
ponds (without special agreement), or into ravines subject to erosion.

Thus a complete ban on sewage discharge into bodies of water
exists only for certain areas of seas, rivers, lakes, reservoirs, and
other surface water bodies for sanitary considerations.

In the remaining areas, only treated sewage may be discharged.

Under the law, the concept "treated sewage" is the sum of requirements which must be met by the quality of the water which is discharged after industrial or domestic use and subsequent treatment by
each owner of an outfall. There is no common concept of treated effluent which is the same for all enterprises, institutions, and organizations that discharge sewage. On the contrary, the agencies concerned with the use and protection of water resources determine separately, for each enterprise, institution, or organization, the condi-

5. *Collected Laws of the USSR*, 1937, No. 35, Article 143.

6. See Article 4 of the Regulations on the Sanitary Protection of
Health Resorts and Areas of Medicinal Importance approved by the
decree of the Council of People's Commissars of the USSR of 10 April
1940 (*Collected Decrees of the USSR*, 1940, No. 12, Article 289).

7. See Articles 4 and 5 of the Sanitary Regulations for the Development and Maintenance of Beaches and Bathing Areas, approved by the
All-Union State Sanitary Inspection on 26 July 1944, in *The Hygiene
of Centers of Population* (Moscow: State Publishing House of Medical Literature, 1962), p. 190.

tions of sewage discharge, including the quality, quantity, and place of discharge. Each enterprise, institution, and organization, therefore, considers the sewage to be treated, if it satisfies the qualitative characteristics and general conditions for discharge that have been sanctioned by the agencies concerned with the use and protection of water resources.

The requirements governing sewage discharge into bodies of water, which have mandatory force for the water users, are determined and established when plans are approved for the construction of new and reconstruction of existing sewerage systems of populated areas and individual enterprises, institutions, and organizations; a similar procedure is followed for the certification of existing outfalls and their routine inspection. All the requirements taken together, which apply to every enterprise that discharges sewage, must ensure the prevention and elimination of pollution by sewage of bodies of water which are used for the drinking water supply, for the cultural and domestic needs of the population, and for the needs of the fish industry. The quality of the water into which sewage is discharged must, therefore, meet all-union standards that have been approved by the appropriate state agencies.[8]

The Regulations for the Protection of Surface Waters from Pollution by Sewage define the conditions of sewage discharge into bodies of water with regard to the extent to which the sewage might be mixed and diluted with water between the place of the outfall and the nearest points of drinking, domestic, and fishery water use. In addition, the sanitary condition of the water in the area of the facility producing the sewage, the sanitary situation above and below the place of discharge of sewage by this facility, and also changes in quantity and quality of sewage per each individual facility, must be taken into account with regard to the prospects for development of these facilities.

The specific conditions for sewage discharge are laid down in decisions of the agencies concerned with the use and conservation of water resources, which permit or prohibit the discharge of sewage by a water user. Decisions permitting discharge of sewage are valid for three years, after which they are subject to revision (that is, to cancellation or renewal).

---

8. See paragraph 12 of the decree of the Council of Ministers of the USSR of 22 April 1960, "On Measures to Regulate Use and Increase Conservation of Water Resources of the USSR" (*Collected Decrees of the USSR*, 1960, No. 9, Article 67); and Appendices 1—5 of the Regulations to Protect Surface Waters from Pollution by Sewage, in *Instructions on the Planning of the External Sewerage of Industrial Enterprises* (Moscow: State Publishing House of Literature on Building [n.d.]), pp. 206—217.

If before the end of the three-year period the conditions of water
use have changed (new enterprises may have been built, the withdrawal of water for water supply or irrigation may have increased, new
areas of drinking and domestic water use may have appeared, and so
on), the agencies concerned with the use and conservation of water
resources have the right to annul their decision permitting sewage
discharge, or to change the requirements agreed upon earlier for the
discharge of sewage by a particular water user so as to conform to the
new circumstances on the body of water, and to fix the period during
which the water user must carry out the corresponding measures. In
this event, the three-year period of operation of the decision is interrupted, and recommences as soon as the requirements for sewage discharge have been revised.

The water user to whom this decision (that is, authorization) applies is obligated to fulfill all the prescribed requirements and does
not have the right to deviate from them.

Under the law, water users do not have the right to change the quality, that is, the content of sewage, at their own discretion. This requirement means that the water user cannot exceed the maximum permissible standards for the content of polluting substances in sewage,
or introduce new substances into sewage which are not specified in
the authorization of the agency concerned with the use and protection
of water resources. But he does have the right, and is obliged, to
achieve the maximum reduction of harmful substances in industrial
wastes until they are no longer discharged into bodies of water.

Exercise of the right to discharge sewage into surface bodies of
water entails the fulfillment of requirements, regarding not only the
quality but also the quantity of sewage.

When plans for building and rebuilding enterprises are approved,
the quantity of sewage of a given quality to be discharged into a body
of water in a given time is established.

Enterprises do not have the right to increase the quantity of sewage
discharged into bodies of water above what has been stipulated in the
plan, except sometimes by a special instruction (decision, authorization) of the agency regulating the use and protection of water resources.
On the contrary, they are obliged in every way possible to achieve a
reduction in the quantity of sewage of permissible quality that is discharged, by showing initiative in improving the technology of production or in the creation of recirculating water supply systems.

Our legislation defining the conditions and requirements governing
the quantity of sewage discharged has been worked out quite well. It
is important to ensure in the first place that the legal requirements be
strictly observed. However, as a further improvement, the law should
regulate not only the quantity of sewage to be discharged during a
fixed period of time, but should require a certain regularity in the removal of used water. It is necessary to prohibit enterprises from de-

liberately making volleyed, concentrated discharges of sewage that
has accumulated in their reservoirs, for such discharges are harmful
to water resources and to the national economy.

The right of enterprises, institutions, and organizations to discharge
treated sewage into surface bodies of water is conditional upon observance of requirements, not only with regard to the quality and quantity of sewage, but also to the location of the effluent outfall. Water
users do not have the right at their own discretion to change the location (that is, the body of water or part of a body of water) of sewage
discharge.

Finally, the rights and obligations of enterprises, institutions, and
organizations which use surface water for the discharge of sewage
entail legal requirements concerning regular control by the water users
themselves over water use.

In compliance with the Regulations for the Protection of Surface
Waters from Pollution by Sewage, the leaders of the enterprises must
maintain constant supervision over the operation of sewage treatment
facilities by analyzing waste liquids and measuring their quantity at
fixed points in the sewerage system and at the outfall into the body of
water. The procedure for control carried out by the water user himself
(frequency and extent of analysis, and so on) is agreed upon with the
agencies concerned with the use and conservation of water resources
in accordance with local conditions on the body of water, the concentration of wastes, the type of facilities, and methods of sewage treatment.

In recent years, particularly since passage of the decree of the
Council of Ministers of the USSR of 22 April 1960, "On Measures to
Regulate Use and Increase Conservation of Water Resources of the
USSR," and the formation of state agencies concerned with the use
and conservation of water resources in the Union Republics, much work
has been done to regulate the discharge of sewage into bodies of water. All sewage outfalls have been inspected and registered, specific
measures to protect water resources have been worked out, treatment
facilities are being constructed for which the state is providing significant appropriations and material means, scientific work is under
way in search of effective methods of treating sewage, scientific
achievements and legislative requirements are being widely publicized,
and persons guilty of polluting bodies of water are being called to account. It is true that all this work is not yet faultless and could be
improved, but great progress has been made. It is reasonable to expect in the not too distant future the complete elimination of pollution
of surface bodies of water, if, of course, no new sources of pollution
are permitted to appear.

As has already been said, the legislation forbids enterprises, departments, and units which discharge sewage to be approved for activation and put into operation, either temporarily or permanently, with-

out the completion of measures to ensure proper treatment of sewage.
But in spite of this, there are new enterprises, departments, and units
being put into operation that discharge untreated wastes into surface
bodies of water.

Thus, according to the Yaroslavskaya Oblast newspaper, *Severnyi
Rabochii*, in September 1962, despite the objections of the agencies
of the State Water Management of the RSFSR, of the state sanitary
supervision, and of fish protection, the second producing unit of the
Novo-Yaroslavl Oil Refinery was put into production without waste
treatment facilities.[9] The Council of Ministers of the RSFSR nonetheless approved the act authorizing activation of the Novo-Yaroslavl
Oil Refinery.

During 1962 and 1963 dozens of enterprises were put into operation
which did not have the necessary sewage treatment facilities (for example the Kotlas Pulp and Paper Mill, the concentrating mills of the
Kursk Magnetic Anomaly Mining Combine, and others).

In order to abolish the faulty practice of building enterprises without at the same time equipping them with treatment facilities, the
Council of Ministers of the USSR has decreed that the leading workers
of building organizations receive bonuses for fulfilling on or ahead of
schedule plans for activation of objects of construction (such as enterprises, departments, and other facilities) that discharge sewage,
only when the main facilities for the proper treatment of sewage are
put into operation at the same time.[10]

However, this condition is frequently not observed and is not even
taken into account in state construction management practice. A particular example is that in July 1964 the State Committee on Labor and
Wages of the Council of Ministers of the USSR, the State Committee
on Construction of the USSR, and the Presidium of the All-Union Central Council of Trade Unions jointly approved the Regulations on Rewarding Workers for Launching the Operation of Industrial Capacities
and Structural Facilities,[11] in which nothing was said about not rewarding leading workers of building organizations if they failed to put into
operation simultaneously both the main structure and the facilities for
proper treatment of sewage.

The need for the strictest observance of legislative requirements
concerned with not permitting the operation of new enterprises, departments, and units that pollute surface bodies of water has grown

----

9. See *Severnyi Rabochii*, 21 December 1962.

10. See the decree of the Council of Ministers of the USSR of 22
April 1960 (*Collected Decrees of the USSR*, 1960, No. 9, Article 67).

11. See the *Regulations on Rewarding Workers for Launching the
Operation of Industrial Capacities and Structural Facilities* (Moscow:
State Publishing House of Literature on Building, 1962).

considerably under modern conditions, with the increased use of chemicals in the national economy which has taken place in accord with
the resolution of the December 1963 Plenum of the Central Committee
of the Communist Party of the Soviet Union. A significant growth of
enterprises of the chemical industry must not be allowed to give rise
to a corresponding increase in water pollution.

Since the principal conditions for sewage discharge into bodies of
water are determined when the technological design and complex of
industrial objects are planned, that is, before relations of water use
arise, a number of legal requirements are addressed to the planning
organizations. A substantial part of these requirements are set out in
a generalized form in construction standards and planning regulations,[12]
the instructions for the planning of the external sewerage of industrial enterprises, approved by the State Construction Committee of the
USSR,[13] and in sanitary regulations for the building and operation of
municipal sewage treatment facilities, approved by the Chief State
Sanitary Inspector of the USSR on 10 April 1959.[14]

The planning of the sewerage system of industrial enterprises must
be carried out on the basis of regional planning projects with a view
to possible joint sewering of enterprises and residential buildings
which are located near one another. When choosing an area for construction of an enterprise, the conditions for removal of sewage into
bodies of water in accordance with existing standards must be worked
out in advance. The planners must ascertain the expediency of extracting and utilizing the valuable substances contained in the sewage
of an enterprise, as well as the possibility of reducing the quantity
of polluted industrial effluent by the application of effective technological processes, a partial or full recirculating water supply system,
or the use of the sewage of one department in other departments.

Of the possible variants of the sewerage system that might be used,
only the one which best satisfies technical-economic considerations
and corresponds to the legal requirements for sewage discharge into
bodies of water is adopted. The location of the outfall and the degree

---

12. See *Construction Standards and Regulations*, Part II, Section
Γ, Chapter 6, "Sewerage Systems, Planning Standards" (SNiP II—5, 6—
62), approved by the State Committee on Construction of the Council
of Ministers of the USSR on 24 August 1962 (Moscow: State Publishing House of Literature on Building, 1962).

13. See *Instructions on the Planning of the External Sewerage
of Industrial Enterprises, Part I, SN 173—61* (approved by the State
Committee on Construction of the Council of Ministers of the USSR
on 13 July 1961 [Moscow: State Publishing House of Literature on
Building, 1961]).

14. *The Hygiene of Centers of Population*, pp. 413—423.

of treatment of the sewage must be agreed upon with the local Council of Workers' Deputies, the local agencies of state sanitary supervision, and the agencies concerned with the use and conservation of water resources and, when the sewage discharge is of significance to fisheries or navigation, with the agencies of fish protection and marine or inland water transport organizations.

If the quantity and content of the sewage is going to change sharply in the course of the day, and it is discharged by volleys in strong concentrations, then it is necessary that the plan should stipulate the construction of additional capacity, permitting an even discharge of industrial sewage to be maintained.

When choosing the method of sewage treatment and the location of the treatment facilities, the possibility and expediency of agricultural use of the sewage after its mechanical purification must first be considered.

Plans for the sewerage system of populated areas and individual enterprises, which have been drawn up in accordance with the established requirements and approved in the appropriate way, are implemented by the building organizations.

The state examining commissions, which authorize the operation of newly created or reconstructed industrial structures and the construction of municipal sewerage systems, must verify that the designing and building organizations observe the law on the conservation of water resources.

In this way all the main conditions governing the exercise by enterprises, institutions, and organizations of the right to discharge sewage (such as methods for removal of sewage, quantity of sewage, content, and place of outfall) are basically determined before relations of water use arise and irrespective of the will of the subject of the law of water use.

On the basis of the foregoing, the law ought to regulate severely the responsibilities of the designing organizations to make the correct technical decisions in order to prevent the discharge of polluted sewage into bodies of water, and to bar state agencies from approving projects for building new and rebuilding existing enterprises, departments, and units if there is not a 100 percent guarantee of protecting the water resources from pollution. The personal responsibility of the guilty officials should be established for the violation of these regulations.

Finally, it is necessary also to stipulate the responsibility of members of state examining commissions who, in violation of the law, authorize the operation of enterprises, departments, and units which have not been provided with the necessary sewage treatment facilities.

New problems in the struggle against the pollution of water resources are arising in connection with the wide use of mineral fertilizers in agriculture. When mineral fertilizers are not used correctly, they can get into water bodies with the surface runoff from fields, which is harmful to agriculture and causes additional pollution of the water. To avoid this, the responsibility of farms, which use mineral fertilizers on their fields, to regulate the surface flow of water appropriately and not to allow fertilizers to get into bodies of water, should be specified.

In conclusion, let us consider briefly the discharge of other wastes (apart from sewage) into bodies of water.

There are no general regulations on this question in the legislation. Only in particular cases that apply to individual categories of bodies of water, or to individual types of substances that must be removed, have rules been established permitting, forbidding, or limiting the discharge of domestic and industrial wastes into water bodies.

The discharge into bodies of water of any wastes whatever is completely forbidden in the first and second zones (belts) of sanitary protection of sources of water supply and health resorts. What is more, the deposit of rubbish and industrial and domestic wastes on the land surface in these zones is prohibited.

Thus, in accordance with the existing Regulations on Planning Zones of Sanitary Protection of a Centralized Water Supply System and Water Sources, in the first and second belts of zones of sanitary protection of sources of water supply there must be no cemeteries, cattle burial grounds, or garbage dumps on the banks of rivers and streams, nor manufactures that might pollute the bodies of water with their wastes. Similar prohibitions are specified in the instructions for the application of the Regulations on the Sanitary Protection of Health Resorts and Areas of Medicinal Importance. These say, in particular, that the creation of dumps and areas for reception of night soil, and the accumulation of hard refuse, and so on, are unconditionally prohibited in the first and second zones of districts of sanitary protection of health resorts.

It is forbidden by the Regulations for the Protection of Surface Waters from Pollution by Sewage to tolerate leakage from produce conveyance facilities and all forms of water transport in any bodies of water.

In the interest of preventing the pollution of bodies of water with solid and liquid refuse, the legislation on the use of fishery waters contains a fairly broad list of forbidden activities. In particular, it is forbidden to empty into fishery waters, or onto the banks or ice of these bodies of water, refuse which is harmful to fish, including chips, bark, sawdust, and similar wastes formed in logging, winter raft-building and building structures for the floating of timber. It is forbidden to empty soil, removed in the course of dredging and clearing the bottoms of water areas, into spawning grounds and wintering holes. The retting of flax, hemp, bast, hides, and so on is not permitted in fishery waters.

Snow which has been removed from pollution centers may be emptied into bodies of water only in special places set aside for this purpose, and with the observance of conditions which are designed to prevent pollution of bodies of water with street rubbish.

3. *Discharge of Sewage into Underground Aquifers*

Prior to 1959 the discharge of domestic and industrial sewage into underground waters was not regulated by law and was unrestricted in practice. As a result of unregulated sewage discharge into underground aquifers, the pollution of underground reserves of drinking and mineral water occurred. This has made it necessary to establish a system of rules regulating sewage discharge into underground aquifers.

The general regulations defining the procedure for sewage discharge into underground aquifers are specified in the decree of the Council of Ministers of the USSR of 4 September 1959, "On Strengthening State Control over the Use of Underground Waters and on Measures for Their Conservation,"[15] and in the Regulations on the Use and Conservation of Underground Waters in the USSR, approved in April 1960 by the Ministry of Geology and Protection of Minerals of the USSR and by the Chief State Sanitary Inspection of the USSR.[16]

Sewage is discharged into underground aquifers by means of specially equipped absorbing wells or drilled wells. The water users in these cases are therefore the owners of the absorbing wells and drilled wells. The corresponding requirements of the legislation on the conditions and procedure for discharging sewage into underground aquifers are addressed to them.

Since 1959 a procedure for authorizing use of underground waters for the discharge of sewage has been in force. This means that the discharge of sewage into underground aquifers is permitted only with the prior authorization of the agencies of geology and the protection of minerals, and with the agreement of the republic agencies of state sanitary inspection. Authorization is given for the construction and operation of absorbing wells and drilled wells (with, in some cases, a number of special requirements).

The discharge of sewage into underground aquifers is permitted only when it is not possible to use other methods of removal. If it is feasible to treat the sewage and subsequently to use it in a recirculating water supply system in the irrigation of agricultural crops, or to discharge it into surface bodies of water, authorization to discharge it into underground aquifers is not issued.

The use of underground waters for the removal of industrial and

---

15. *Collected Decrees of the USSR*, 1959, No. 17, Article 135.
16. See *The Hygiene of Centers of Population*, pp. 347–362.

domestic wastes must not lead to the pollution of natural reserves of water that are suitable for water supply. The drilling and construction of absorbing wells for the discharge of the industrial and human wastes of enterprises is, therefore, forbidden in all cases where the wells could become sources of pollution of an underground aquifer which is being used, or is intended for use, or might be used, for a drinking water supply system or for medicinal purposes.

In the interest of preventing the pollution of groundwater the legislation provides for prior and subsequent control over the observance of the requirements for the protection of water resources.

Prior control means that enterprises, institutions, and organizations interested in discharging sewage into underground aquifers conduct special hydro-geological and sanitary-bacteriological investigations, the results of which are submitted to the agencies of geology and protection of minerals and to the agencies of state sanitary supervision, together with an application for permission to drill absorbing wells. The agencies of geology and protection of minerals and the agencies of state sanitary supervision consider this material and give permission for absorbing wells to be drilled, if it can be shown that the sewage discharge will not cause any harm to an aquifer which contains natural reserves of water suitable for a drinking water supply and medicinal purposes, or to open bodies of water and adjacent areas, and provided that the absorbing aquifer has sufficient receiving capacity.

Subsequent control over fulfillment of the requirements for the protection of groundwater from pollution is carried out in the course of the operation of absorbing wells. Where sewage is pumped into underground aquifers, systematic laboratory observations of the quality of the water in nearby water intakes and other wells and pits must be carried out by the owners of the absorbing wells, in accordance with a plan agreed upon with the local agencies of state sanitary supervision.

The general requirements for enterprises, institutions, and organizations which discharge sewage into underground aquifers in many ways resemble the requirements governing the discharge of sewage into surface bodies of water. At the same time they have their own special features.

In particular, as in the discharge of sewage into surface bodies of water, when sewage is discharged into underground aquifers, the place of sewage outfall—the place where the absorbing well is located—is strictly regulated.

It is forbidden to construct and operate absorbing wells in the first and second belts of zones of sanitary protection of sources of water supply. In addition, when sewage is discharged into the ground, the depth of the well and absorbing aquifer must be precisely established. The water user does not have the right at his own discretion to change either the location of the absorbing well or its depth. He must discharge sewage only into the aquifer indicated in the authorization issued by the agency of geology and protection of minerals. In order to protect the upper aquifers, through which the absorbing well passes, from pollution by sewage, the owner of the well must ensure that its walls are reliably insulated.

When sewage is discharged into underground aquifers, the quantity of sewage pumped through each absorbing well in a period of time is regulated and controlled. The quantity of sewage to be discharged into groundwater is determined by the agencies of geology and protection of minerals and by the agencies of state sanitary supervision when they issue the authorization to drill or to construct the absorbing wells. The water user does not have the right to increase the quantity of sewage above that indicated in the authorization. If it is necessary to increase the quantity of sewage discharged, the conditions of discharge are liable to reconsideration by the agencies of geology and protection of minerals and the agencies of state sanitary supervision.

Unlike the sewage discharge into surface waters, which is permitted only after treatment, the law does not demand prior treatment of sewage discharged into underground aquifers. Consequently, polluted sewage containing any substance, other than radioactive, may be discharged into underground aquifers. But in exceptional cases, after special investigation, sewage containing radioactive substances may be discharged into underground aquifers by joint authorization of the Ministry of Health of the USSR and the Ministry of Geology of the USSR.

Since the existing legislation does not demand prior treatment of sewage discharged into underground aquifers, neither does it specify the responsibility of owners of waste water absorbing wells to maintain the same composition of substances in the discharged sewage and to control the quality of the sewage. Enterprises, institutions, and organizations which use underground water for the removal of wastes are obliged only to keep a daily record of the amount discharged into the absorbing wells.

The legal problems involved in the rational use and conservation of water resources in the USSR are not completely taken care of by the regulation of water use. Some of these problems are associated with the organization and work of the state water management agencies, with the implementation of the right of exclusive state ownership of the waters, and with the application of measures of accountability to violators of Soviet water law, which requires independent study.

But there is now reason to conclude that the legal regulation of water use should occupy a central place in Soviet water law, because it is the scientifically based conditions and requirements of water use, brought within the framework of law, that primarily ensure the rational use and conservation of the water resources of the USSR.

Appendix

Index

Principles of Water Law of the USSR and Union Republics

As a result of the victory of the Great October Socialist Revolution, water, like other natural resources in our country, was nationalized and became the property of the people.

State ownership of water constitutes the basis of water relations in the USSR, creates favorable conditions for carrying out the planned and complex use of water to the greatest effect for the national economy, and makes it possible to provide the Soviet people with the best working, living, recreation, and public health conditions.

The development of social production and urban construction, and the improvement in the material well-being and cultural level of the population increase the all-round requirements for water and the importance of rational use and conservation of water.

Soviet water law is called upon to promote actively the most effective, scientifically based use of water and its protection from pollution, obstruction, and depletion.

I. General Provisions

Article 1. Goals of Soviet Water Law

The goals of Soviet water law shall be the regulation of water relations in order to ensure the rational use of water for the needs of the

Translated from *Izvestiya* of 11 December 1970.

population and the national economy, to protect water from pollution, obstruction, and depletion, to prevent and eliminate the harmful action of water, and to improve the condition of water bodies; and also the protection of the rights of enterprises, organizations, institutions, and citizens, and the strengthening of the law in the field of water relations.

Article 2. Water Law of the USSR and the Union Republics

Water relations in the USSR shall be regulated by these Principles and, issued in accord with them, by other acts of water law of the USSR, and by the water codes and other acts of water law of the Union Republics.

Land, forest, and mining relations shall be regulated by corresponding legislation of the USSR and Union Republics

Article 3. State Ownership of Water in the USSR

In accordance with the Constitution of the USSR, water in the Union of Soviet Socialist Republics is state property, that is, the property of all the people.

Water in the USSR is the exclusive property of the State, and use of it only is granted. Actions that infringe, either directly or indirectly, on the right of state ownership of water, shall be prohibited.

Article 4. A Single State Water Resource

All the waters (bodies of water) of the USSR constitute a common state resource. This indivisible state water resource includes: (1) rivers, lakes, reservoirs, other surface bodies of water and water sources, and also canals and ponds; (2) underground waters and glaciers; (3) inland seas and other inland sea waters of the USSR; (4) territorial waters (territorial seas) of the USSR.

Article 5. The Competence of the USSR in the Sphere of the Regulation of Water Relations

The following shall be subject to the jurisdiction of the USSR in the field of the regulation of water relations:

(1) the administration of the common state water resource within the limits of the authority of the USSR in accordance with the Constitution of the USSR;

(2) the establishment of basic provisions for water use, the protection of water from pollution, obstruction, and depletion, and the prevention and elimination of the harmful action of water;

(3) the establishment of all-union standards for water use and water quality, and methods for evaluating water quality;

(4) the establishment of a single system for the whole country of state water accounts, of water use and the registration of use, and of a state water cadastre;

(5) the approval of schemes for the complex use and conservation of water and for water resource balances, having all-union importance;

(6) the planning of all-union measures for the use and conservation of water and for the prevention and elimination of its harmful action;

(7) state control over the use and conservation of water and the establishment of a procedure for implementing it;

(8) the definition of water bodies, regulation of the use of which is carried out by agencies of the USSR.

Article 6. The Competence of the Union Republics in the Field of the Regulation of Water Relations

The following shall be subject to the jurisdiction of the Union Republics in the field of the regulation of water relations outside the competence of the USSR: the administration of the single state water resource on the territory of the republic; the establishment of a procedure for the use of water, its protection from pollution, obstruction, and depletion, and the prevention and elimination of the harmful action of water; the planning of measures for the use and conservation of water and the prevention and elimination of its harmful effects; the approval of schemes for the complex use and conservation of water and for water resource balances; the exercise of state control over the use and conservation of water, and also the regulation of water relations on other questions that do not fall within the competence of the USSR.

Article 7. State Administration in the Field of the Use and Conservation of Water

State administration in the field of the use and conservation of water shall be carried out by the Council of Ministers of the USSR, the Councils of Ministers of the Union Republics, the Councils of Ministers of the Autonomous Republics, the executive committees of the local Councils of Workers' Deputies, and also by specially authorized state agencies for regulating the use and conservation of water, either directly or through the basin (territorial) administrations and other agencies in accordance with the law of the USSR and Union Republics.

Article 8. State Control over the Use and Conservation of Water

State control over the use and conservation of water shall aim to secure the observance by all ministerial, departmental, state, cooperative, and public enterprises, organizations, institutions, and citizens of the established procedure for the use of water, the fulfillment of obligations for the conservation of water and the prevention and elimination of its harmful action, the rules for maintaining water resource balances, and other regulations established by water law.

State control over the use and conservation of water shall be exercised by the local Councils of Workers' Deputies, their executive and administrative agencies, and also by specially authorized state agencies within the procedure established by legislation of the USSR.

Article 9. The Participation of Public Organizations and Citizens in Implementing Measures for the Rational Use and Conservation of Water

Trade unions, youth organizations, societies for the protection of nature, scientific societies, and other public organizations, as well as citizens, shall render assistance to state agencies in the implementation of measures for the rational use and conservation of water.

Public organizations shall take part in activities directed toward ensuring the rational use and conservation of water in accordance with their charters (regulations) and the law of the USSR and Union Republics.

Article 10. The Siting, Designing, Construction, and Putting into Operation of Enterprises, Installations, and Other Facilities Affecting the Condition of Water

In the siting, designing, construction, and putting into operation of new and reconstructed enterprises, installations, and other facilities, and in the introduction of new technological processes affecting the condition of water, the rational use of water must be ensured, with priority for meeting the drinking water and daily needs of the population. In this connection, measures are envisaged for the keeping of records on water removed from water bodies and returned thereto, the protection of water from pollution, obstruction, and depletion, the prevention of the harmful action of water, for keeping the flooding of land to the minimum, protecting land from salinization, rising groundwater, or desiccation, and also for preserving favorable natural conditions and landscapes.

In the siting, designing, construction, and putting into operation of new and reconstructed enterprises, installations, and other facilities on fishery waters, measures must also be taken at the proper time to protect the fish and other aquatic fauna and flora as well as conditions for their reproduction.

The sites for the construction of enterprises, installations, and other facilities influencing the condition of water shall be determined in agreement with the agencies regulating the use and conservation of water, the executive committees of the local Councils of Workers' Deputies, the agencies exercising state sanitary supervision, the agencies for the protection of fish reserves, and other agencies, in accordance with the law of the USSR and Union Republics. Designs for the construction of these enterprises, installations, and other facilities shall be subject to agreement with the agencies regulating the use and conservation of water and other agencies in instances and within the procedures established by the law of the USSR.

It shall be forbidden to put into operation the following: new and reconstructed enterprises, shops, aggregates, and communal and other facilities that are not equipped with devices for preventing the pollution and obstruction of water or its harmful action; irrigation and watering systems, reservoirs, and canals, before the implementation of measures provided for in the plans to prevent flooding, rising groundwater, waterlogging, and salinization of the land, and soil erosion; drainage systems, before the preparation of water-intake and other devices in accordance with the approved plans; water-intake installations without devices for the protection of fish in accordance with the approved plans; hydrotechnical installations before the preparation of devices for the passage of floodwater and fish in accordance with the approved plans; drilled wells that are not equipped with water-regulating devices and without establishing, where necessary, the zones of sanitary protection.

It shall be forbidden to fill reservoirs before the measures specified in the plan for the preparation of the reservoir bed have been carried out.

Article 11. The Procedure for the Performance of Work on Water Bodies and Littoral Areas (Zones)

Building, dredging, and detonating operations, the extraction of useful minerals and aquatic plants, the laying of cables, pipes, and other communications, the cutting of timber, and drilling, agricultural, and other work on bodies of water and their littoral belts (zones), which affect the condition of the water, shall be carried out with the agreement of the agencies regulating the use and conservation of water, the executive committees of the local Councils of Workers' Deputies, and with other agencies in accordance with the law of the USSR and Union Republics.

II. Water Use

Article 12. Water Users

Water users in the USSR may be state, cooperative, and public enterprises, organizations, institutions, and citizens of the USSR.

In cases specified in the legislation of the USSR, other organizations and persons may also be water users.

Article 13. *Objects of Water Use*

Use shall be granted of the bodies of water enumerated in Article 4 of these Principles.

The use of bodies of water, having special importance for the State or a special scientific or cultural value, may be partially or completely prohibited according to the procedure established by the Council of Ministers of the USSR and the Councils of Ministers of the Union Republics.

Article 14. *Forms of Water Use*

The use of water bodies shall be granted with the observance of the requirements and conditions established by law for meeting the drinking water, everyday, medicinal, resort, health-improvement, and other needs of the population, and agricultural, industrial, power, transport, fishery, and other state and public needs. The use of bodies of water for the discharge of wastes may be permitted only in cases and with the observance of special requirements and conditions specified by the law of the USSR and Union Republics.

A distinction shall be made between general water use—carried out without the application of facilities or technical devices affecting the condition of the water—and special water use—carried out with the application of such facilities or devices. Related to special water use in certain cases may be also the use of water bodies without the application of facilities or technical devices, but affecting the condition of the water.

A list of types of special water use shall be drawn up by the agencies regulating the use and conservation of water.

Bodies of water may be in joint or individual use.

Enterprises, organizations, and institutions that have been granted the individual use of bodies of water shall be the primary water users, but in cases stipulated by the law of the USSR and Union Republics, they shall have the right to permit secondary water use to other enterprises, organizations, institutions, and citizens, in agreement with the agencies regulating the use and conservation of water.

Article 15. *Procedure and Conditions for Granting the Use of Water Bodies*

Use of bodies of water shall be granted first of all in order to meet the drinking and daily needs of the population.

Bodies of water shall be granted for individual use either fully or in part on the basis of a decree of the Council of Ministers of a Union

Republic or the Council of Ministers of an Autonomous Republic, or of a decision of the executive committee of the appropriate Council of Workers' Deputies or other state agency so empowered, according to the procedure established by the law of the USSR and Union Republics.

Special water use shall be carried out on the basis of authorizations issued by the agencies regulating the use and conservation of water and, in cases stipulated by the law of the USSR and Union Republics, by the executive committees of the local Councils of Workers' Deputies. Such authorizations shall be issued after agreement with the agencies concerned with state sanitary supervision and the protection of fish, and also with other interested agencies. The procedure for approving and issuing authorization for special water use shall be established by the Council of Ministers of the USSR.

General water use shall be carried out without authorization according to the procedure established by the law of the Union Republics. General water use shall be permitted on water bodies granted for individual use on conditions laid down by the primary water user in agreement with the agencies regulating the use and conservation of water, and if necessary may be prohibited.

Water use shall be carried out free of charge. Special water use may be subject to a fee in such case and according to the procedure established by the Council of Ministers of the USSR.

Article 16. Time Periods of Water Use

Bodies of water shall be granted for indefinite or temporary use.

Indefinite (permanent) means water use without a time limit set in advance.

Temporary use may be short-term—up to three years—or long-term—from three to twenty-five years. When necessary, the period of water use may be extended for a period not exceeding the time limit for short-term or long-term temporary use, whichever shall be appropriate.

General water use shall not be subject to a time limit.

Article 17. The Rights and Obligations of Water Users

Water users shall have the right to use water bodies only for those purposes for which use has been granted.

In cases specified by the law of the USSR and Union Republics, the rights of water users may be limited in the interests of the State and in the interests of other water users. In this connection the conditions for the use of water bodies for drinking water and the everyday needs of the population must not be allowed to deteriorate.

Water users shall be obliged: to utilize bodies of water rationally, to be concerned about the economic use of water, and about restoring and improving the quality of water; to take measures to limit fully the discharge of sewage containing pollutants into bodies of water; not to violate the rights granted to other water users, nor to cause damage to economic facilities or natural resources (lands, forests, living things, useful minerals, and so forth); to maintain in good condition purification and water management installations and technical devices affecting the condition of the water, to improve their operational qualities, and in specified cases to keep a record of water use.

*Article 18. Grounds for Discontinuing the
Right to Water Use*

The right of enterprises, organizations, institutions, and citizens to the use of water shall be subject to termination in the following instances: (1) termination of the need for or renunciation of water use; (2) expiration of the time period for water use; (3) liquidation of the enterprise, organization, or institution; (4) transfer of water-management installations to other water users; (5) emergence of the necessity to remove a body of water from individual use.

The right to water use of enterprises, organizations, institutions, and citizens (except the right to use water for drinking water and everyday needs) may also be discontinued in the event of violation of the regulations on the use and conservation of water, or if the body of water is used for a purpose other than that for which use is granted.

Other grounds for terminating the right of enterprises, organizations, institutions, and citizens to use water may be stipulated by the law of Union Republics.

*Article 19. The Procedure for Terminating the
Right to Water Use*

The right to water use shall be terminated as follows: annulment of the authorization for special, and also secondary, water use; withdrawal of bodies of water granted for individual use.

Termination of special water use shall be by decision of the agency that issued authorization for it.

Secondary water use may be terminated by decision of the primary water user, with the concurrence of the agency regulating the use and conservation of water.

The withdrawal of bodies of water from individual use shall be carried out in accordance with the procedure established by the law of the USSR and Union Republics.

The withdrawal of bodies of water from the individual use of enterprises, organizations, and institutions of union subordination shall occur with the agreement of the water users and the Ministries and Departments to which they are directly subordinate.

*Article 20. Compensation for Losses Caused in
Carrying Out Water Management Measures, by the
Termination or Change of Conditions of Water Use*

Losses caused to enterprises, organizations, institutions, and citizens in carrying out water management measures (hydrotechnical operations and so on), and also by the termination or change of conditions of water use must be compensated for in cases and according to the procedure specified by the Council of Ministers of the USSR.

*Article 21. The Use of Bodies of Water for
Drinking, Everyday, and Other Needs of the Population*

Bodies of water, in which the quality of water corresponds to the established sanitary requirements, shall be granted for the drinking, everyday water supply, and other needs of the population.

The use of underground water of potable quality for needs not related to the drinking and everyday water supply shall not be permitted as a rule. In areas where the necessary surface water sources are lacking and there are sufficient reserves of underground water of potable quality, the agencies regulating the use and conservation of water may authorize the use of this water for purposes not related to the drinking and everyday water supply.

*Article 22. The Use of Bodies of Water for
Medicinal, Resort, and Health-Improvement Purposes*

Water bodies, falling according to the established procedure into the category of medicinal, shall be used first of all for medicinal and resort purposes. In exceptional cases, the agencies regulating the use and conservation of water may authorize the use of water bodies, coming within the category of medicinal, for other purposes in agreement with the appropriate public health and resort management agencies.

The discharge of sewage into bodies of water, coming within the category of medicinal, shall be prohibited.

The procedure for the use of waters for recreation and sport shall be established by the law of the USSR and Union Republics.

*Article 23. Use of Bodies of Water for the
Needs of Agriculture*

The use of bodies of water for agricultural needs shall be accomplished according to the procedure of both general and special water use.

In the case of special water use, irrigation, water supply, drainage, and other water-management installations and systems shall be used which belong to state organizations, state and collective farms, and other water users.

Collective and state farms and other enterprises, organizations, institutions, and citizens, using bodies of water for agricultural needs, shall be obliged to observe the established plans, regulations, standards, and regimen of water use, to undertake measures to reduce loss of water through seepage and evaporation in land-improvement systems and to prevent inefficient removal of water from them, to prevent fish from fishery waters getting into land-improvement systems, and also to create the most favorable soil conditions.

The irrigation of agricultural lands with sewage shall be authorized by the agencies regulating the use and conservation of water in agreement with the agencies exercising state sanitary and veterinary supervision.

The provisions of this article shall extend also to the irrigation and drainage of land occupied by forests, forest belts, and forest nurseries.

Article 24. Use of Bodies of Water for Industrial Purposes

Water users, using bodies of water for industrial purposes, shall be obliged to observe the established plans, technological standards and regulations for water use, to undertake measures to reduce water consumption, and to discontinue the discharge of sewage by improving production technology and water supply schemes (the use of water-free technological processes, air cooling, recycled water supply, and other technical methods).

In the event of natural disaster, accident, or in other exceptional circumstances, and if an enterprise exceeds the established limit for use of water from the water supply, the executive committees of the local Councils of Workers' Deputies shall have the right to limit or prohibit consumption for industrial purposes of drinking water from communal water supplies and to limit temporarily consumption for industrial purposes from departmental economic and drinking water supplies, in the interests of meeting primarily the drinking water and other needs of the population.

Underground water (fresh, mineral, thermal) which does not come into the category of drinking or medicinal water, may, according to the established procedure, be used for technical water supply, for extracting the mineral elements it contains, for generating thermal energy and other production needs, with the observance of the requirements for the rational use and conservation of water.

*Article 25. The Use of Bodies of Water
for Hydroelectric Needs*

The use of bodies of water for the needs of hydroelectricity shall
be carried out with consideration for the interests of other branches
of the national economy and with the observance of requirements for
the complex use of water, if no other direct provision has been made
by decree of the Council of Ministers of the USSR or decrees of the
Councils of Ministers of the Union Republics, and, in the appropriate
cases, by decision of the agency regulating the use and conservation
of water.

*Article 26. The Use of Bodies of Water for the
Needs of Water Transport and the Floating of Timber*

The rivers, lakes, reservoirs, canals, inland seas, and other inland sea waters of the USSR, and also the territorial waters (territorial
seas) of the USSR, shall be waterways of general use, with the exception of those cases where their use for these purposes has been fully
or partially prohibited, or if they have been granted for individual use.
The procedure for categorizing waterways as suitable for shipping or
timber-floating, and the establishment of regulations for the operation
of waterways, shall be defined in the legislation of the USSR and
Union Republics.

Floating of loose timber and also of rafts without a towboat shall
be forbidden: (1) on shipping routes; (2) on bodies of water, the list
of which shall be approved by the Council of Ministers of the USSR
or the Councils of Ministers of the Union Republics, which have
special importance for the fishing industry, water supply, or other
purposes of the national economy.

On the remaining bodies of water the above-mentioned forms of
timber-floating shall be permitted on the basis of authorizations issued by the agencies regulating the use and conservation of water,
after agreement with the agencies concerned with the protection of
fish.

The timber-floating organizations shall be obliged to clear sunken
wood regularly from the routes used for floating.

*Article 27. Use of Bodies of Water for the
Needs of Air Transport.*

The procedure for the use of water bodies for the stationing, take-
off, and landing of aircraft and for other needs of air transport shall
be established by the law of the USSR.

*Article 28. The Use of Bodies of Water for the
Needs of the Fishing Industry*

On fishery waters, or on sections having particular importance for
the preservation and reproduction of valuable species of fish and of
other objects of the water industry, the rights of water users may be
limited in the interests of the fishing industry. Lists of such bodies
of water or sections of them and the types of limitation on water use
shall be drawn up by the agencies regulating the use and conservation
of water on the basis of presentations by the agencies concerned with
the protection of fish.

In the operation of hydrotechnical and other installations on fishery waters, measures must be taken at the proper time to ensure the
protection of the fish and conditions for their reproduction.

The procedure for the use of bodies of water for the needs of the
fishing industry shall be established by the law of the USSR and Union
Republics.

*Article 29. The Use of Bodies of Water for the
Needs of the Hunting Industry*

On rivers, lakes, and other water bodies providing habitat for waterfowl and valuable fur-bearing animals (beaver, muskrat, desman, nu-
tria, and so on), the primary right of water use by enterprises and organizations of the hunting industry may be established by the agencies
regulating the use and conservation of water, with consideration for
the requirements of complex water use.

The procedure for the use of bodies of water for the needs of the
hunting industry shall be established by the law of the USSR and
Union Republics.

*Article 30. The Use of Bodies of Water for the
Needs of Preserves*

Bodies of water having special scientific or cultural value, in accordance with the procedure established by the law of the USSR and
Union Republics, shall be declared preserves and be granted for the
permanent individual use of the preserves for the purposes of the protection of nature and scientific research.

The procedure for the use of the waters of the preserves shall be
determined by the regulations on the preserves.

The withdrawal of bodies of water from the use of the preserves
shall be permitted only in cases of extreme necessity on the basis of
a decree of the Council of Ministers of the Union Republic.

Article 31. The Use of Bodies of Water for the
Discharge of Sewage

The use of bodies of water for the discharge of industrial, everyday communal, drainage, and other wastes may occur only with the
authorization of the agencies regulating the use and conservation of
water after agreement with the agencies concerned with state sanitary
supervision and the protection of fish and other interested agencies.

The discharge of sewage shall be permitted only if it does not lead
to an increase in the amount of pollutants in the water body above the
established levels, and on condition that the water user treat the
sewage to the extent laid down by the agencies regulating the use and
conservation of water.

If these requirements are violated, the discharge of sewage must
be limited, suspended, or prohibited by the agencies regulating the
use and conservation of water, and the work of the industrial plants,
shops, enterprises, organizations, or institutions must if necessary
be halted. In cases where public health is threatened, the agencies
exercising state sanitary supervision shall have the right to halt the
discharge of sewage, if necessary by discontinuing the operation of
the industrial and other plants, with notification to the agencies regulating the use and conservation of water.

The procedure and conditions for the use of water bodies for the
discharge of sewage shall be established by the law of the USSR and
Union Republics.

Article 32. The Use of Bodies of Water for
Fire Protection and Other State and Public Needs

The withdrawal of water from any body of water shall be permitted
for fire suppression needs.

The procedure for the use of water bodies for fire suppression needs
and other state and public needs shall be established by the law of
the USSR and Union Republics.

Article 33. The Operation of Reservoirs

Enterprises, organizations, and institutions operating water-raising,
water-passage or water-intake installations on reservoirs shall be
obliged to observe the regime for increase and decrease of storage of
the reservoirs that has been established with consideration for the interests of water and land users in the zones affected by the reservoirs.

The procedure for the operation of reservoirs shall be defined by
regulations approved by the agencies regulating the use and conserva-

tion of water for each reservoir, cascade, or system of reservoirs, in agreement with the agencies concerned with state sanitary supervision and the protection of fish, and with other interested agencies.

The organization and coordination of measures to ensure the proper technical condition and comprehensive equipping of reservoirs, and the observance of the regulations for their operation, shall be carried out by the agencies regulating the use and conservation of water according to the procedure established by the Council of Ministers of the USSR and Councils of Ministers of the Union Republics.

The provisions of this article shall extend also to the operation of lakes and other bodies of water used as reservoirs.

Article 34. Regulation of the Use of Bodies of Water
Situated on the Territory of More Than One Union Republic

Regulation of the use of bodies of water situated on the territory of two or more Union Republics, in areas affecting the interests of these Republics, shall be carried out by agreement between agencies of the interested Republics, with the exception of those bodies of water, the regulation of which falls within the competence of the USSR.

Article 35. The Procedure for Settling Disputes on
Water Use

Disputes on water use shall be settled by the Councils of Ministers of the Union Republics, the Councils of Ministers of the Autonomous Republics, the executive committees of the local Councils of Workers' Deputies, and by the agencies regulating the use and conservation of water and other state agencies so empowered, according to the procedure established by the law of the USSR and Union Republics.

Disputes between the water users of one Union Republic and the water users of another Union Republic on the use of water shall be examined by a commission, made up on the basis of parity, of representatives of the interested Union Republics. In the event of the commission's not reaching an agreed decision, the dispute shall be subject to examination in accordance with the procedure defined by the Council of Ministers of the USSR.

Property disputes connected with water relations shall be resolved according to the procedure established by the law of the USSR and Union Republics.

Article 36. The Use of Border Waters of the USSR

Use of the border waters of the USSR shall be carried out on the basis of international agreement.

Where water in the Soviet section of border waters is not regulated by international agreements to which the USSR is a party, regulation shall be carried out in accordance with the law of the USSR and Union Republics.

The procedure for the use of border waters of the USSR shall be established by the competent agencies in agreement with the border troops command.

III. *The Conservation of Water and Prevention of Its Harmful Action*

Article 37. The Conservation of Water

All waters (bodies of water) shall be subject to protection from pollution, obstruction, and depletion that may cause harm to the health of the population, the diminution of fish reserves, the deterioration of water supply conditions, and other unfavorable effects resulting from changes in the physical, chemical, and biological properties of the water, reducing its capacity for natural purification, and upsetting the hydrological and hydro-geological regime.

Enterprises, organizations, and institutions, whose activity affects the condition of water, shall be obliged to carry out technological, forest-improvement, agrotechnical, hydrotechnical, sanitary, and other measures agreed upon with the agencies regulating the use and conservation of water, the executive committees of local Councils of Workers' Deputies, the agencies concerned with state sanitary supervision and the protection of fish, and other interested state agencies, or according to instructions from state agencies so empowered. These measures are to secure the protection of water from pollution, obstruction, and depletion, and to improve the conditions and regime of the water. Measures for the conservation of water shall be specified in the state plans for the development of the national economy.

Article 38. The Protection of Water from Pollution and Obstruction

The discharge into bodies of water of industrial, everyday, and other forms of wastes shall be prohibited. The discharge of sewage is permitted only with the observance of the requirements laid down in Article 31 of these Principles.

The owners of means of water transport, pipelines, floating and other installations on bodies of water, timber-floating organizations, and other enterprises, organizations, and institutions shall be obliged not to permit the pollution and obstruction of water resulting from the loss of oil, wood, chemical, petroleum, and other products.

Enterprises, organizations, and institutions shall be obliged not to permit the pollution and obstruction of the surface of drainage systems, the ice-cover of bodies of water, and the surface of glaciers by industrial, everyday, or other wastes and discharges, and by oil and chemical products whose contact with water entails a deterioration in the quality of surface and underground water.

The administrations of state water management systems, collective and state farms, and other enterprises, organizations, and institutions shall be obliged to prevent the pollution of water by fertilizers and toxic chemicals.

In order to protect water used for drinking and everyday water supply, medicinal, resort, and health-improvement needs of the population, regions and zones of sanitary protection shall be established in accordance with the law of the USSR and Union Republics.

Article 39. The Protection of Water from Depletion

In order to maintain the favorable water regime of rivers, lakes, reservoirs, underground water, and other water bodies so as to prevent erosion, silting up of water bodies, and deterioration in the habitat of aquatic animals, and to reduce fluctuations in flow, and so on, forest water-conservation zones shall be established, and forest-improvement, antierosion, hydrotechnical, and other measures shall be undertaken according to the procedure specified by the law of the USSR and Union Republics.

In approving questions concerning the siting and construction of enterprises, installations, and other objects affecting the condition of water, and in issuing authorization for special water use, the agencies regulating the use and conservation of water must be guided by schemes for the complex use and conservation of water and by water-resource balances, which take into consideration the interests of water and land users.

If, when carrying out drilling and other mining operations connected with the prospecting, surveying, and exploitation of deposits of gas, petroleum, coal, and other useful minerals, underground aquifers are discovered, the organizations conducting the mining operations shall be obliged to inform immediately the agency regulating the use and conservation of water, and, in accordance with the established procedure, to take measures for the protection of the underground water.

Self-discharging wells shall be equipped with regulating devices, or be temporarily closed or dismantled, according to the procedure established by the law of the USSR and Union Republics.

Article 40. The Prevention and Elimination of the
Harmful Action of Water

Enterprises, organizations, and institutions shall be obliged to carry out measures agreed upon with the agencies regulating the use and conservation of water, the executive committees of the local Councils of Workers' Deputies and other interested state agencies, or on the instructions of state agencies so empowered, to prevent and eliminate the following harmful actions of water: floods, inundations, and rising groundwater; the destruction of banks, protective dikes, and other installations; waterlogging and salinization of land; and soil erosion, the creation of ravines, landslides, flash floods, and other harmful phenomena.

The implementation of urgent measures to prevent and eliminate natural disasters caused by the harmful action of water shall be regulated by the law of the USSR and Union Republics.

Measures for the prevention and elimination of the harmful action of water shall be specified in the state plans for the development of the national economy.

IV. *State Record-Keeping and Planning the Use of Water*

Article 41. The Goals of State Record-Keeping and Planning the Use of Water

The state record-keeping on water and its use shall aim to establish the quantity and quality of water and data on water use for the needs of the public and the national economy.

Planning water use must ensure the scientifically based distribution of water between water users, with consideration for meeting primarily the drinking water and everyday needs of the population and for the conservation of water and the prevention of its harmful action. In planning water use, data of the state water cadastre, water resource balances, and schemes for the complex use and conservation of water shall be taken into consideration.

Article 42. The State Water Cadastre

The state water cadastre shall include record-keeping data on water according to quantitative and qualitative indices, the registration of water use, and record-keeping data on the use of water.

Article 43. Water Resource Balances

Water resource balances, evaluating the presence and extent of water use, shall be compiled by basins, economic regions, Union Republics, and the USSR.

Article 44. Schemes for the Complex Use and Conservation of Water

General and basin (territorial) schemes for the complex use and conservation of water shall determine the basic water-management and other measures to be carried out in order to meet the long-term needs for water of the population and the national economy, and in order to conserve water and prevent its harmful action.

Article 45. The Procedure of Keeping the State Records on Water and Its Use, Maintaining the State Water Cadastre, Compiling Water Resource Balances, and Working Out Schemes for the Complex Use and Conservation of Water

The state record-keeping on water and its use, the maintenance of the state water cadastre, the compilation of the water resource balances, and the development of schemes for the complex use and conservation of water shall be carried out by the State and in accordance with a common system for the USSR.

The procedure for keeping the state records on water and its use, the maintenance of the state water cadastre, the compilation of the water resource balances, and the development and approval of schemes for the complex use and conservation of water shall be established by the Council of Ministers of the USSR.

V. *Liability for the Violation of Water Law*

Article 46. Liability for the Violation of Water Law

Ceding the right to water use and other transactions that violate, overtly or covertly, the right of state ownership of water shall be invalid.

Persons guilty of these transactions or of: the unauthorized seizure of bodies of water or unauthorized water use; the withdrawal of water in violation of the plans of water use; pollution and obstruction of water; putting into operation enterprises, communal, and other facilities without installations and devices to prevent the pollution and obstruction of water and its harmful action; uneconomic use of water (extracted or drained from bodies of water); violation of the water-conservation regime in drainage systems, causing pollution, soil erosion, and other harmful effects; unauthorized hydrotechnical operations; damaging water-management installations and devices; violating the regulations for the operation of water-management installations and devices shall be criminally or administratively liable in accordance with the law of the USSR and Union Republics.

Liability for other forms of violation of water law may be established by the law of the Union Republics.

Willfully seized water bodies shall be returned to the proper quarter without the reimbursement of expenses incurred during the period of illegal use.

Enterprises, organizations, institutions, and citizens shall be obliged to compensate for losses caused by the violation of water law, to the extent and according to the procedure established by the law of the USSR and Union Republics. Responsible persons and other workers, through whose fault the enterprises, organizations, and institutions incurred expenses connected with compensation for losses, shall be materially liable according to the established procedure.

On Measures to Regulate Use and Increase Conservation of Water Resources of the USSR

Decree of the Council of Ministers
of the USSR, 22 April 1960

For purposes of regulation of the complex use and conservation of the water resources of the country, and the early elimination of water pollution, the Council of Ministers of the USSR decrees:

1. To entrust the Councils of Ministers of Union Republics with responsibility for planning the use of surface and underground waters on the territory of the Union Republics, for protecting them from depletion, obstruction, and pollution by industrial, domestic and other sewage, and miscellaneous discharges, and also for undertaking measures to combat the harmful action of water (flooding, waterlogging, leaching, soil erosion, and so on).

2. To commission the Councils of Ministers of Union Republics to organize specialized agencies of the Councils of Ministers of Union Republics to be concerned with the use and conservation of surface and groundwater resources, with inspections for the basins of the main rivers (bodies of water) in the territory of the Republics.

To entrust the agencies of the Councils of Ministers of Union Republics concerned with the use and conservation of water resources, in particular with:

(a)* keeping systematic records on quantitative and qualitative indices of surface and groundwater resources on the territory of the Republics, and ensuring their systematic use;

Extracted from *Collected Decrees of the USSR*, 1960, No. 9, Article 67.

*Latin alphabetic order used for enumeration of subparagraphs in the translation.

(b) organizing the development of water-management balances and long-range schemes for the use and conservation of water resources for river basins, industrial regions, and the Republic as a whole;

(c) control over measures to combat the harmful action of water: flooding, rising groundwater, waterlogging, soil erosion, formation of gullies, and so on;

(d) the preparation of overall plans for the use of surface and underground waters in the main basins, and of regulations for the complex use of reservoirs in the headrace and tailrace canals by hydroelectric stations, water transport, and other branches of the national economy;

(e) the current regulation of the dispatching of water on the basis of the approved overall plan and the prevailing water situation of the year, and ensuring interrepublic and intersystem exchanges of water as stipulated in the plan;

(f) state supervision over the keeping of records and the rational use of water by enterprises, and over the implementation by these enterprises of measures to protect water bodies from pollution, obstruction, and depletion.

The agencies of the Councils of Ministers of Union Republics concerned with the use and conservation of water resources shall have the right to suspend the work of enterprises if they fail to implement on time the government decrees on measures for the treatment of sewage;

(g) the issue of mandatory orders dealing with plans for the construction of new and the reconstruction of existing enterprises, where such plans are connected with the use and conservation of water resources and the struggle to combat the harmful action of water;

(h) the registration and certification of the principal hydrotechnical constructions and systems connected with the use and conservation of water resources and the struggle to combat the harmful action of water;

(i) the preparation of interrepublic agreements on the use and conservation of surface and groundwater resources in joint use.

To establish that supervision over the proper condition of water bodies and the elaboration of measures to protect water sources shall be carried out by the agencies of the Councils of Ministers of Union Republics concerned with the use and conservation of water resources, with the participation of sanitary, shipping, and fishery supervisions, and communal and agricultural agencies (as appropriate), with consideration for the primary use of water for the domestic and drinking needs of the population.

3. To prohibit the granting of authorization for, and the launching of, permanent or temporary operation of enterprises, shops, and units which discharge sewage without completion of measures for the treatment of the sewage. And in this connection to establish that com-

mencement of operation of these enterprises, shops, and units shall be permitted only with the authorization of the State Sanitary Inspection.

To establish that rewards to leading workers of building organizations for fulfilling, on or ahead of schedule, the plan for launching the operation of objects of construction (enterprises, shops, and other installations), which discharge sewage, shall be granted only when the principal sewage treatment facilities are put into operation simultaneously.

4. That the Councils of Ministers of Union Republics, ministries, and departments of the USSR and councils of national economy shall:

(a) beginning in 1961, specify in the plans the allocation of capital investments and material-technical means for the specific purpose of undertaking measures for the rational use of water resources and for the elimination of water pollution, having registered all industrial enterprises and other objects which pollute water sources;

(b) prohibit any cutting, over and above the plan, of upland forests which are important for water conservation and provide for the regeneration of the vegetative cover, particularly forests, as the most effective means to combat soil erosion.

5. To create a Department of Water Resources in the State Planning Committee of the USSR, with a staff of thirty-five in addition to the staff of the central establishment, which shall be entrusted with the regulation and coordination of water resource use and conservation in the country, with the promulgation of the principal regulations for carrying out water management and planning water resource development in accord with the plan for the development of the national economy of the USSR, and which shall also be entrusted with the coordination of all water management work affecting the interests of adjacent Republics and border States.

6. To recognize the expediency of organizing departments (subdepartments) of water-management planning in the State Planning Committees of the Union Republics and, likewise, special groups on water management in the councils of national economy, ministries, and departments which are directly concerned with questions of the use and conservation of water.

[7. omitted]

8. To require the State Scientific-Economic Council of the Council of Ministers of the USSR, together with the Chief Office of Hydrometeorology under the Council of Ministers of the USSR, the Ministry of Electrostation Construction, the Ministry of Transport Construction, the Ministry of Agriculture of the USSR, and the Ministry of Inland Water Transport of the RSFSR to draw up a plan for the development and study of the water resources of the country, with regard for the long-term plan for the development of the national economy of the USSR over twenty years.

9. To entrust the Ministry of Electrostation Construction with developing, on the instructions of the State Scientific-Economic Council of the Council of Ministers of the USSR, schemes for the use and conservation of water resources, both in the country as a whole and in individual Republics, and especially in the main drainage basins; and also with drawing up a general long-term scheme for the complex use of the water resources of the country and measures for their conservation over the next twenty years.

[10. omitted]

11. In addition to the decree of the Council of Ministers of the USSR of 4 September 1959, No. 1036, to ensure that the drilling of new wells for water, the reequipment of exploratory wells for operation, and the construction and reequipment of water-intake structures for use of underground water shall be carried out with the agreement also of the agencies of the Councils of Ministers of Union Republics concerned with the use and conservation of water, the decision of such agencies relative to the safeguarding of the underground water of the population and its distribution among different branches of the national economy being mandatory.

12. To ensure that All-Union standards regarding quality for surface and groundwater used for domestic and cultural needs shall be approved by the Ministry of Health of the USSR, that standards regarding the quality and conditions for fishery waters shall be approved by the Chief State Fishery Waters Administration [Glavgosrybvod] under the Council of Ministers of the RSFSR, and that standards regarding the quality and conditions for bodies of water used for agriculture and livestock breeding shall be approved by the Ministry of Agriculture of the USSR, in coordination with the State Planning Committee of the USSR.

13. To commission the Ministry of Health of the USSR, in coordination with the State Planning Committee of the USSR, to approve regulations for the protection of surface and groundwater from pollution.

[14.-17. omitted]

18. To require the Ministry of Higher and Secondary Special Education of the USSR to include questions of sewage treatment in programs of special disciplines of higher and secondary special educational institutions, having regard for the specific character of production.

19. To require the ministries and departments of the USSR and councils of national economy to work out and implement by 1963 measures to prevent the pollution of water bodies with the effluent from the steam-cleaning and washing of railway tanks for oil and chemical products, and also with wastes from seagoing and river vessels.

[20. omitted]

21. To commission the State Planning Committee of the USSR and the Ministry of Finance of the USSR, with the participation of the

Council of Ministers of the Union Republics and interested ministries and departments of the USSR, to review the present system of levying fines for the discharge of untreated wastes, having in view that the present system of penalty sanctions is not sufficiently conducive to the implementation of measures to eliminate water pollution, and to submit proposals to the Council of Ministers of the USSR by 1 November 1960.

On Measures to Regulate Use and Increase Conservation of Water Resources of the RSFSR

Decree of the Council of Ministers
of the RSFSR, 6 August 1960

In fulfillment of the decree of the Council of Ministers of the USSR of 22 April 1960, No. 425, and for purposes of regulation of the complex use and conservation of the water resources of the RSFSR and early elimination of water pollution, the Council of Ministers of the RSFSR decrees:

1. To recognize the necessity of organizing a State Committee of the Council of Ministers of the RSFSR to be concerned with the use and conservation of surface and groundwater resources, with inspections in the basins of the main rivers (bodies of water) of the RSFSR.

To submit to the Presidium of the Supreme Soviet of the RSFSR a draft edict on this matter.

2. To require the State Planning Committee of the RSFSR, the Supreme Council of National Economy, the Councils of Ministers of Autonomous Republics, regional executive committees, oblast executive committees, the Moscow city executive committee, the Leningrad city executive committee, ministries and departments of the RSFSR, and councils of national economy, starting in 1961, to specify in the plans the allocation of capital investments and material-technical means for the specific purpose of undertaking measures for the rational use of water resources and the elimination of water pollution, having registered all the industrial enterprises and other objects which pollute water sources.

3. To require the Councils of Ministers of Autonomous Republics,

Collected Decrees of the RSFSR, 1960, No. 28, Article 133.

regional executive committees, oblast executive committees, the Moscow city executive committee, the Leningrad city executive committee, ministries and departments of the RSFSR, and councils of national economy:

(a)[*] to check as soon as possible the condition of the sewage-treatment facilities of existing enterprises and to establish time limits for these facilities to be put into proper condition in the course of the years 1960 to 1963, after guaranteeing their effective operation; and at the same time to organize systematic laboratory control over the functioning of the treatment facilities;

(b) to prevent an increase in sewage and discharges at these enterprises or a deterioration in the quality of the sewage, without all the necessary technical treatment measures being first carried out;

(c) to prohibit any cutting, over and above the plan, of upland forests which are important for water conservation, and also to provide for the regeneration of the vegetative cover, particularly forests, as the most effective means to combat soil erosion;

(d) to ensure that all water management objects shall be put into good condition within a three-year period, and regularly to carry out dredging, channel-correcting, and other necessary works, as well as to clear rivers, canals, ponds, reservoirs, and other bodies of water from debris;

(e) to prevent the granting of authorization for and launching of temporary or permanent operation of enterprises, shops, and units that discharge sewage without completion of measures for treatment of the sewage. The commencement of operation of these enterprises, shops, and units shall be permitted only with the authorization of the State Sanitary Inspection.

Awards to leading workers of building organizations for fulfilling, on or ahead of schedule, plans for launching the operation of objects of construction (enterprises, shops, and other structures), which discharge sewage, shall be granted only when the principal sewage treatment facilities are put into operation simultaneously.

4. To commission the State Planning Committee of the RSFSR, together with the Supreme Council of National Economy and the Ministry of Finance of the RSFSR, to submit within a month to the Council of Ministers of the RSFSR proposals: on the organization of special groups on water management in the councils of national economy and ministries and departments of the RSFSR that are directly concerned with questions of the use and conservation of water; on the organization of special scientific institutions for the amalgamation and development of scientific research in the field of water use and con-

---

[*]Latin alphabetic order used for enumeration of subparagraphs in the translation.

servation and the struggle against the harmful action of water, on the basis of amalgamating the existing scientific research institutes in the RSFSR conducting analagous work, with appropriate reinforcement of the scientific research base.

5. To require the ministries and departments of the RSFSR and councils of national economy to work out and implement by 1963 measures to prevent the pollution of bodies of water with effluent from the steam-cleaning and washing of railway tanks for oil and chemical products, and also with the wastes from seagoing and river vessels.

Criminal Code of the RSFSR of 1960

Article 223. Water and Air Pollution

The pollution of rivers, lakes, and other bodies of water and water sources with untreated sewage, discharges, and effluents from industrial and communal enterprises, presenting a hazard to human health or to agricultural production or to stocks of fish, and equally the pollution of the air by industrial wastes harmful to human health, shall be punished by corrective labor for a period of up to one year or by a fine of up to three hundred rubles.

Index